Trace
Elements

Trace
Elements

*Proceedings of the Conference Held at the
Ohio Agricultural Experiment Station
Wooster, Ohio, October 14-16, 1957*

EDITED BY

C. A. Lamb, O. G. Bentley
and J. M. Beattie

1958

ACADEMIC PRESS INC.

NEW YORK and LONDON

LIST OF CONTRIBUTORS

S. AARONSON, *Haskins Laboratories, New York, New York*

DANIEL I. ARNON, *Laboratory of Plant Physiology, Department of Soils and Plant Nutrition, University of California, Berkeley, California*

H. BAKER, *Department of Chemistry, Mount Sinai Hospital, New York, New York*

JAMES M. BEATTIE, *Ohio Agricultural Experiment Station, Wooster, Ohio*

KENNETH C. BEESON, *United States Plant, Soil and Nutrition Laboratory, Agricultural Research Service, Ithaca, New York*

ORVILLE G. BENTLEY, *Ohio Agricultural Experiment Station, Wooster, Ohio*

THOMAS E. BROWN, *Charles F. Kettering Foundation, Yellow Springs, Ohio*

A. CURY, *Institute of Microbiology, University of Brazil, Rio de Janeiro, Brazil*

GEORGE K. DAVIS, *Florida Agricultural Experiment Station, Gainesville, Florida*

C. A. ELVEHJEM, *University of Wisconsin, Madison, Wisconsin*

H. CLYDE EYSTER, *Charles F. Kettering Foundation, Yellow Springs, Ohio*

S. GRANICK, *The Rockefeller Institute for Medical Research, New York, New York*

FREDERIC L. HOCH, *The Biophysics Research Laboratory of the Department of Medicine, Harvard Medical School, and Peter Bent Brigham Hospital, Boston, Massachusetts*

D. J. HOFF, *Ohio Agricultural Experiment Station, Wooster, Ohio*

S. H. HUTNER, *Haskins Laboratories, New York, New York*

RONALD R. JOHNSON, *Ohio Agricultural Experiment Station, Wooster, Ohio*

RICHARD F. KEELER, *Department of Agricultural Biochemistry, Ohio State University, Columbus, Ohio*

S. KIRKWOOD, *Department of Agricultural Biochemistry, University of Minnesota, Saint Paul, Minnesota*

E. O. McLEAN, *Ohio Agricultural Experiment Station, Wooster, Ohio*

HENRY R. MAHLER, *Indiana University, Bloomington, Indiana*

H. J. MEDERSKI, *Ohio Agricultural Experiment Station, Wooster, Ohio*

A. L. MOXON, *Ohio Agricultural Experiment Station, Wooster, Ohio*

ALVIN NASON, *McCollum-Pratt Institute, The Johns Hopkins University, Baltimore, Maryland*

H. A. NATHAN, *Haskins Laboratories, New York, New York*

ANDRÉ PIRSON, *Botanical Institute, University of Marburg, Marburg, Germany*

J. D. SAYRE, *Agricultural Research Service, United States Department of Agriculture, and the Ohio Agricultural Experiment Station, Wooster, Ohio*

S. SCHER, *Department of Botany, Rutgers University, New Brunswick, New Jersey*

G. S. SERIF, *Department of Agricultural Biochemistry, University of Minnesota, Saint Paul, Minnesota*

JOHN SKOK, *Argonne National Laboratory, Lemont, Illinois*

HOWARD A. TANNER, *Charles F. Kettering Foundation, Yellow Springs, Ohio*

E. J. UNDERWOOD, *Institute of Agriculture, University of Western Australia, Nedlands, Australia*

BERT L. VALLEE, *The Biophysics Research Laboratory of the Department of Medicine, Harvard Medical School, and Peter Bent Brigham Hospital, Boston, Massachusetts*

J. E. VARNER, *Department of Agricultural Biochemistry, Ohio State University, Columbus, Ohio*

G. W. VOLK, *Ohio State University, Columbus, Ohio*

H. F. WINTER, *Ohio Agricultural Experiment Station, Wooster, Ohio*

FOREWORD

During 1957 the Ohio Agricultural Experiment Station celebrated its Diamond Jubilee. In addition to planning numerous special days and events it was felt that to hold several scientific symposia would be a fitting way to commemorate the great contributions to science made by members of the staff during the institution's 75-year history.

Through the interest of Dr. Charles F. Kettering and financial support provided by him through the Kettering Foundation, it was possible to hold a three-day symposium on the role of trace elements in plants, animals, and microorganisms.

The response to invitations to present papers and attend the conference was most gratifying. Registration totaled 338, of which number 198 were from outside Ohio. Seven foreign countries and twenty-one states were represented. Participants in the program were drawn from academic institutions, foundations, and commercial laboratories from this country and abroad where outstanding work on the subject matter theme had been done or was in progress.

The need for more basic research and the role an experiment station can play in contributing to basic knowledge was made evident by the exchange of ideas stimulated during the conference and the apparent relationships between this type of research and improved technology.

To those whose responsibility it was to prepare the program and other details, to those who made such noteworthy contributions to the program, to those who attended, and to Dr. Charles F. Kettering and Dr. H. A. Tanner of the Kettering Foundation for their participation and financial support, our deepest appreciation is herewith extended.

L. L. RUMMELL, *Director*
W. E. KRAUSS, *Associate Director*

PREFACE

The areas of activity within a large agricultural experiment station cover a wide range of interests in both the plant and animal fields. Trace elements was a happy choice as the topic for a symposium to celebrate an important milestone in the history of the host institution, because it is of direct interest and importance to so many research workers.

The metabolic and physiological functions of trace elements in the fields of plants, animals, and microorganisms were discussed. The participants maintained a fine balance in the approach to their subjects, with sufficient basic material for good understanding, adequate review of recent developments, and stimulating reports on current research. An important feature of the presentations was the stress placed on micronutrient interrelationships, with many specific illustrations. The role of trace elements as enzyme activators, as constituents of metalloproteins and metalloenzymes, and the function of these compounds in biological systems was emphasized by many of the speakers.

The first session introduced the subject in a general way. The role of trace elements in plants was introduced by Dr. D. I. Arnon, University of California; in animals by Dr. E. J. Underwood, University of Western Australia; and in microorganisms by Dr. S. H. Hutner, Haskins Laboratories, New York City. The soil-plant-animal relationship was ably integrated by Dr. K. C. Beeson, Plant, Soil and Nutrition Laboratory, A.R.S., Ithaca, N. Y.

The remaining sessions were concerned with individual elements. Manganese was introduced by Dr. André Pirson, University of Marburg, Germany; Selenium by Dr. A. L. Moxon, Ohio Agricultural Experiment Station; Cobalt by Dr. G. K. Davis, University of Florida; Boron by Dr. John Skok, Argonne Laboratory; Iodine by Dr. Sam Kirkwood, University of Minnesota; Molybdenum and Vanadium by Dr. Alvin Nason, McCollum-Pratt Institute; Copper by Dr. H. R. Mahler, Indiana University; Zinc by Dr. F. L. Hoch, Harvard Medical School; and Iron by Dr. S. Granick, Rockefeller Institute for Medical Research. Supplementing these distinguished speakers were presentations of more specific aspects of trace element research by staff members of the Ohio Agricultural Experiment Station, the Ohio State University, and the Kettering Foundation.

A notable feature of the program was the concluding summarization of the proceedings by Dr. C. A. Elvehjem, University of Wisconsin. He, as did many of the other speakers, emphasized the importance of funda-

ix

mental research on trace elements in the search for solutions to many practical agricultural problems. There has probably been no area in which the application of results to the practical field has been more important or more spectacular. The examples are legion where the identification of deficiencies or toxicities has led to complete correction of difficulties easily and cheaply. And still we seem to have barely scratched the surface in reaching an understanding of how and why the cures have worked. Perhaps the greatest contribution of the conference lay in calling attention to the incompleteness of the knowledge now at hand and the great potential that lies in further work.

The symposium offered a challenge to the station workers, and provided background for understanding and a stimulus for further work. It is hoped and believed that it will do as much for the reader.

C. A. LAMB
O. G. BENTLEY
J. M. BEATTIE

Wooster, Ohio,
April, 1958

CONTENTS

LIST OF CONTRIBUTORS v

FOREWORD vii

PREFACE ix

1. The Role of Micronutrients in Plant Nutrition with Special
   Reference to Photosynthesis and Nitrogen Assimilation . .   1
   DANIEL I. ARNON

2. Trace Elements in Animals   33
   E. J. UNDERWOOD

3. Trace Elements in Microorganisms: The Temperature Factor
   Approach   47
   S. H. HUTNER, S. AARONSON, H. A. NATHAN,
   H. BAKER, S. SCHER, and A. CURY

4. The Relation of Soils to the Micronutrient Element Content of
   Plants and to Animal Nutrition   67
   KENNETH C. BEESON

5. Manganese and Its Role in Photosynthesis   81
   ANDRÉ PIRSON

6. Manganese Deficiency in Soybeans   99
   H. J. MEDERSKI and D. J. HOFF

7. Chemical Methods of Estimating Available Soil Manganese . 109
   D. J. HOFF and H. J. MEDERSKI

8. Manganese Problems in the Production of Concord Grapes . 117
   JAMES M. BEATTIE

9. Manganese Toxicity: A Possible Cause of Internal Bark Necrosis
   of Apple 125
   H. F. WINTER

10. Physiological Effects of Manganese Deficiency 135
    THOMAS E. BROWN, H. CLYDE EYSTER, and
    HOWARD A. TANNER

11. Mineral Requirements for *Chlorella pyrenoidosa* under Auto-
    trophic and Heterotrophic Conditions 157
    H. CLYDE EYSTER, THOMAS E. BROWN, and HOWARD
    A. TANNER

12. Selenium: Its Occurrence in Rocks and Soils, Absorption by Plants, Toxic Action in Animals, and Possible Essential Role in Animal Nutrition 175
   A. L. Moxon

13. Metabolic Function and Practical Use of Cobalt in Nutrition . 193
   George K. Davis

14. Cobalt and the Synthesis of Vitamin B_{12} and Vitamin B_{12}-like Substances by Rumen Microorganisms 213
   Ronald R. Johnson and Orville G. Bentley

15. The Role of Boron in the Plant Cell 227
   John Skok

16. The Accumulation of Boron in Margins of Corn Leaves . . . 245
   J. D. Sayre

17. Boron for Alfalfa and Other Crops on Ohio Soils 251
   E. O. McLean and G. W. Volk

18. Enzyme Systems Concerned with the Synthesis of Monoiodo-tyrosine: I. The Occurrence and Behavior of Soluble and Mitochondrial Systems 257
   G. S. Serif and S. Kirkwood

19. The Metabolic Role of Vanadium and Molybdenum in Plants and Animals 269
   Alvin Nason

20. The Metabolism of Molybdate and Tungstate in *Azotobacter* 297
   Richard F. Keeler and J. E. Varner

21. The Role of Copper in Some Enzyme-Catalyzed Oxidation Reactions 311
   Henry R. Mahler

22. The Metabolic Role of Zinc 337
   Frederic L. Hoch and Bert L. Vallee

23. Iron Metabolism in Animals and Plants 365
   S. Granick

24. Summary of Trace Elements Symposium 383
   C. A. Elvehjem

Author Index 393
Subject Index 407

CHAPTER 1

The Role of Micronutrients in Plant Nutrition with Special Reference to Photosynthesis and Nitrogen Assimilation

DANIEL I. ARNON

Laboratory of Plant Physiology
Department of Soils and Plant Nutrition
University of California, Berkeley, California

                                                                    Page
I. The Recognition of Micronutrients   1
II. Discovery of New Micronutrients   3
    A. Search for Methods   3
    B. Criteria of Essentiality   5
    C. The Essentiality of Vanadium for Green Algae   7
    D. Diversity of Micronutrient Requirements   11
    E. Is the List of Essential Elements Complete?   13
III. Micronutrients in Nitrogen Metabolism. The Role of Molybdenum . . .   15
    A. Molybdenum and Nitrogen Assimilation in *Scenedesmus*   15
    B. Molybdenum and Nitrogen Metabolism of Blue-Green Algae   18
IV. Micronutrients in Photosynthesis   23
V. Quantitative Requirements of Micronutrients. The Molybdenum Require-
    ment of a Single Cell   28
    References   31

I. THE RECOGNITION OF MICRONUTRIENTS

It is particularly fitting that a symposium on micronutrient elements be held under the auspices of an agricultural experiment station celebrating its 75th anniversary. The birth of this subject preceded by only a few years the founding of this experiment station. For it was in 1869 that Raulin discovered the role of zinc in the nutrition of *Aspergillus niger* and concluded, with a remarkable insight for his day, that zinc and other inorganic elements were not merely "useful stimulants, which could, rigorously speaking, be dispensed with but were, on the contrary, indispensable"; growth, in what was believed to be their absence, was possible only because, as he suggested, these elements were required by plants in

1

minute quantity and were present as impurities in the external medium (Raulin, 1869).

But it is not only the chronological coincidence which is worthy of recollection today. Micronutrients are a part of the broader subject of the inorganic nutrition of plants—a subject which marks the beginning of the application of science to agriculture. The wave of scientific enthusiasm which swept the agriculture of Western Europe in the middle of the 19th century was based on the recognition, for the first time in the long history of man's association with green plants, of the crucial concepts of plant nutrition. In 1804, de Saussure, in his classical treatise "Recherches chimiques sur la vegetation" provided a cogent and unified concept of plant nutrition which, 40 years later, through the work of men like Boussingault in France, Lawes and Gilbert in England, and Liebig in Germany, ushered in the scientific revolution in agriculture.

The extent of this revolution may be measured by one fact: from the days of the Roman Empire to 1804 when de Saussure's book was published, the average yield of wheat in Western Europe remained between 6 and 10 bushels per acre (Kellogg, 1951). One hundred years later, yields three times as high were commonplace in Western Europe. Let us not forget that this increase in yields in one century occurred before the development of modern fungicides and insecticides for the control of crop diseases and pests, before the use of plant growth substances or the development through scientific breeding of hybrid seed and disease-resistant strains, and prior to the use of agricultural machinery based on electricity or the internal combustion engine. This marked rise in crop yields rested principally on the application of the new knowledge of plant nutrition to crop production.

What was the crucial concept of plant nutrition formulated by de Saussure and his successors which made this revolution in crop production possible? New evidence, derived from controlled experiments, revealed that land plants are made of chemical elements from three sources: air, water, and soil. The novel and revolutionary aspect of this concept was the realization that the bulk of plant substance, usually about 90 per cent of its dry weight, was made up of the three elements assimilated during photosynthesis: carbon, oxygen, and hydrogen. These three elements are derived from air and water. The inorganic elements derived from soil accounted for the remaining 10 per cent of the plant substances.

Despite their relatively small quantitative contribution to the bulk of plant substance, the elements derived from the soil soon became the object of more extensive and vigorous investigation than the process of photosynthesis. The reason for the preoccupation with the inorganic, or, as it was often called, mineral nutrition of plants, did not lie in the underestimation of the cosmic importance of photosynthesis, but rather in the recognition that this process was, for all practical purposes, beyond control. Little could be done to alter light or CO_2 supply in the field. By contrast, the inorganic elements which plants absorb from the soil were subject to control and modification, as was soon demonstrated by striking increases in crop production from the application of chemical fertilizers.

The immediate question which confronted students of inorganic nutrition of plants was which elements were indispensable for plant life. At first, it appeared that the plant required, *in toto*, only ten chemical elements for growth and reproduction: three—carbon, hydrogen, and oxygen—derived from water and air; and seven, normally supplied by the soil—nitrogen, phosphorus, potassium, calcium, magnesium, sulfur, and iron. However, Raulin's discovery of the zinc requirements of *Aspergillus niger* opened the possibility that an entirely new group of essential inorganic elements was overlooked because the small quantities in which they were required were usually supplied by the impurities in the nutrient medium.

We need no reminder today of how correct Raulin's hypothesis proved to be in the next 75 years. The new elements which became known as "trace elements" or "micronutrients" were found to be of great theoretical and practical importance to cellular physiology and agriculture. In introducing at this symposium the subject of micronutrient elements in relation to plant growth, I shall attempt to fulfill my assignment by discussing only certain selected topics which are closely bound to this broad field of inquiry. Since my treatment of them is to be illustrative rather than comprehensive, I shall, in the main, limit my discussion to the work with which I am most familiar; that is the work of my own laboratory.

II. Discovery of New Micronutrients

A. Search for Methods

In assessing the essentiality of inorganic elements in plant nutrition, they can be roughly divided into two categories. One category comprises elements whose essentiality is obvious since they form cellular constituents indispensable to life. Carbon, hydrogen, oxygen, nitrogen, sulfur, and phosphorus fall in this category as well as magnesium for its part in the chlorophyll molecule and iron as a component of respiratory enzymes, irrespective of what other functions these elements may perform in the plant. The inclusion of calcium in this category could also be argued, at least for higher plants, from the fact that it combines with pectic acid to form calcium pectate in the middle lamella of the cell wall.

The second category consists of elements which, like potassium, have not yet been identified for certain with any essential cellular constituent. The essentiality of potassium for plants, and indeed for all life forms, is so readily demonstrable that it has never been called in question. However the status of this element exemplifies the need for formulating definite criteria of essentiality for those inorganic elements whose role in cellular economy is more apparent in the realm of cellular function than in cellular structure. The problem is particularly acute for micronutrients. Their small quantitative requirement points to their catalytic function in the cell. An assessment of their essentiality is usually needed well in advance of the recognition of a specific enzyme system in which they may play an activating role.

At one time the mere presence of an element in the plant, particularly if it occurred with great regularity among diverse species, was taken in itself as evidence of essentiality. It was soon recognized, however, that the green plant has the capacity, within rather wide limits, of indiscriminate absorption; it absorbs from the soil essential as well as superfluous or even harmful elements. Every essential element must, of course, be present in the plant, but not every element present is essential.

Since the composition of the plant offered no reliable guide as to the essentiality of the constituent elements, it was found more profitable to turn to the external medium in which the plant grows. An obvious approach was to remove from the external medium, one at a time, its constituent elements and to observe what effect this had on the plant. If the plant failed to grow as a consequence of removing element A but not element B, the conclusion would be drawn that element A is essential and element B is dispensable. This straightforward approach, however, was not found applicable to the natural soil medium in which plants grow. Apart from the few clear-cut single element deficiencies in natural soils, the attempt to remove completely an element from a soil entailed, for most nutrients, a chemical treatment which would have altered the soil from a natural to an artificial medium.

For this and other reasons which are discussed in more detail elsewhere (Arnon, 1952), a paradoxical conclusion seemed justified, that the natural growth medium of land plants, the soil, was least adapted for the study of the essentiality of plant nutrients of which it was the source. As a consequence, special techniques of artificial nutrient solutions, synthetic water and sand cultures, were developed for the study of essential plant nutrients normally obtained by land plants from the soil.

Artificial culture techniques have served as a powerful and discriminating tool for evaluating the indispensability of inorganic nutrients in plant nutrition. With the aid of this tool, four new essential elements were discovered in the first 30 years of the present century: boron, manganese, copper, and zinc. The discovery of these four new micronutrients was made possible by the development of special techniques for their removal as accidental impurities in the synthetic nutrient medium. The same approach has also been used more recently in the detection of the new micronutrients, to be discussed later.

It is interesting to note that the recent history of plant nutrition offers no case of a discovery of a new essential element through soil treatments. For every one of the new micronutrients, evidence of its indispensability was obtained from artificial nutrient solution experiments, well in advance of any response obtained in the field. The practical significance of these discoveries made by an exacting laboratory technique remote from field practice, was attested by a vast and ever-growing list of hitherto obscure diseases of field crops which were soon recognized as micronutrient deficiencies.

B. Criteria of Essentiality

With the addition of boron, manganese, copper, and zinc to the list of essential elements for green plants, the question arose whether other, hitherto unrecognized, micronutrients might not be present as ubiquitous impurities in synthetic nutrient media even after purification by the methods then in use. These considerations moved the late D. R. Hoagland to prepare several so-called A–Z solutions, containing a rather large number of elements in minute quantities which were to be used in supplementing the standard nutrient solutions. In an experiment with strawberries, Hoagland and Snyder (1933) gained the distinct impression that plants receiving an enlarged A–Z solution, containing twenty-two elements in addition to the four known micronutrients, were superior to all others. This observation, although strongly suggestive, did not lend itself to quantitative evaluation. Soon afterwards, in an investigation of the relative merits of ammonium and nitrate as sources of nitrogen, another indication was obtained of a possible physiological role of one or more new elements: molybdenum, chromium, or nickel improved the growth of barley plants in a culture solution supplied with ammonium salts as the sole source of nitrogen (Arnon, 1937).

These observations led to the undertaking of a systematic investigation to test the hypothesis that the list of micronutrients, then confined to boron, manganese, zinc, and copper, was incomplete. This was done by arranging a number of elements in groups and by observing how the addition of a given group affected the growth of plants in culture solutions (Arnon, 1938). Three supplementary solutions, each containing different elements in minute quantity, were prepared. One solution, designated A4, furnished the recognized 4 micronutrients, boron, manganese, copper, and zinc. The basic culture solution, supplemented with the A4 solution, therefore furnished the plant with a seemingly complete list of essential elements. Another supplementary solution, designated B7, contained the following 7 elements: molybdenum, vanadium, chromium, nickel, cobalt, tungsten, and titanium—a somewhat arbitrary grouping based on the consideration that each of these could assume various valency levels and hence, conceivably, participate in oxidation-reduction processes within the plant cell. The already-mentioned findings on the role of metals in the nitrogen nutrition of barley (Arnon, 1937) suggested this particular grouping. The third supplementary solution, designated C13, supplied thirteen elements: Aluminum, arsenic, cadmium, strontium, mercury, lead, lithium, rubidium, bromine, iodine, fluorine, selenium, and beryllium. Sodium and chlorine, though not singled out, were provided from several sources in these solutions.

In experiments with lettuce and asparagus, a marked improvement in growth was observed from supplying, in addition to A4, the B7 solution. The further addition of thirteen more elements supplied by the C13 solution produced no measurable effect on either the lettuce or the asparagus plants (Arnon, 1938).

These findings indicated that one or more of the seven elements contained in the B7 solution was capable of benefiting plant growth markedly. The question arose as to the significance which was to be attached to an increase in growth in evaluating the essentiality of an element in plant nutrition. When is a "beneficial" element to be considered indispensable? For example, mention was already made of the beneficial effects of molybdenum, chromium, and nickel under special conditions of nitrogen nutrition of barley. It was undertaken, therefore, to formulate definite criteria of essentiality by means of which the status of each of the seven elements comprising the B7 group could be tested.

The following criteria were set up (Arnon and Stout, 1939a): an element is not considered essential unless (a) a deficiency of it makes it impossible for the plant to complete the vegetative or reproductive stage of its life cycle; (b) such deficiency is specific to the element in question and can be prevented or corrected only by supplying this element, and (c) the element is directly involved in the nutrition of the plant quite apart from its possible effects in correcting some unfavorable microbiological or chemical condition of the external medium.

The criterion of foremost physiological significance is the requirement of an inorganic element for the successful completion of the life cycle of a plant. This is, of course, different from merely demonstrating a favorable effect on growth. The experimental procedure involved in putting this criterion to a test must be based on removing the element in question from the nutrient medium of the plant. This, however, is beset with difficulties; first, it is impossible to remove completely an element that may be contained in the seed or inoculum. Second, the same obstacle applies to the nutrient medium. Regardless of how effective purification procedures are, they cannot be considered as having removed the last atom of a contaminant originally present in the water and nutrient salts, or one that is derived from the container in which the plants are grown, or one gaining access to the nutrient medium in the course of an experiment.

Experimentally, the problem resolves itself into selecting a species which has a high requirement for a given micronutrient and using purification procedures capable of reducing to a minimum the level of contamination in the nutrient medium. Different species vary greatly in their requirement for a given micronutrient. Beans, for example, have a far greater requirement for boron than barley. Alfalfa is capable of absorbing enough zinc from a medium in which corn shows acute deficiency symptoms. The extent to which it is necessary to purify the culture medium in order to produce deficiency symptoms may be reduced through selection of plants having a high requirement for an element. Obviously a deficiency will be observed only when the requirement for an element exceeds its supply.

The application of these criteria of essentiality and the use of refined methods for the purification of the nutrient medium (Stout and Arnon, 1939) soon led to the discovery that molybdenum is an essential element for higher plants (Arnon and Stout, 1939b; also see review, Arnon, 1952). Molybdenum was therefore removed from the B7 group of elements and placed with the A4 group of proven essential elements. The A4 and B7 supplementary micronutrient solutions were thenceforth redesignated A5 and B6 solutions.

C. The Essentiality of Vanadium for Green Algae

Our earlier studies of micronutrients were at first limited to higher (flowering) plants. Since higher plants represent a marked degree of biochemical uniformity in their principal metabolic pathways, it was not surprising to find a remarkably similar pattern in their requirements of micronutrients. By contrast with higher plants, the photoautotrophic microorganisms, such as algae, exhibit a biochemical diversity shown, for example, in their differing pigment composition and ability to use molecular nitrogen. The biochemical diversity of algae could conceivably be reflected in varying requirements for biocatalysts, including micronutrients, and possibly provide a clue to the metabolic function of an element.

Apart from their biochemical diversity, algae appeared to possess other advantages for micronutrient research. Their fundamental metabolism, notably that of the green algae (Chlorophyceae), is similar to that of higher plants, and they can be grown much more readily with maximum control of environmental variables. Of particular significance is their lack of specialized cells and organs. Each viable algal daughter cell must therefore contain all of the inorganic constituents essential for metabolism. Rapid reproduction by cell division would, in the absence of an added supply, quickly dilute, below a level critical for normal cell function, the concentration of an essential micronutrient initially present in abundance in the mother cell or derived from a residual impurity in a purified nutrient medium.

Our investigation of the micronutrient requirements of algae began with a representative of the green algae (Chlorophyceae), *Scenedesmus obliquus*. Applying the criteria of essentiality formulated for higher plants, evidence was soon obtained that "a second element of the original B7 group," vanadium, is essential for this alga (Arnon and Wessel, 1953). The identification of this new micronutrient resulted from experiments concerned with iron nutrition. When *Scenedesmus* was grown in a purified basic nutrient solution supplemented with all the known essential micronutrients for higher plants (manganese, boron, copper, zinc, and molybdenum), a marked increase in growth was observed with increasing iron concentration. In these as in previous experiments, the purification of the nutrient solution was limited to macronutrient salts and water. Iron salts were not purified on the assumption that, since they were used in small amounts, they could serve only as a negligible source of impurities. It seemed possible, therefore, that the observed increase in growth at high iron concentrations resulted from some unknown essential micronutrient commonly present as an impurity in iron salts.

This hypothesis was tested by purifying ferric chloride, as a source of iron, by a procedure (Grahame and Seaborg, 1938) particularly effective for the removal of cobalt but also likely to remove or reduce other metal impurities such as nickel and vanadium. The algae were grown at three levels of iron supply: 0.1, 1.0, and 4.0 mg. of iron per liter of nutrient solution. To one series of cultures was added a supplementary solution (B3) which provided 10 micrograms per liter each of cobalt, nickel, and vanadium. The results are shown in Fig. 1. In this, as in all subsequent experiments, measurements of growth by dry weight (shown here), and by the additional criteria of fresh weight (packed cell volume), cell count, and chlorophyll content, gave concordant results.

One-tenth (0.1) mg. iron per liter was clearly insufficient for growth regardless of the addition of the supplementary solution B3. However, at 1.0 and 4.0 mg. iron, a marked increase in growth has resulted from the addition of a mixture of cobalt, nickel, and vanadium. At iron concentrations adequate for vigorous growth, i.e., 1 mg. or more per liter, the

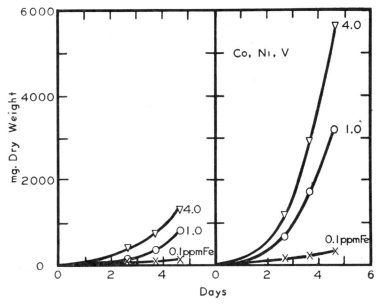

Fig. 1. Effect of a mixture of cobalt, nickel, and vanadium (B3 solution) on growth of *Scenedesmus* in a purified medium at 3 levels of iron: 0.1, 1.0, and 4.0 p.p.m. (1 p.p.m. = 10^{-3} g. per liter). Left: growth (mg. dry weight per liter of nutrient solution) without the addition of the B3 solution. Right: the effect of adding the B3 solution. The B3 solution supplied 10 micrograms per liter of Co, Ni, and V as $Co(NO_3)_2$, $NiSO_4$, and NH_4VO_3, respectively.

growth of algae was distinctly limited by the insufficiency of at least 1 of the 3 elements in the B3 solutions. Figure 2 shows that vanadium was the effective element. The addition of cobalt or nickel gave no measurable increase in growth. In another experiment, 4 parallel cultures were grown in a purified medium without the addition of vanadium. On the 4th day, when a deficiency was apparent, the addition of vanadium to 2 of the cultures was followed by a sharp increase in growth (Fig. 3).

The specificity of vanadium was shown by the finding that 16 other elements, titanium, chromium, tungsten, aluminum, arsenic, cadmium, strontium, mercury, lead, lithium, rubidium, bromine, iodine, fluorine, selenium, and beryllium, the remaining elements in the B7 and C13 solutions (Arnon, 1938), added jointly to the vanadium-deficient cultures, failed to substitute for vanadium.

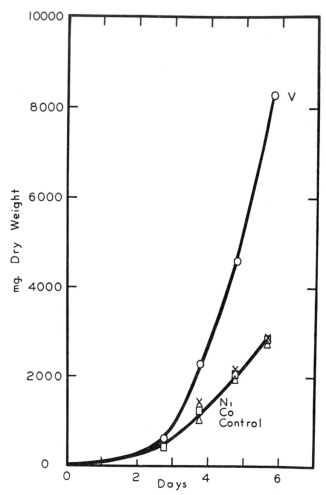

FIG. 2. Effect of adding singly nickel, cobalt, and vanadium (supplied from sources and in amounts given in legend to Fig. 1) on growth (mg. dry weight per liter of nutrient solution). 1 p.p.m. Fe was supplied as $FeCl_3$.

The search for a physiological role of vanadium in *Scenedesmus* (Arnon and Ichioka, unpublished data, 1953; Arnon, 1954) yielded evidence that this element is involved in photosynthesis (see Section IV). Warburg and his collaborators (Warburg and Krippahl, 1954; Warburg *et al.*,

1955) found a role for vanadium in photosynthesis by *Chlorella*. With the recognition of a physiological role for vanadium, it seemed justified, on the basis of our three criteria of essentiality, to add this element to those required for the growth of green algae.

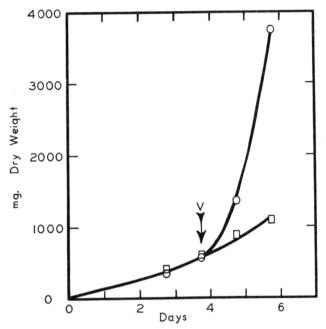

FIG. 3. Effect of adding vanadium on growth of vanadium-deficient cultures. At the time indicated by arrow, 20 micrograms of V (as NH_4VO_3) were added per liter of nutrient solution. Growth is expressed in milligrams dry weight per liter of nutrient solution. One p.p.m. Fe was supplied as $FeCl_3$.

Although there is no evidence at present for the indispensability of vanadium for plants other than green algae, this element is widely distributed in the plant kingdom; of 62 species analyzed by Bertrand (1941, 1942), all contained vanadium.

D. Diversity of Micronutrient Requirements

It has already been stated that similar requirements of inorganic nutrients in different species of plants are most likely to be correlated with similar metabolic and biochemical patterns. Support for this generalization is found in Table I which summarizes the known inorganic requirements of higher plants and those of 2 species of algae investigated in this laboratory: *Scenedesmus obliquus*, similar in its pigment composi-

TABLE I

Elements Required by Green Plants in Macro- or Microquantities

Elements	Higher plants	Green algae (*Scenedesmus obliquus*)	Blue-green algae (*Anabaena cylindrica*)
C, H, O, N, P, S, K, Mg	Macro	Macro	Macro
Fe, Mn, Cu, Zn	Micro	Micro	Micro
Ca	Macro	Micro	Macro
Mo	Micro	Micro	Micro ($\times$ 100)
Na	Micro (?)	Micro (?)	Macro
V	Micro (?)	Micro	Micro (?)
B	Micro	Micro (?)	Micro (?)
Cl	Micro	Micro (?)	Micro (?)
Co	Micro (?)	Micro (?)	Micro

tion and nitrogen metabolism to higher plants and *Anabaena cylindrica* (Myxophyceae), a nitrogen-fixing filamentous blue-green alga, with a pigment system differing from that of green algae and higher plants, notably in the absence of chlorophyll b and in the presence of phyco-cyanin.

Of the elements listed in Table I, the "classical" elements which are required in macroquantities by all the species tested comprise a group of eight: carbon, oxygen, hydrogen, nitrogen, phosphorus, sulfur, potassium, and magnesium. There can also be little question about the general essentiality of iron, manganese, copper, and zinc. The other elements in Table I give a diverging picture both qualitatively and quantitatively with regard to their known requirements.

Calcium is needed in macroquantities by higher plants and by blue-green algae (Allen and Arnon, 1955a) but only in microquantities by green algae (Myers, 1951; Stegman, 1940; Walker, 1953). Molybdenum is an essential micronutrient for all groups of plants, but its requirement by blue-green algae was found to be about 100 times higher than that for higher plants and green algae. Sodium is an essential element for blue-green algae (Allen and Arnon, 1954, 1955b; Kratz and Myers, 1955), but there is as yet no evidence of its indispensability, as tested by our criteria of essentiality, for green algae or higher plants. Although the essentiality of boron is undisputed for higher plants, there is as yet no unequivocal evidence for the requirement of this element by algae. Likewise, the recent report of a chlorine requirement by higher plants (Broyer *et al.*, 1954) raises the question of the need for this ubiquitous element by other plant forms. For another element, cobalt, there is so far only evidence for a requirement by blue-green algae (Holm-Hansen *et al.*, 1954; Buddhari and Arnon, unpublished data).

These differences in requirements among different species are of great methodological importance in the study of essentiality of inorganic nutrients. As already suggested, a given experimental technique may be adequate for demonstrating the essentiality of an element only in those species in which its quantitative requirement is high. Thus, a judicious or a fortuitous selection of species may permit an early discovery of a new essential element, whose requirements for other plants will be demonstrable only by additional refinements in experimental procedures. The history of micronutrient research contains a number of instances of this sort.

E. Is the List of Essential Elements Complete?

The diversity of inorganic requirements by different species raises the question whether evidence for the essentiality of an element by one species always indicates a universal requirement for this element by all plants. Is vanadium, for example, which, so far, was found to be essential only for green algae, to be also regarded as an essential micronutrient for all green plants? No unequivocal answer can be given to this question without further evidence of its general function in photosynthesis. It is certain that an element must be considered universally essential if it can be identified with a specific cellular reaction or a constituent common to all plants. But such evidence is not yet available even for the well-recognized essential elements, potassium and boron.

The recognition of the function of an inorganic nutrient may, in certain cases, impose limits on the definition of its essentiality. Thus, as will be discussed later, the requirement for molybdenum in *Scenedesmus* was found to be linked with the nitrogen source. Molybdenum met the criteria of essentiality when nitrate was the nitrogen source but not with ammonia or urea. Requirements for inorganic elements could thus be linked with certain metabolic pathways, but not with those which could serve as physiological alternatives.

In the absence of any definite knowledge of function for a new inorganic element suspected of being essential, the most reliable evidence of its status can only come from clear-cut growth experiments. As a matter of historical interest it is well to recall that all of our now known essential micronutrients were discovered by this route, well in advance of any knowledge of their function within the plant. Once the essentiality of an inorganic nutrient is established by growth experiments for any one species, it is, of course, desirable to try it with other species as well. But no matter how many species are tested, many more will always remain untried. Methodologically, it will always be useful to work with species which have an "exaggerated" requirement for a certain micronutrient. For these reasons, it seems that in the future as in the past, a well-documented requirement for a new micronutrient, even if established for only one or a few species, is likely to apply to all other plants characterized by the same type of metabolism.

The question is sometimes asked whether elements other than those hitherto investigated might be essential for green plants. It would seem best to attempt to answer this question in a quantitative rather than a qualitative manner: to determine analytically whenever possible the upper limit of impurity for a given element that may be contained in the nutrient medium and to measure a growth response with and without a further addition of the element in question. This can be illustrated as follows: It was found with the dithizone test that when the combined zinc, copper, lead, cadmium, and mercury content of a nutrient solution was less than 0.0001 mg. per plant, severe deficiency symptoms occurred in the tomato. Recovery was brought about by adding 0.002 mg. of copper and 0.002 mg. of zinc, but no further improvement was produced by supplying 0.0005 mg. each of lead, cadmium, and mercury. These results, while confirming the indispensability of zinc and copper in amounts greater than those found in the nutrient medium, were interpreted as permitting no final conclusion as to the role of cadmium, lead, and mercury. The possibility that one of these elements, or others studied by a similar technique, may be required in amounts smaller than the incidental impurities which could not be removed from culture solution by the present technique cannot be *a priori* excluded.

If these views are accepted, there can be no objection to regarding almost every element in the periodic table, and particularly those most frequently encountered in plant tissues, as susceptible of being shown at some time to be essential for plants. What can be asserted definitely is that, if an element now regarded as dispensable for a given plant should at some future time be found essential, it will be shown to be required in exceedingly small amounts that are within the limits of contamination still encompassed by the refined methods now used for purifying the nutrient medium. This quantitative approach to the problem of essentiality of micronutrients is regarded not as a mere theoretical generalization but as a point of view conducive to a search for more refined analytical methods and procedures for growing plants, which would make it possible to investigate the status of a number of new elements in plant nutrition.

III. Micronutrients in Nitrogen Metabolism. The Role of Molybdenum

It has already been mentioned that the minute quantities in which micronutrients are required in cellular metabolism have pointed early to their role as catalysts. Their catalytic role is of special interest in the two processes which occupy a key position in the economy of green plants: photosynthesis and nitrogen assimilation.

Research on these aspects of micronutrients has been under way in several laboratories, as we shall hear in more detail in this Symposium. In what follows, I shall present examples of this phase of research from our laboratory at Berkeley.

A. *Molybdenum and Nitrogen Assimilation in* Scenedesmus

Although the status of molybdenum as an essential micronutrient for higher plants has been well established, its role in the nutrition of algae was unknown. Recent reviews of mineral requirements of algae could adduce no evidence for the essentiality of molybdenum (Myers, 1951; Ketchum, 1954). More recently, however, evidence was presented for a molybdenum requirement of *Scenedesmus obliquus* (Arnon *et al.*, 1953; Arnon, 1954) and of *Chlorella pyrenoidosa* (Walker, 1953; Loneragan and Arnon, 1954).

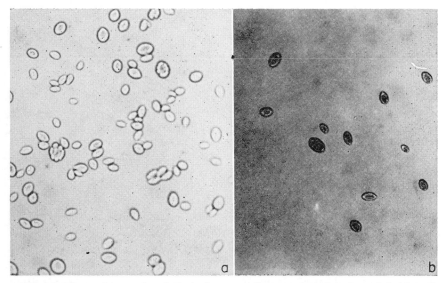

Fig. 4. Photomicrographs of *Scenedesmus* cells stained with iodine. (*a*) Normal; (*b*) molybdenum-deficient.

In later experiments with *Scenedesmus* (Arnon *et al.*, 1955) in which more effective procedures were used for removing traces of molybdenum impurities, there was almost complete failure of growth without added molybdenum in nutrient media containing nitrate as the sole source of nitrogen. The molybdenum-deficient cells showed symptoms of extreme nitrogen starvation as seen in parallel cultures to which molybdenum was added but from which nitrogen was omitted. In both the −Mo and −N

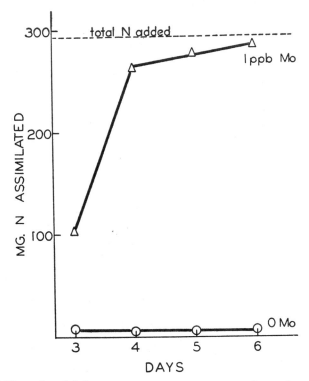

Fɪɢ. 5. Effect of molybdenum on nitrate nitrogen assimilation by *Scenedesmus*. Ordinate represents mg. N assimilated by cells contained in one liter of nutrient solution.

cultures there was a marked accumulation of starch and no evidence of cell division. This is shown in Fig. *4a, b,* which are photomicrographs of suspensions of *Scenedesmus* cells from normal and −Mo cultures stained with a dilute iodine solution. The molybdenum-deficient cells stained blue indicating an accumulation of starch.

The nitrogen starvation suggested by the appearance of the molybdenum-deficient cells was borne out by chemical determinations of their nitrogen assimilation. As illustrated in Fig. 5, the molybdenum-deficient cells assimilated only a minute amount of the nitrogen supplied as nitrate in the nutrient solution. Nitrogen assimilation in the normal cells proceeded vigorously up to the 4th day, when almost all of the nitrogen added to the medium was used up.

An entirely different picture was found however, when a reduced form of combined nitrogen, ammonia or urea, was substituted for nitrate (Ichioka and Arnon, 1955). As shown in Fig. 6, the omission of molybdenum had no effect on growth with either urea or ammonia nitrogen. In the nitrate series no growth occurred without added molybdenum.

These results, presented in more detail elsewhere (Ichioka and Arnon,

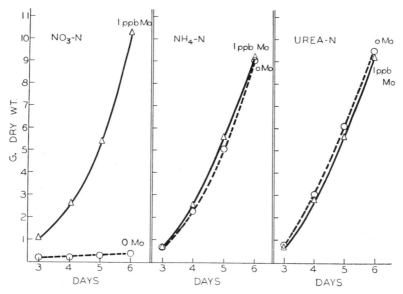

Fig. 6. Effect of molybdenum on growth of *Scenedesmus* supplied with nitrate, ammonia, or urea nitrogen. (Ordinate represents g. dry weight of cells per liter of nutrient solution.)

1955), suggest that in *Scenedesmus* the function of molybdenum is limited to nitrate reduction. They seem to provide the first instance in the nutrition of green plants in which the essentiality of an inorganic element is linked with only one metabolic step. The by-passing of the specific "metabolic block" of nitrate reduction caused by the deficiency of molybdenum rendered this essential element dispensable. With other organisms the substitution of a reduced form of nitrogen for nitrate has not abolished the requirement for molybdenum. Steinberg (1937) and Nicholas and McElroy (1954), working with fungi, and Mulder (1948) and Hewitt and McCready (1954), working with higher plants, concluded that even though the molybdenum requirement was greatly reduced it could not be completely abolished when ammonium replaced nitrate as the sole source of nitrogen (Meagher, 1952; Agarwala, 1952). In these species, molybdenum has been thought to perform other functions (Hewitt and McCready, 1954; Spencer and Wood, 1954) in addition to its principal one of catalyzing the reduction of nitrate. However, for another alga related to *Scenedesmus, Chlorella pyrenoidosa,* Walker (1953) found a requirement for molybdenum only when nitrate (but not urea) was the sole source of nitrogen.

B. Molybdenum and Nitrogen Metabolism of Blue-Green Algae

Many members of the blue-green algae (Myxophyceae) combine a photosynthetic habit of life with an ability to fix molecular nitrogen. Since

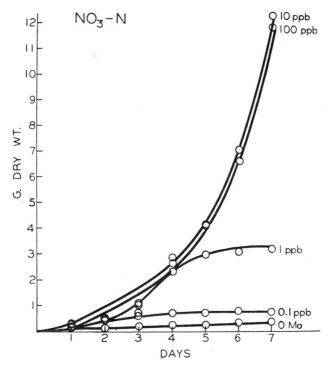

Fig. 7. Effect of molybdenum on the dry weight (g. dry weight of cells per liter of nutrient solution) of *Anabaena cylindrica* supplied with nitrate nitrogen (10^{-6} g. Mo per liter of nutrient solution = 1 p.p.b.). (Arnon and Ichioka, unpublished data.)

these organisms can also assimilate nitrogen they afford an opportunity for a comparison of the molybdenum requirement under the divergent conditions of nitrogen fixation and nitrate reduction. Figures 7 and 8 provide such a comparison for *Anabaena cylindrica*.

As shown in Fig. 7, assimilation of nitrate nitrogen by *Anabaena*, measured by the total dry weight produced, was strictly dependent on

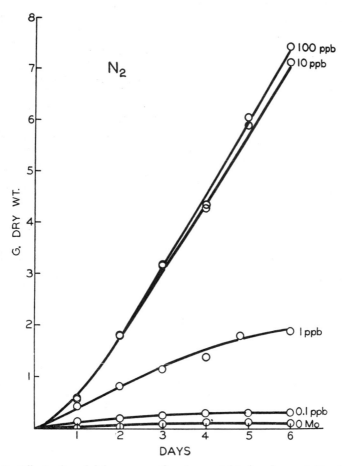

Fig. 8. Effect of molybdenum on the dry weight (g. dry weight of cells per liter of nutrient solution) of *Anabaena cylindrica* grown at the expense of atmospheric nitrogen (10^{-6} g. Mo per liter of nutrient solution = 1 p.p.b. Mo). (Arnon and Ichioka, unpublished data.)

molybdenum. *Anabaena* was found to differ from *Scenedesmus* in requiring an approximately 100-fold higher supply of molybdenum for effective utilization of nitrate nitrogen. For *Anabaena* the range from limiting to adequate concentration of molybdenum in the nutrient medium was from

10^{-6} to 10^{-5} g. molybdenum per liter (Fig. 7) whereas for *Scenedesmus* it was from 10^{-8} to 10^{-7} g. molybdenum per liter of nutrient solution (Arnon *et al.*, 1955).

The molybdenum requirement for fixation of molecular nitrogen by *Anabaena* was found to be approximately the same as that for nitrate reduction, i.e., the range from limiting to adequate concentration was from 10^{-6} to 10^{-5} g. molybdenum per liter of nutrient solution (Fig. 8).

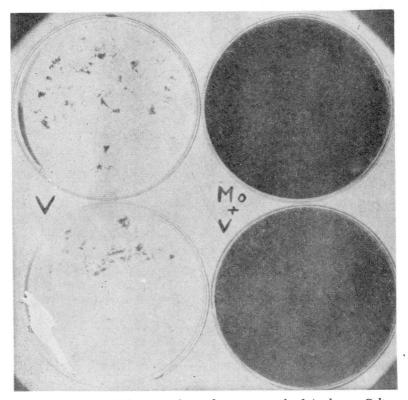

FIG. 9. Effect of molybdenum and vanadium on growth of *Anabaena*. Cultures on right received 10^{-5} g. Mo and 10^{-5} g. V, those on left received 10^{-5} g. V per liter of nutrient solution, but no molybdenum.

The molybdenum requirement for nitrate reduction was specific and not replaceable by other elements including vanadium. This is in accord with the findings of Nicholas and Nason (1945a, b) that molybdenum is the specific metal component of nitrate reductase in *Neurospora*. There is ample evidence, however, that molybdenum in its catalytic function in nitrogen fixation by bacteria (Burk, 1934) is replaceable by vanadium. Following the work of Bortels (1940) this conclusion has also been generally extended to nitrogen fixation by blue-green algae. However, an examination of Bortels' experimental results shows that the evidence for the replaceability of molybdenum by vanadium was not as definite as it has been accepted to be. Bortels studied 18 cultures of various Myxophyceae. The growth of 13 of these was stimulated by molybdenum, but not by vanadium, 2 of them were stimulated by both molybdenum and vanadium, and 3 did not respond to the addition of either of these elements.

The nonreplaceability of molybdenum by vanadium in nitrogen fixation by *Anabaena* is illustrated in Fig. 9. Growth at the expense of molecular nitrogen could not proceed when molybdenum was replaced by vanadium. The yield of *Anabaena* without the addition of either molybdenum or vanadium was 0.28 g. dry weight per liter, the addition of vanadium resulted in a yield of 0.36 g. per liter, and the addition of molybdenum raised the yield to 5.8 g. per liter. The reason for the replaceability of molybdenum by vanadium in nitrogen fixation by *Azotobacter* (Burk, 1934) and not by *Anabaena* is not clear at the present time.

The ability to fix molecular nitrogen combined with a photosynthetic habit of life places *Anabaena* and other blue-green algae among the most completely autotrophic living organisms requiring only light and a few inorganic elements for growth. Organisms of this kind could be of great importance to agriculture as a source of combined nitrogen for crop use. This has already been recognized for a number of years in rice culture (see review by Fogg, 1947). But because it was believed their growth was slow with atmospheric nitrogen, the potential quantitative contribution of blue-green algae to the nitrogen economy of crops was considered to be limited.

This conclusion does not seem to be justified in the light of recent evidence (Allen and Arnon, 1955a). By proper adjustment of the inorganic nutrient medium, including the provision of an optimal supply of micronutrients, *Anabaena cylindrica* produced at the expense of atmospheric nitrogen as much as 25 g. of dry weight of cells per square meter of illuminated surface in 24 hours, an increase of approximately 200-fold over the yields previously reported for this and other blue-green algae. These high yields have resulted not from the attainment of higher growth rate constants (K) than those previously reported for these organisms, but rather from the maintenance of high growth rates at *high cell densities*.

The potential significance of this rate of growth of blue-green algae to the nitrogen economy of soils is shown in Table II. Under otherwise similar culture conditions, the growth of *Anabaena* with atmospheric nitrogen was about half that of *Scenedesmus*, grown with nitrate nitro-

TABLE II

Yield (Dry Weight Basis) and Nitrogen Economy of a Green and a Blue-Green Alga

Alga	Nitrogen source	Density of cells at harvest		Highest daily (24 hrs.) yield of cells	Highest daily (24 hrs.) nitrogen use[a]	Calculated highest nitrogen use[a] for a month
		(g. per liter)	(g. per sq. meter)	(g. per sq. meter)	(g. N per sq. meter)	(lb. N per acre)
Scenedesmus obliquus	NO_3^-	13.9	158.	56.8	2.84[b]	780[b,d]
Anabaena cylindrica	N_2	7.6	86.5	25.0	1.75[c]	480[c,e]

[a] Computed on basis of 7 per cent nitrogen of dry weight of *Anabaena* and 5 per cent of *Scenedesmus*.

[b] The nitrogen was absorbed by the algal cells from the nutrient solution as nitrate.

[c] The nitrogen was fixed by the algal cells from nitrogen gas in the air.

[d] Corresponds to 3700 pounds of ammonium sulfate.

[e] Corresponds to 2300 pounds of ammonium sulfate.

gen, and accounted for the fixation in an organic form of 480 pounds of gaseous nitrogen per acre per month. This figure is, of course, an extrapolation of laboratory results to field conditions and must be used with great caution. It suggests, however, that under favorable conditions blue-green algae could make a substantial contribution to the nitrogen economy of soils. Even if only a small fraction of their nitrogen-fixing capacity were used, it would be important by comparison with nitrogen fixation as reported for other biological agents, e.g., 40 pounds by nonsymbiotic bacteria and 100–200 pounds by the *legume-Rhizobium* association, per acre per year (Waksman, 1931).

The ability of blue-green algae to supply combined nitrogen to plants unable to use molecular nitrogen, already observed in the field (see review, Fogg, 1947), was tested (jointly with M. B. Allen) in preliminary experiments with rice seedlings in a greenhouse. Rice seedlings were germinated and grown in sand culture with nutrient solutions lacking nitrogen. One series was inoculated with a pure culture of *Anabaena cylindrica.* As shown in Fig. 10, the rice seedlings in the uninoculated cultures failed to grow once the nitrogen reserves in the seed were used up. By contrast, the rice plants in the inoculated cultures made appreciable growth at the expense of the atmospheric nitrogen fixed by *Anabaena.*

This quasi symbiosis between rice and *Anabaena,* two independent

FIG. 10. Effect of *Anabaena cylindrica* on the growth of rice seedlings in a nutrient solution free of nitrogen compounds. (*a*) Control; (*b*) culture inoculated with *Anabaena cylindrica*.

photoautotrophic plants, constituted a more stringent test of nitrogen fixation than a similar association would under field conditions. In the greenhouse experiment, the rice seedlings were dependent on nitrogen fixed concurrently by the blue-green algae, whereas in the field, rice plants would be able to draw on nitrogen fixed by algae in prior events.

IV. MICRONUTRIENTS IN PHOTOSYNTHESIS

Special attention is being given in our laboratory to the effects of molybdenum, vanadium, and manganese on photosynthesis. Bové and Bové (unpublished data) have observed an effect of molybdenum on photosynthesis by the blue-green alga, *Nostoc,* grown at the expense of molecular nitrogen. On a unit-chlorophyll basis, total carbon assimilation, measured by a 15-minute photosynthesis experiment with $C^{14}O_2$, was reduced approximately by half in the molybdenum-restricted cultures as compared with cells which have received an adequate supply of molybdenum throughout the growing period. The addition of molybdenum to the molybdenum-restricted cultures, 11 hours prior to the photosynthesis experiment, increased total CO_2 fixation and produced a marked shift in the distribution of radioactivity among the assimilatory products (Table III). The addition of molybdenum has resulted in a decrease in sugars accompanied by a marked increase of glutamine and amino acids, particularly aspartic and glutamic acid (Table III). These results are in

TABLE III

Effect of Molybdenum on Photosynthesis by *Nostoc*

(Fifteen minutes illumination, 20°C. Molybdenum added, where indicated, 11 hours before the experiment. "Low Mo" cultures received 5×10^{-7} g. Mo per liter of culture solution.)

	% $C^{14}O_2$ fixed in sol. fraction	
	Low Mo	Mo added
Sugar phosphate	75.	55.5
Sucrose	5.	3.
Malate	2.5	1.
Glutamine	Trace	5.
Amino acids, total	6.	26.5
Aspartic	4.	17.
Glutamic	0.5	5.5
Other amino acids	1.5	4.
Total C^{14} fixed (c.p.m.)	8.9×10^5	16×10^5

harmony with the previously discussed (Section III, B) role of molybdenum in nitrogen fixation by blue-green algae, but they do not constitute evidence for a direct participation of this element in photosynthesis. The observed accumulation of sugars accompanied by a decrease in total CO_2 fixation can be most simply explained as a result of impaired nitrogen fixation and assimilation, under conditions of molybdenum insufficiency.

In another series of experiments (Arnon and Ichioka, unpublished data; Arnon, 1954) vanadium deficiency in *Scenedesmus* resulted in a substantially lower chlorophyll content (Table IV). Photosynthesis of plus- and minus-vanadium *Scenedesmus* cells was studied at a high (20,000 lux) and a low light intensity (2000 lux). The rate of photo-

TABLE IV

Effect of Vanadium on Chlorophyll and Photosynthesis in *Scenedesmus obliquus*

Experiment	Chlorophyll (Per cent dry wt.)		Photosynthesis (mm.³ O₂/mg. chl./hr.)			
			2000 lux		20,000 lux	
	−V	+V	−V	+V	−V	+V
A	1.7	2.3	1500	1500	2400	5200
B	1.7	2.3	1600	1600	2900	4600
C	1.7	3.1	1200	1600	1900	4000
D	1.3	2.3	800	1200	1600	4000
E	1.2	2.6	900	1400	1200	3700
F	1.2	2.6	1100	1200	1200	3400
G	1.0	1.8	1400	1700	1500	3200

synthesis, expressed on a *unit-chlorophyll* basis, was twice as high in the plus-vanadium cells as in the minus-vanadium cells, but only in strong light (Table IV). In the weaker light there was no significant difference between the two cultures in the rate of photosynthesis. The effects of vanadium deficiency at high and low light intensity are graphically represented in Figs. 11 and 12.

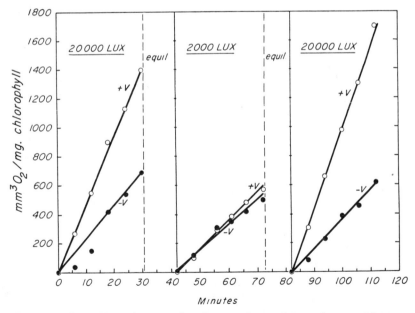

Fig. 11. Effect of vanadium on the photosynthesis of *Scenedesmus obliquus* at a high and a low light intensity. The same cells were exposed successively to high and to low and again to high light intensity with intervening equilibration periods.

The effects of vanadium on photosynthesis invite comparison with those of manganese observed in parallel experiments in this laboratory (Tsujimoto and Arnon, unpublished data; also compare Arnon, 1954). Manganese deficiency, unlike that of vanadium, did not reduce significantly the chlorophyll content of *Scenedesmus*. Total growth as measured by cell count, packed cell volume, and dry weight was arrested, but the chlorophyll content of the manganese-deficient cells was approximately the same as that of the controls.

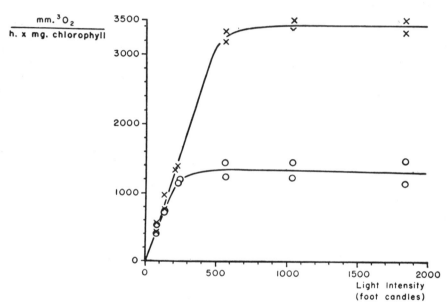

FIG. 12. The rate of photosynthesis of plus-vanadium (crosses) and minus-vanadium (circles) *Scenedesmus obliquus* cells as a function of light intensity. (These experiments were carried out by Dr. A. W. Frenkel.)

The rate of photosynthesis in the manganese deficient cells was also investigated under a high and a low light intensity. The results (Fig. 13), expressed again on a unit chlorophyll basis, differ in one interesting respect from those found in vanadium deficiency (Fig. 11). Manganese deficiency was found to reduce the rate of photosynthesis in both weak and strong light (Fig. 13), suggesting that manganese may be involved in the photochemical reactions at all light intensities.

This direct participation of manganese-catalyzed reactions in the photochemical events of photosynthesis is also shown in Fig. 14. The lower rate of photosynthesis of cells grown without added manganese

$(-Mn)$ was restored within about 20 minutes to that of the normal cells $(+Mn)$ by the addition of manganese to the minus-manganese cells $(-Mn + Mn)$ whether this addition was made while the cells were illuminated or kept dark. By contrast, the addition of vanadium to the minus-vanadium cells restored the normal rate of photosynthesis at high light intensity only after several hours. The prompt restoration of a normal rate of photosynthesis in the minus-Mn cells by the addition of manganese suggests a direct catalytic participation of this micronutrient

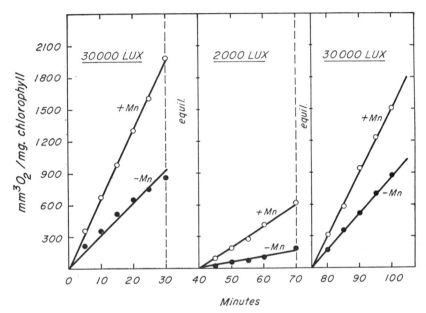

FIG. 13. Effect of manganese on the photosynthesis of *Scenedesmus obliquus* at a high and a low light intensity. The same cells were exposed successively to high, to low, and again to high light intensity with intervening equilibration periods.

in photosynthetic reactions. These effects of manganese on photosynthesis in *Scenedesmus* are fundamentally in agreement with the earlier work of Pirson *et al.* (1952), on *Ankistrodesmus*.

The effects of manganese described so far concern photosynthesis as measured at the cellular level. Evidence was recently obtained that manganese increases photosynthesis by isolated chloroplasts as measured by carbon dioxide fixation (Arnon *et al.*, 1954, 1956; Allen *et al.*, 1955). The nature of the manganese effect in this cell-free photosynthetic system is currently under investigation.

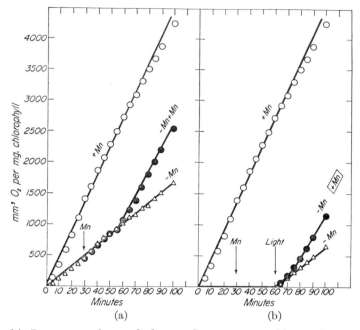

Fɪɢ. 14. Restoration of normal photosynthetic rates on addition of manganese to —Mn cells. The addition of Mn was made, at the time indicated by arrows, to —Mn cells kept either in the light (a) or in the dark (b). —Mn cells which were kept in the dark (b) were exposed to light at the time indicated by the second arrow.

V. QUANTITATIVE REQUIREMENTS OF MICRONUTRIENTS. THE MOLYBDENUM REQUIREMENT OF A SINGLE CELL

The recurrent emphasis on the small requirements of micronutrients makes it desirable to illustrate in specific terms, for at least one element, molybdenum, the relation which was observed between its concentration in the external medium and that within the cells of a *Scenedesmus* culture, grown with nitrate as the sole source of nitrogen (Section III, A).

As shown in Fig. 15, 10^{-9} g. molybdenum per liter of nutrient solution (0.001 p.p.b. molybdenum) was clearly insufficient throughout the entire growth period. 10^{-8} g. molybdenum per liter was sufficient almost up to the 3rd day but began limiting growth when production of dry cell matter exceeded 2 g. per liter. 10^{-7} g. molybdenum per liter was fully adequate to sustain vigorous growth. No increase in growth was obtained by a 10-fold increase in concentration (10^{-6} g. molybdenum per liter). A further 10-fold increase in concentration (10^{-5} g./l.) appeared to be only slightly inhibitory. These and previous results (Arnon, 1954) demonstrate the low level of external concentration of molybdenum which is sufficient for growth. The results also confirm the remarkably great spread, characteristic for this element, between the adequate and toxic

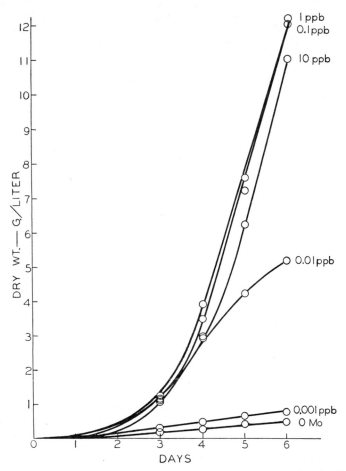

Fig. 15. Effect of molybdenum on the dry weight (g. dry weight of cells per liter of nutrient solution) of *Scenedesmus* (10^{-6} g. Mo per liter of nutrient solution = 1 p.p.b.).

levels of supply, as was noted in the first experiments on the essentiality of molybdenum for green plants (Arnon and Stout, 1939b).

If the quantitative requirement for molybdenum by *Scenedesmus* is expressed in terms of concentration of this element in the nutrient solution, excellent agreement is found with the low values reported by Agarwala and Hewitt (1954) for cauliflower. The supply levels at which molybdenum deficiency could be shown were 10^{-8} g. molybdenum per liter for *Scenedesmus* as against 5×10^{-8} g. molybdenum per liter of nutrient solution for cauliflower.

The unicellular character of *Scenedesmus* has also made it possible to determine the molybdenum requirement in terms of atoms per single cell. The number of cells in the minus-molybdenum culture served as a blank, since it represented growth at the expense of the molybdenum contained in the inoculum and in the residual impurities of the nutrient medium. By subtracting this blank from the number of cells in the cultures to which molybdenum was added, net cell counts representing growth as a function of molybdenum concentration were obtained.

The values for the molybdenum requirement per cell, given in Table V, represent maximum figures, since it was assumed that all the molybde-

TABLE V

Number of Molybdenum Atoms per Cell in *Scenedesmus*

	Restricted Mo supply				Adequate Mo supply	
	(10^{-9} g./l.)		(10^{-8} g./l.)		(10^{-7} g./l.)	
Age of culture (days)	Net[a] cell count $\times 10^{-8}$/l.	Atoms Mo per cell[b]	Net[a] cell count $\times 10^{-8}$/l.	Atoms Mo per cell[b]	Net[a] cell count $\times 10^{-8}$/l.	Atoms Mo per cell[b]
0	0.1	630,000	0.1	6,300,000	0.1	63,000,000
3	23	2,700	290	2,200	450	14,000
4	40	1,600	340	1,800	1500	4,200
5	37	1,700	430	1,500	2300	2,700
6	37	1,700	420	1,500	2600	2,400

[a] Obtained by subtracting the number of cells in the $-$Mo culture.

[b] Computed by the formula: $\dfrac{\text{gram-atoms Mo}}{\text{net-cell count}} \times$ Avogadro's number.

num added to the nutrient solution was used by the algae. The molybdenum requirement per cell was computed at three different levels of molybdenum concentration in the nutrient solution: two representing a restricted, and one an adequate level of supply (Fig. 15). At all three levels the most rapid cell division occurred when the molybdenum supply was above 3000 atoms per cell. In the molybdenum-restricted cultures no cell division occurred when the molybdenum supply dropped to 1500–1700 atoms per cell.

Considering the large errors inherent in this type of computation, the quantitative agreement between the molybdenum requirement per cell reported earlier (Arnon, 1954) and that found in the different cultures used in the more recent investigation reported here, is considered excellent. The molybdenum requirements of *Scenedesmus* invite comparison with those reported by Burk (1934) for *Azotobacter*. He found that an *Azotobacter* cell required 10,000 atoms of Mo for optimum nitrogen fixation. Taking the average diameter of a *Scenedesmus* cell as 12 microns and that of *Azotobacter* as 2 microns (Burk, 1934), one arrives at the ratio of the cell volumes of *Scenedesmus* to *Azotobacter* as 216 : 1 (ratio of the diameters cubed). This suggests that on a unit cell volume basis, the concentration of molybdenum needed by *Azotobacter* is approximately 700 times as great as in *Scenedesmus*.

REFERENCES

Agarwala, S. C. 1952. *Nature* **169**, 1099.
Agarwala, S. C., and Hewitt, E. J. 1954. *J. Hort. Sci.* **29**, 278–290.
Allen, M. B., and Arnon, D. I. 1954. Paper presented before American Society of Plant Physiologists, Gainseville, Florida.
Allen, M. B., and Arnon, D. I. 1955a. *Plant Physiol.* **30**, 366–372.
Allen, M. B., and Arnon, D. I. 1955b. *Physiol. Plantarum* **8**, 653–660.
Allen, M. B., Arnon, D. I., Capindale, J. B., Whatley, F. R., and Durham, L. J. 1955. *J. Am. Chem. Soc.* **77**, 4149–4155.
Arnon, D. I. 1937. *Soil Sci.* **44**, 91–121.
Arnon, D. I. 1938. *Am. J. Botany* **25**, 322–325.
Arnon, D. I. 1952. *In* "Mineral Nutrition of Plants," pp. 313–341. Univ. Wisconsin Press, Madison, Wisconsin.
Arnon, D. I. 1954. *8ᵉ Congr. intern. botan., 8ᵉ Congr. Paris.* Sect. 11, 73–80.
Arnon, D. I., and Stout, P. R. 1939a. *Plant Physiol.* **14**, 371–375.
Arnon, D. I., and Stout, P. R. 1939b. *Plant Physiol.* **14**, 599–602.
Arnon, D. I., and Wessel, G. 1953. *Nature* **172**, 1039–1040.
Arnon, D. I., Fujiwara, A., Wessel, G., and Woolley, J. T. 1953. Paper presented before American Society of Plant Physiologists, Madison, Wisconsin.
Arnon, D. I., Allen, M. B., and Whatley, F. R. 1954. *Nature* **174**, 394–396.
Arnon, D. I., Ichioka, P. S., Wessel, G., Fujiwara, A., and Woolley, J. T. 1955. *Physiol. Plantarum* **8**, 538–551.
Arnon, D. I., Allen, M. B., and Whatley, F. R. 1956. *Biochim. et Biophys. Acta* **20**, 449–461.
Bertrand, D. 1941. *Bull. soc. chim. France,* [5ᵉ] **9**, 121–135.
Bertrand, D. 1942. *Ann. institut Pasteur* **68**, 58–69.
Bortels, H. 1940. *Arch. Mikrobiol.* **11**, 155–186.
Broyer, T. C., Carlton, A. B., Johnson, C. M., and Stout, P. R. 1954. *Plant Physiol.* **29**, 526–531.
Burk, D. 1934. *Ergeb. Enzymforsch.* **3**, 23–56.
de Saussure, T. 1804. "Recherches chimiques sur la vegetation." Reprinted by Gauthier-Villars, Paris, 1957.
Fogg, G. E. 1947. *Endeavour* **6**, 172–175.
Grahame, D. C., and Seaborg, G. T. 1938. *J. Am. Chem. Soc.* **60**, 2524–2528.
Hewitt, E. J., and McCready, C. C. 1954. *Nature* **174**, 186–187.
Hoagland, D. R., and Snyder, W. C. 1933. *Proc. Am. Soc. Hort. Sci.* **30**, 288–294.
Holm-Hansen, O., Gerloff, C. D., and Skoog, F. 1954. *Physiol. Plantarum* **7**, 665–675.

Ichioka, P. S., and Arnon, D. I. 1955. *Physiol. Plantarum* **8**, 552–560.
Kellogg, C. E. 1951. *J. Politics* **13**, 325–344.
Ketchum, B. H. 1954. *Ann. Rev. Plant Physiol.* **5**, 55–74.
Kratz, W. A., and Myers, J. 1955. *Am. J. Botany* **42**, 282–287.
Loneragan, J. F., and Arnon, D. I. 1954. *Nature* **174**, 459.
Meagher, W. R. 1952. Ph.D. Thesis, University of California, Berkeley, California.
Mulder, E. G. 1948. *Plant and Soil* **1**, 94–119.
Myers, J. 1951. *Ann. Rev. Microbiol.* **5**, 157–180.
Nicholas, D. J. D., and McElroy, W. D. 1954. *J. Biol. Chem.* **207**, 341–351.
Nicholas, D. J. D., and Nason, A. 1954a. *J. Biol. Chem.* **207**, 353–360.
Nicholas, D. J. D., and Nason, A. 1954b. *J. Biol. Chem.* **211**, 183–197.
Pirson, A., Tichy, C., and Wilhelmi, G. 1952. *Planta* **40**, 199–253.
Raulin, J. 1869. *Ann. sci. nat.* [5ᵉ] **11**, 93–299.
Spencer, D., and Wood, J. G. 1954. *Australian J. Biol. Sci.* **7**, 425–434.
Stegmann, G. 1940. *Z. Botan.* **35**, 385–422.
Steinberg, R. A. 1937. *J. Agr. Research* **55**, 891–902.
Stout, P. R., and Arnon, D. I. 1939. *Am. J. Botany* **26**, 144–149.
Waksman, S. A. 1931. "The Soil and the Microbe." Wiley, New York.
Walker, J. B. 1953. *Arch. Biochem. Biophys.* **46**, 1–11.
Warburg, O., and Krippahl, G. 1954. *Angew. Chem.* **66**, 493–496.
Warburg, O., Krippahl, G., and Buchholz, W. 1955. *Z. Naturforsch.* **10b**, 422.

CHAPTER 2

Trace Elements in Animals

E. J. UNDERWOOD

Institute of Agriculture
University of Western Australia,
Nedlands, Western Australia

		Page
I.	The Nature of Trace Elements	33
	A. The Essential Trace Elements	34
	B. The Probably Essential Elements	34
	C. The Toxic Trace Elements	36
	D. The Physiologically Inactive Trace Elements	36
II.	The Discovery of the Trace Elements	37
III.	Interrelations among the Trace Elements	39
IV.	Mode of Action of the Trace Elements	41
V.	Sources of the Trace Elements	43
	References	44

I. THE NATURE OF TRACE ELEMENTS

A very large number of elements is known to occur in the tissues of higher animals—many of them in such small quantities that the early workers, who were unable to measure precise concentrations with the methods then available, frequently referred to them as occurring in "traces." For this reason they became known as trace elements, a term which has remained, although a high proportion of them can now be estimated with considerable precision. "Micronutrient elements" is the more correct term, but the shorter colloquial name with its historical associations seems destined to remain in popular usage.

No completely satisfactory line of demarcation can be drawn between those elements which can be classed as trace elements and the macronutrient elements. In animal physiology it is customary to regard any element which normally occurs in, or is required by, the higher forms of animal life in amounts greater than those of iron as a macronutrient and to include among the micronutrients all those elements which normally occur or are required in amounts no greater than those of iron. This is a fairly satisfactory division, although it must be realized that

33

large quantitative differences occur among the trace elements both in
the concentrations in which they generally occur in living tissues and in
the minimum requirements of animals. For instance, the requirements of
mammals for copper are many times those of iodine, and the levels of zinc
in animal tissues are normally many times those of manganese. Moreover,
some trace elements, like silicon and rubidium, regularly occur in the
blood and tissues of animals in concentrations many times those of most
of the essential trace elements, although no physiological functions have
yet been assigned to them.

The trace elements can conveniently be divided into four groups,
as follows: (1) the essential; (2) the probably essential; (3) the toxic;
and (4) the physiologically inactive elements.

There is some overlapping in these groups, and the location of a
particular element in a group is likely to change as research proceeds.
Nevertheless, a division of this sort is helpful in discussion.

A. The Essential Trace Elements

Thirty years ago the only trace elements which could be legitimately
called essential for animals were iron and iodine. At the present time,
copper, zinc, manganese, and cobalt must be added, making six essential
trace elements in animal nutrition. Ruminants, however, are the only
class of animal for which cobalt, as such, can be called essential. Essentiality in these cases is determined by the following criteria: (1) repeated
demonstration of a significant growth response to dietary supplements of
the element and this element alone; (2) development of the deficiency
state on diets otherwise adequate and satisfactory, i.e., containing all
other known dietary essentials in adequate amounts and proportions and
free from toxic properties, and (3) correlation of the deficiency state
with the occurrence of subnormal levels of the element in the blood or
tissues of animals exhibiting the response.

B. The Probably Essential Elements

These are fluorine, bromine, selenium, molybdenum, barium, and
strontium, which cannot yet be classed as essential trace elements because
they have not so far been shown to meet all of the above criteria. There
is no doubt, for instance, that the fluoride ion at appropriate levels of
intake assists in the prevention of dental caries, but a fluorine-deficient
diet which limits the growth or reproductive capacity or affects the well-
being of the animal organism as a whole has not been produced. Bromine,
another halogen, has recently been shown to induce a small but significant
growth increase in chicks fed a semisynthetic diet and in mice fed a diet
containing iodinated casein (Huff et al., 1956), but this interesting finding

awaits confirmation with the use of more satisfactory basal diets and measurements of the bromine status of the body under the conditions of presumed deficiency.

Barium and strontium are at present in much the same equivocal position as is bromine. Thus Rygh (1949) fed rats and guinea pigs on diets highly purified by special techniques which produced satisfactory growth and tooth and bone development when supplemented with a "complete" mineral mixture. The omission of either barium or strontium from the mineral supplement resulted in a depression in growth, while the omission of strontium alone resulted further in an impairment of the calcification of the bones and teeth and in a higher incidence of carious teeth than occurred in the strontium-supplemented animals. This important piece of basic research needs confirmation and extension, especially in view of the present interest in Sr^{90} and the paucity of modern data on the normal occurrence of stable strontium in living tissues.

Molybdenum is in a rather more satisfactory position. It is known to be a component of the enzyme, xanthine oxidase (Richert and Westerfield, 1953; DeRenzo et al., 1953) and molybdenum-low diets have been devised which deplete liver and intestinal xanthine oxidase levels in the rat. The addition of molybdenum to these diets raised the xanthine oxidase levels in the tissues, but it was not accompanied by any improvement in the growth or metabolic performance of the animals, although the basal diets contained only 0.02 p.p.m. molybdenum (Westerfield and Richert, 1954). Subsequently a significant growth response from added molybdenum has been reported in chicks (Reid et al., 1956). These animals were fed diets containing 1 p.p.m. molybdenum or more, which is about 50 times that of the diet found adequate for rats, and the growth response was obtained from a supplement supplying only 0.0126 p.p.m. molybdenum. This highly interesting finding has not yet been fully confirmed elsewhere, although the addition of tungsten, which is apparently a molybdenum antagonist, enabled a growth response in chicks from added molybdenum to be readily demonstrated (Higgins et al., 1956; Norris, 1957).

The most recent element to be added to the list of possible essential trace elements is selenium. In a series of elegant experiments two groups of workers have independently shown that this element, in the form of selenite, can perform many of the functions of vitamin E. Selenite protects against the necrotic liver degeneration which develops in rats fed a vitamin E-free diet in which torula yeast is the sole source of protein and against the exudative diathesis which occurs in chicks fed similar diets (Schwarz et al., 1957; Schwarz and Foltz, 1957; Patterson et al., 1957). It is not yet known if selenium is required in the presence of vitamin E but if so then this requirement must be less than 0.04 p.p.m. selenium, since this is approximately the selenium content of the diet which gives good growth and no signs of disease when vitamin E, and vitamin E alone, is included.

C. The Toxic Trace Elements

It is, of course, a truism that any element or nutrient can be toxic to animals if consumed in large enough amounts or for sufficiently long periods. Certain of the trace elements, however, owe their biological importance, or originally owed their biological importance, to their toxic effects on animals in very small or trace quantities. Fluorine, selenium, and molybdenum are outstanding examples of these because of their natural occurrence in the food and drinking water of certain areas of the world in sufficiently high concentrations to induce gross signs of disease in animals confined to these regions. Chronic copper poisoning in sheep has also been reported, under naturally occurring conditions, in certain restricted areas in Australia (Albiston *et al.*, 1940; Bull, 1951). Toxic conditions from other trace minerals, such as arsenic, lead, and zinc, can also occur under special conditions as a result of industrial contamination or the excessive use of particular fungicides, pesticides, or anthelmintics.

One aspect of the investigation of these toxicity problems which is of the greatest scientific and practical importance has been the revelation that the metabolism, and hence toxicity, of an element can be markedly influenced by the degree to which other elements or nutrients are present in the diet. It was the study of naturally occurring molybdenosis in cattle in England (Ferguson *et al.*, 1938, 1940, 1943) and in New Zealand (Cunningham, 1950) which first revealed the relation between copper intakes and molybdenum toxicity and the study of chronic copper poisoning in sheep in Australia which led to the remarkable findings of Dick (1952, 1953, 1954) that not only does molybdenum act as a copper antagonist in the animal body but that this antagonistic action is dependent upon the levels of inorganic sulfate in the diet. These and other trace element interactions are discussed more fully later.

D. The Physiologically Inactive Trace Elements

The physiologically active elements so far mentioned represent only a small proportion of the total trace elements which have been shown to occur regularly in living tissues. Spectrochemical studies in many laboratories have revealed the presence of a further 20 to 30 elements, the nature of which vary, one suspects, more with the techniques used than with actual differences in distribution. It is difficult to evaluate these investigations and still more difficult to resist teleological reasoning from some of the intriguing facts which have emerged. For instance, is there any physiological significance in the fact that rubidium occurs in animal tissues and organs, including fetal tissues and milk, in the remarkably high and fairly consistent proportion of 20 to 40 p.p.m. on the dry basis (Lundergardh, 1929; Ramage and Sheldom, 1931)? Why is it that about 80 per cent of the arsenic in normal blood is concentrated in the red cells (Hove *et al.*, 1938)? Is this in any way related to the persistent, but experimentally inconclusive, claims that arsenic is of value in the treatment of human anemias? What significance attaches to the fact that lead occurs in greatest concentration in the outer enamel of both erupted and unerupted teeth and decreases in concentration in the inner layers, whereas no such pattern of distribution occurs with tin or copper, to which the animal is equally exposed (Brudevold and Steadman, 1955)? It may be that the consistent concentration of certain elements in particular organs or tissues merely reflects a higher tolerance or greater chemical affinity of one organ or tissue compared with that of another. Nevertheless it seems likely that as techniques improve, many of these "accidental" trace elements will be found to have physiological functions. It should not be forgotten that only a few short years ago copper, zinc, manganese, and cobalt were regarded as adventitious contaminants and molybdenum and selenium solely as toxic elements.

II. The Discovery of the Trace Elements

The history of the discovery of the trace elements and of their physiological significance is one of the most fascinating and rewarding in the whole field of animal biology. Advances have come equally from many different countries and from workers with entirely different backgrounds and different objectives. The applied scientist with his urge to solve a serious field problem, no less than the pure scientist with his interest in the basic nutritional needs of animals, has made significant contributions to our present knowledge and understanding.

Work with trace elements can be said to have begun about a century ago when scientists interested themselves in a number of special compounds of limited biological significance such as turacin, a porphyrin compound containing copper which occurs in the feathers of certain birds (Church, 1869); hemocyanin, another copper compound found in the blood of certain snails (Harless, 1847); sycotypin, a zinc-containing pigment in the blood of mollusca (Mendel and Bradley, 1905); and a vanadium-containing respiratory compound present in the blood of sea squirts (Henze, 1911). For many years these substances were regarded merely as scientific curiosities and little idea of a generalized function for the trace elements emerged from such studies.

Early in this century, however, chemists became greatly interested in the chemical composition of biological materials, particularly as spectro-chemical techniques became available and conventional methods of analysis progressed to the point where small concentrations of elements could be measured with more confidence. During this period it became evident, for the first time, that plant and animal tissues contained, in addition to the major elements, a great array of other elements present in minute but fairly consistent concentrations. The attitude toward these trace elements at this time was predominantly chemical rather than biological but this "distributional" phase in trace element history served two important purposes. It drew the attention of nutritionists to the possible significance of many elements hitherto regarded as, at most, interesting contaminants, and it saw the beginning of the development of microanalytical methods. The availability of methods capable of estimating with delicacy and precision the minute amounts involved has been, and still is, a highly potent factor in facilitating our understanding of the trace elements. The advent of radioactive isotopes of these elements has, it is true, placed a new and powerful weapon in the hands of the physiologist, but it has not eliminated the need for more sensitive and accurate methods of analysis by more conventional means.

In the 1920's, particularly in France and the United States, a direct attack on the role of trace elements in animal nutrition began with the use of highly purified or specially constituted diets fed to small laboratory animals. At first these were largely unsuccessful because the diets used were usually so deficient in other respects, especially in vitamins, that even with the addition of the element under study the animals soon died or made very little growth. In 1928, however, Hart and associates (1928) at Wisconsin demonstrated conclusively that copper is an essential element in the nutrition of the rat. This classic work initiated the trace element era in the modern sense. It was quickly followed by demonstrations of the essentiality of copper for other species and of manganese and zinc in mammalian and avian nutrition (see Underwood, 1956). Advances in other branches of nutritional science gradually enabled more and more satisfactory basal diets to be devised and more acute deficiency states to be developed. Attention was then turned to the functions and mode of action of the new essential elements in the cells and tissues of the animal body. Knowledge of the relation of the trace elements to various enzyme systems emerged from such studies and represented a most significant step forward in our understanding of their role in nutrition.

While these fundamental researches were proceeding, and even earlier in the case of iodine, there began the investigations of a number of naturally occurring nutritional diseases of man and his domestic animals which were destined to give a new and powerful stimulus to the study of trace elements. Outstanding examples of these were the demonstration that, (1) lack of iodine in the food and water supply in certain areas is the primary cause of endemic goiter of man and farm stock. This was conclusively shown early in the century (see Harington, 1933); (2) a deficiency of cobalt in the soils and pastures of restricted areas in Australia and New Zealand is the cause of a drastic wasting disease (marasmus) in sheep and cattle, confined to these pastures (Lines, 1935; Marston, 1935; Underwood and Filmer, 1935); (3) lack of copper in the grazing is associated with a range of disabilities in sheep and cattle in certain parts of Australia, Europe, and the United States (see Underwood, 1956); (4) a deficiency of manganese is the primary cause of the diseases of poultry, "perosis" and "chondrodystrophy," which arise when the birds are fed certain types of commercial diets (Wilgus et al., 1936; Lyons and Insko, 1937); (5) "alkali disease" and "blind staggers" of stock depastured on particular range areas in the Great Plains region of the United States are manifestations of chronic and acute selenium poisoning, respectively (Robinson, 1933; Beath et al., 1935), and (6) excessive intakes of molybdenum from the herbage are responsible for the severe and debilitating diarrhea which occurs in cattle confined to certain pastures in England (Ferguson et al., 1938, 1940, 1943).

Very considerable scientific effort was concentrated upon these and other field problems because of their great economic significance to the countries concerned. As a result, cheap and simple solutions in most cases were found which completely revolutionized the productivity of the affected areas. In addition, a great stimulus was given to basic studies of the mode of action of the trace elements within the animal body, until at the present time it is impossible to distinguish between such fundamental researches which sprang from the attempts to solve and understand practical field problems and those which developed as a result of the "pure science" approach with small, laboratory animals.

III. INTERRELATIONS AMONG THE TRACE ELEMENTS

In the naturally occurring trace element abnormalities, just mentioned, attention was at first concentrated upon a single element, or in some cases upon a pair of elements, like cobalt and copper, deficiencies of which existed together in the same area. As investigations proceeded, a number of anomalies became apparent in the results reported from different parts of the world. These have led to the concept that simple or uncomplicated deficiencies or excesses rarely occur under natural conditions. They are frequently ameliorated or accentuated, i.e., "conditioned," by other dietary factors peculiar to the environment where the disease occurs. The demonstration of the nature of some of these "conditioning" factors and of the profound importance of balance among the trace elements constitutes one of the most fruitful and challenging advances in animal physiology in recent times. Several examples of such findings will now be given.

For instance, "swayback," which is the local name given to an ataxic condition which affects lambs in certain parts of England, fulfills some of the criteria of copper deficiency but not others. It can be controlled by feeding copper supplements to the ewe during pregnancy, and subnormal concentrations of copper can be demonstrated in the blood and tissues of ewes and affected lambs, as in Australia, but the copper contents of the pastures of swayback areas are quite normal. Pasture copper levels of 7 to 14 p.p.m. are usual compared with the levels of 2 to 5 p.p.m. which are common in copper-deficient areas elsewhere. In other words, the swayback lambs and their mothers exhibit copper deficiency while ingesting apparently adequate amounts of copper. It seems, therefore, that the affected pastures contain some factor or factors which affect copper utilization by the animal and that swayback must be regarded as a conditioned copper deficiency. So far the English workers have not been able to identify the factors concerned, although neither molybdenum, lead nor zinc, each of which has been shown to affect copper metabolism under appropriate conditions, appears to be implicated.

In parts of New Zealand, a disease of cattle known as "peat scours" has been established by Cunningham (1950) as a molybdenosis conditioned by copper deficiency. It develops in cattle confined to pastures which are high in molybdenum and low in copper and can be completely controlled merely by raising the copper intake of the animals to normal levels. Massive dosage with copper is *not* necessary to control the scouring as it is in the "teart" areas of England where the molybdenum contents of the pastures are very much higher than they are in peat scours. It is apparent, therefore, that copper is antagonistic to molybdenum in the animal and that the copper-molybdenum ratio in the diet can be of great metabolic importance.

Further striking evidence of the importance of copper-molybdenum balance emerged from the work of Bull (1951) and Dick (1952, 1953, 1954) on chronic copper poisoning of sheep in Australia, previously mentioned. This disease occurs under three different sets of conditions, only one of which is relevant to the present discussion. This is in an area where the pastures are normal or high-normal in copper content but exceedingly low in molybdenum, in fact rarely exceeding 0.1 to 0.2 p.p.m. molybdenum. Under such conditions the animals are consuming a diet with a very high copper-molybdenum ratio, which favors the development of a high body copper status and hence leads to copper poisoning. When the copper-molybdenum ratio was lowered by molybdate supplementation, both the amount of copper retained by the animals and the incidence of copper poisoning were reduced.

The most far-reaching and significant finding of these workers was that molybdenum exerts its effect on copper retention only in the presence of adequate dietary intakes of inorganic sulfate. The profound influence of inorganic sulfate on molybdenum and copper metabolism has since been confirmed with other species (VanReen, 1954 and VanReen and Williams, 1956), but much remains to be learned of the mechanism of this action and of the copper-molybdenum inorganic sulfate interaction and its quantitative significance. It is apparently a very complex process in which still other elements will almost certainly be implicated. It is already evident, however, that the occurrence of copper deficiency and toxicity, and of molybdenum deficiency and toxicity, can each be markedly influenced by the dietary levels of both these elements and of inorganic sulfate.

Other examples of trace element interactions can be given. The protective effect of arsenic against selenium toxicity was shown some years ago, and more recently the significance of the calcium level in the diet to the incidence of zinc deficiency (parakeratosis) in swine has been revealed (Lewis et al., 1956; Stevenson and Earle, 1956). Furthermore, high intakes of zinc are known to induce copper deficiency in rats (Smith and Larson, 1946), mainly, it seems by reducing copper absorption (Grant-Frost and Underwood, unpublished data). So far we are only at the beginning of an understanding of the mechanisms involved. Nevertheless it is apparent that dietary balance is no less important with the trace elements than it is with other nutrients, and that metabolic studies with these elements can be frustrating and misleading unless the nature of the whole diet is taken into account.

IV. Mode of Action of the Trace Elements

The only characteristic which the trace elements have in common is their capacity to function in the body in small quantities as catalysts or activators involved in hormones, vitamins, or enzyme systems. During the last two decades, the number of trace elements known to function in this way has expanded rapidly, and more and more enzymatic functions for the trace metals are becoming known as more highly purified preparations are obtained. Certain enzymes may be activated by a number of different metals—others have particular trace metals as specific and integral components, upon which they are completely dependent for their activity. Examples of these specific metalloenzymes containing iron are the cytochromes, catalase, peroxidase, cytochrome-c reductase, and fumaric hydrogenase; of those containing copper, ascorbic acid oxidase, tyrosinase, laccase, uricase, and butyryl CoA dehydrogenase; of those containing zinc, carbonic anhydrase, carboxypeptidase, and a number of pyridine nucleotide dehydrogenases (Vallee and Hock, 1955, 1956; Vallee and Walker, 1956; Vallee et al., 1955); those containing manganese, arginase, and prolidase; and those containing molybdenum, xanthine oxidase, aldehyde oxidase, and nitrate reductase.

It is clear from this list that trace metals, no less than those other micronutrients, the vitamins, lie at the root of metabolic processes. Deficient or excessive intakes of these elements would, therefore, be expected to produce the most profound metabolic disturbances in the animal. In many cases changes in the amounts or activities of certain metalloenzymes in the tissues have been nicely correlated with the dietary status of the animal, notably in the case of copper (Gallagher et al., 1956); in many more cases no such correlation has yet been demonstrated, in spite of the most severe clinical disturbances in the animal. In the zinc-deficient rat and pig, for instance, serious impairment of growth is observed before any reduction in the activity of any enzymes so far studied can be detected. Even when the rat is in extremis during the terminal stages of zinc deficiency, there appears to be no reduction in the carbonic anhydrase activity of its blood and tissues.

These findings clearly reveal the need for further research by enzymologists and nutritionists working together—research aimed at delineating the ultimate biochemical lesions which exist in the animal as a result of trace metal deficiencies, excesses, or imbalances. Only in this way will we arrive at a full understanding of their mode of action within the body and of their real significance in animal physiology.

Two other trace elements, iodine and cobalt, deserve special mention because of their unique position—unique because in each case the element appears to function solely as an integral part of a single physiologically active substance. No other function for iodine in the animal body is known other than as part of the thyroid hormone or hormones, whether this be thyroxine or triiodothyronine, and the whole of the physiological activity of cobalt can at present be accounted for by vitamin B_{12}. In the ruminant, the situation with cobalt is doubly unique, since these animals not only appear to utilize the trace element solely as an integral part of a vitamin but are directly and wholly dependent upon the activities of gastrointestinal microorganisms for their supply of this vitamin. The fact that neither cobalt nor iodine has been shown to be required by the higher plants can probably be related to the further fact that neither vitamin B_{12} nor thyroxine fulfills any functional role, or perhaps even exists, in plant tissues.

V. Sources of the Trace Elements

It cannot be too strongly emphasized that all animals and man depend ultimately upon the soil for their supplies of all mineral elements. Where naturally occurring deficiencies or excesses occur to such a degree that gross signs of animal disease arise, as in cobalt-deficient or seleniferous areas, this dependence is obvious, but it applies equally, although not so dramatically, where no such disease conditions develop. The soil-plant-animal relationship in human nutrition is complicated by the ever-widening sources of supply of the great variety of foods which comprise modern human dietaries and by the increasing amount of processing to which they are subjected. The former provides the opportunity of balancing possible mineral abnormalities of foods grown in one area with those of foods grown in another area under different environmental conditions. The latter provides the opportunity for contamination, especially with trace elements, from metals and chemicals used in processing and preservation.

In the nutrition of farm animals, similar considerations apply, although not yet to the same extent, and mineral supplements containing a wide range of elements are being increasingly used. Nevertheless, it has to be remembered that plants, which comprise the bulk of all animal feeds, reflect in their mineral composition the species or variety used and the soil and climatic conditions under which they are grown. Each of these is subject to considerable modification by man in his efforts to obtain more productivity from the land. The plant breeder is constantly evolving faster-growing and heavier-yielding types, while at the same time heavier and heavier dressings of fertilizer are being applied. The increased *quantity* of production which results may not always be accompanied by a parallel improvement in quality or even by the maintenance of existing levels of quality. It is possible, for instance, that the recent increase in incidence of parakeratosis in swine may be related to reduced concentrations of zinc in corn as a result of increases in yield. No evidence for this exists, as far as I am aware, but it certainly warrants consideration. The significance of plant species differences is evident also from recent findings in New Zealand that certain strains of rye grass differ markedly and consistently in iodine content, even when grown under the same soil conditions (Johns, 1956). It is apparent, therefore, that a continual watch must be kept on the quality, or nutritive value of feeds, as well as on their yields, in relation to changing production practices. The trace elements, no less than the essential amino acids, the vitamins, and major minerals constitute a vital part of that nutritive value and may be equally influenced by changes in farm or factory practices.

REFERENCES

Albiston, H. E., Bull, L. B., Dick, A. T., and Keast, J. C. 1940. *Australian Vet. J.* **16**, 233.
Beath, O. A., Eppson, H. F., and Gilbert, C. S. 1935. *Wyoming Agr. Expt. Sta. Bull.* **206**.
Brudevold, F., and Steadman, L. T. 1955. *J. Dental Research* **34**, 209, 674.
Bull, L. B. 1951. *Proc. Specialist Conf. in Agr. Australia, 1949*, p. 300.
Church, A. W. 1869. *Phil. Trans. Roy. Soc. London* **159**, 627.
Cunningham, I. J. 1950. *Symposium on Copper Metabolism* pp. 246–273.
DeRenzo, E. C., Kaluta, E., Heytler, P. G., Oleson, J. J., Hutchings, B. L., and Williams, J. H. 1953. *Arch. Biochem. Biophys.* **45**, 247.
Dick, A. T. 1952. *Australia Vet. J.* **28**, 30.
Dick, A. T. 1953. *Australian Vet. J.* **29**, 18, 233.
Dick, A. T. 1954. *Australian Vet. J.* **30**, 196.
Ferguson, W. S., Lewis, A. H., and Watson, S. J. 1938. *Nature* **141**, 553.
Ferguson, W. S., Lewis, A. H., and Watson, S. J. 1940. *Jealott's Hill Research Sta. Bull.* **1**.
Ferguson, W. S., Lewis, A. H., and Watson, S. J. 1943. *J. Agr. Sci.* **33**, 44.
Gallagher, C. H., Judah, J. D., and Rees, K. R. 1956. *Proc. Roy. Soc.* **B145**, 134.
Harless, E. 1847. *Arch. Anat. u. Physiol.* **148**.
Harington, C. R. 1933. "The Thyroid Gland: Its Chemistry and Physiology. Oxford Univ. Press, London and New York.
Hart, E. B., Steenbock, H., Waddell, J., and Elvehjem, C. A. 1928. *J. Biol. Chem.* **77**, 798.
Henze, M. 1911. *J. Physiol. Chem.* **72**, 494.
Higgins, E. S., Richert, D. A., and Westerfeld, W. W. 1956. *Federation Proc.* **15**, 895.
Hove, E., Elvehjem, C. A., and Hart, E. B. 1938. *Am. J. Physiol.* **124**, 205.
Huff, J. W., Bossardt, D. K., Miller, O. P., and Barnes, R. H. 1956. *Proc. Soc. Exptl. Biol. Med.* **92**, 216, 219.
Johns, A. T. 1956. *Proc. 7th Intern. Grassland Conf., New Zealand*, p. 251.
Lewis, P. K., Jr., Hoekstra, W. G., Grummer, R. H., and Phillips, P. H. 1956. *J. Animal Sci.* **15**, 741.
Lines, E. W. 1935. *J. Council Sci. Ind. Research* **8**, 117.
Lundegårdh, H. G. 1929. *Naturwissenschaften* **22**, 572.
Lyons, M., and Insko, W. M. 1937. *Kentucky Agr. Expt. Sta. Bull.* **371**.
Marston, H. R. 1935. *J. Council. Sci. Ind. Research* **8**, 111.
Mendel, L. B., and Bradley, H. C. 1905. *Am. J. Physiol.* **14**, 313; **17**, 167 (1906).
Norris, L. C. 1957. *Proc. Poultry Sci. Congr. Columbia, Missouri*.

Patterson, E. L., Milstrey, R., and Stokstad, E. L. R. 1957. *Proc. Soc. Exptl. Biol. Med.* **95**, 617.

Ramage, H., and Sheldon, J. H. 1931. *Nature* **128**, 376.

Reid, B. L., Kurnick, A. A., Svacha, R. L., and Couch, J. R. 1956. *Poultry Sci.* **35**, 1167.

Richert, D. A., and Westerfeld, W. W. 1953. *J. Biol. Chem.* **203**, 915.

Robinson, W. O. 1933. *J. Assoc. Offic. Agr. Chemists* **16**, 423.

Rygh, O. 1949. *Bull. soc. chim. biol.* **31**, 1052, 1403, 1408.

Schwarz, K., and Foltz, C. M. 1957. *J. Am. Chem. Soc.* **79**, 3292.

Schwarz, K., Bieri, J. G., Briggs, G. M., and Scott, M. L. 1957. *Proc. Soc. Exptl. Biol. Med.* **95**, 621.

Smith, S. E., and Larson, E. J. 1946. *J. Biol. Chem.* **163**, 29.

Stevenson, J. W., and Earle, I. P. 1956. *J. Animal Sci.* **15**, 1036.

Underwood, E. J. 1956. "Trace Elements in Human and Animal Nutrition." Academic Press, New York.

Underwood, E. J., and Filmer, J. F. 1935. *Australian Vet. J.* **11**, 84.

Vallee, B. L., and Hoch, F. L., 1955. *Proc. Natl. Acad. Sci. U.S.* **41**, 327.

Vallee, B. L., and Hoch, F. L. 1956. *Federation Proc.* **15**, 619.

Vallee, B. L., and Walker, W. E. C. 1956. *J. Am. Chem. Soc.* **78**, 1771.

Vallee, B. L., Adelstein, S. J., and Olson, R. 1955. *J. Am. Chem. Soc.* **77**, 5196.

VanReen, R. 1954. *Arch. Biochem. Biophys.* **53**, 77.

VanReen, R., and Williams, M. A. 1956. *Arch. Biochem. Biophys.* **63**, 1.

Westerfeld, W. W., and Richert, D. A. 1954. *Ann. New York Acad. Sci.* **57**, 896.

Wilgus, H. S., Norris, L. C., and Heuser, G. F. 1936. *Science* **84**, 252.

CHAPTER 3

Trace Elements in Microorganisms: The Temperature Factor Approach

S. H. HUTNER, S. AARONSON, H. A. NATHAN,
H. BAKER, S. SCHER, AND A. CURY

Haskins Laboratories, New York, New York; Department of Chemistry, Mount Sinai Hospital, New York, New York; Department of Botany, Rutgers University, New Brunswick, New Jersey; and Institute of Microbiology, University of Brazil, Rio de Janeiro, Brazil

	Page
I. Introduction	47
II. *Ochromonas* as Humanoid: Metabolic Stress as a Taxonomic Character	48
III. *Euglena gracilis* as Guide to Metaphyte Metabolism	50
IV. Vitamin B_{12}, Cobalt, and Temperature Factors	51
A. Generalities; *Ochromonas, Euglena,* and Vertebrates	51
B. *Crithidia fasciculata* and Pneumococcus	52
C. Other Protists	54
D. Cobalt as a B_{12} Tracer	56
E. Vitamin B_{12} and Inhibition Analysis	57
F. Vitamin B_{12} and Cobalt as Ecological Factors	58
V. Design of Inorganic Portions of Culture Media for Temperature Experiments	59
A. General Techniques	59
B. Chelating Agents and Trace Elements	59
1. Boron, Cobalt, and Vanadium	59
2. Selenium	60
3. Sodium and Halides	60
4. Silicon	61
C. Nonspecific Effects	61
VI. Summary	61
Acknowledgments	63
References	64

I. INTRODUCTION

J. B. S. Haldane describes animals as organisms that wander about in search of fuel and spare parts—a preposterous way to make a living alongside our plant ancestor's simple appetite for sunlight and minerals. Despite our evolutionary improbability, let us think about the spare parts needed when our metabolic engine is pushed to full capacity, as when repairing itself after profound damage such as deep irradiation while simultaneously withstanding the fever which in mammals follows general damage. This paper suggests (a) that certain trace metals are urgent spare parts for animals undergoing metabolic stress, and (b) that phago- trophic chrysomonad flagellates are good tools for identifying such trace metals. We discuss elsewhere the question of a thermal component in radiation damage (Hutner et al., 1957a).

II. OCHROMONAS AS HUMANOID: METABOLIC STRESS AS A TAXONOMIC CHARACTER

With a bow toward the unity of biochemistry, one may ask, *which microorganisms are the best guides to the workings of higher plants and animals?* We nominate for the post of "humanoid" the yellow-brown, photosynthetic, phagotrophic (particle-ingesting) flagellate *Ochromonas malhamensis*. The original assumptions were: (a) metazoa came from protozoa which, like metazoa, contain vitamin B_{12}—the green plants, higher fungi, and the ciliates contain no B_{12} whatever; (b) the protozoan ancestors of metazoa were asymmetric, as are metazoan spermatozoa. Chrysomonad and some other brown-pigmented flagellates meet these specifications. Later, *O. malhamensis* turned out to have a B_{12} require- ment gratifyingly identical with that of birds and mammals—which still leaves shaky our argument by exclusion.

It is well established that the chick and rat fed thyroactive materials have much-enhanced nutritional requirements, notably for vitamin B_{12} and thiamine (references in Hutner et al., 1957a). If the extra nutritional demands imposed by the metabolic stress of fever or hyperthyroidism were known both for vertebrates and for a variety of the invertebrates, one might discern a common denominator for metazoa. Suppose, also, that different microorganisms responded differently to metabolic stress, as shown by needs for different extra nutritional requirements. If among all the protists tested, one group alone has the metazoan pattern, then we might more reasonably call it "humanoid" as a shorthand description, as- suming its other metabolic characters agreed with the metazoan ones.

How, in protists, to induce the metabolic equivalent of thyroid- induced or fever stress? Exposing them to an incubation temperature at the precise limit for growth in "ordinary" media might be one such way; another, treatment with dinitrophenol. Our unpublished results with *O. malhamensis* and *Euglena gracilis* indicate that it is elevated incubation temperature and not dinitrophenol poisoning which may parallel mammalian fever; dinitrophenol toxicity is antagonized by L-glutamic acid and related compounds, which is in accord with findings by Caughey *et al.* (1957) that dinitrophenol interferes with glutamic acid dehydrogenase. (We do not know whether the interference of dinitrophenol with oxidative phosphorylation impairs utilization of phosphate and substrates; if it does interfere, it is less conspicuous than interference with glutamate utilization.)

To grow *O. malhamensis* at elevated temperatures, it must be given additional B_{12} and thiamine, and, as extra metabolites, folic acid, purines,

TABLE I

Metals as Temperature Factors for *Ochromonas malhamensis*

	34°C.		35.9°C.		36.3°C.	
	No addition	HEDTA[b] 0.05%	No addition	HEDTA[b] 0.05%	No addition	HEDTA[b] 0.05%
Medium[a] 0.4 ×	0.48[c]	0.62	0.86	0.88	0	0.73
Medium 0.8 ×	1.32	1.00	0.88	1.10	0	1.31
Medium 1.2 ×	1.74	1.80	0.30	1.30	0	0.60
Medium 1.6 ×	2.36	2.20	0.17	1.48	0	0
Medium 2.0 ×	2.66	2.56	—	0.47	0	0
Fe 0.4 mg. %	1.68	1.53	0.29	1.52	0	0
Fe 0.8 mg. %	1.68	1.73	0.12	0.12	0	0
Fe 1.2 mg. %	1.96	2.00	0.09	0.10	0	0
Zn 0.5 mg. %	1.54	1.35	1.60	2.04	0.50	1.92
Zn 1.0 mg. %	1.62	1.38	0.98	1.96	0.25	1.92
Zn 1.6 mg. %	1.80	1.43	0.38	2.14	0.15	2.10
Mn 0.05 mg. %	1.44	1.24	1.27	2.20	0.52	2.12
Mn 0.2 mg. %	1.48	1.26	2.00	2.18	1.52	0.91
Mn 0.8 mg. %	1.52	1.34	1.29	2.28	1.30	2.15
Cu 0.04 mg. %	1.50	—	1.92	1.72	1.14	2.00
Cu 0.1 mg. %	1.53	1.34	1.06	1.12	—	1.98
Cu 0.2 mg. %	1.45	1.38	1.62	2.00	0	0
Cu 0.4 mg. %	1.54	1.43	1.50	2.30	0	0

[a] Medium modified from Hutner *et al.*, 1957a.

[b] HEDTA = Hydroxylethylethylenediaminetriacetic acid; neutralized with Quadrol [*N,N,N',N'*-tetrakis (2-hydroxypropyl)ethylenediamine] to pH 4.8–5.2.

[c] In this and later tables, growth is expressed in optical density units.

and pyrimidines (e.g., adenosine, thymine, and thymidine), amino acids (phenylalanine, leucine, isoleucine, valine, and tryptophan), and additional zinc, manganese, and copper (Table I). This diversity of nutrients indicates that many kinds of compounds can enter *O. malhamensis*— which imparts much flexibility to experimentation; this nutritional versatility is to be expected from the observations that *O. malhamensis* will freely ingest particles its own size or smaller, including oil droplets and microbial bodies; it is truly a microanimal or animalcule.

III. Euglena gracilis as Guide to Metaphyte Metabolism

Nominating a microorganism to be surrogate for higher green plants is less adventuresome than proposing one for metazoa. The photosynthetic apparatus of green algae and euglenoid flagellates resembles that of higher plants (Wolken, 1956; for earlier literature see Hutner and Provasoli 1951, 1954). Green flagellates such as *Chlamydomonas* may well be like the protistan ancestor of the land plants as shown by chloroplast structure (Sager and Palade, 1957); the euglenoids are perhaps an offshoot from a *Chlamydomonas*-like form. Some strains of *Euglena gracilis* grow profusely on easily purified organic substrates, and enough is clear about their B_{12} requirement (Hutner *et al.*, 1956a) for them to rank among the most useful of all the domesticated green-pigmented forms, perhaps surpassing even the venerated *Chlorella*. *Chlorella* uses sugar readily in simple media at neutral *p*H; *Euglena* does not—which puts *Chlorella* closer to the higher plants, avid sugar-utilizers all. The pronounced heterotrophy of a *Euglena* such as the *z* strain makes it attractive for temperature studies: it utilizes a wide range of nutritional supplements even though it is not phagotrophic. The irreversible bleaching of *Euglena* by elevated temperatures (bleached strains may be maintained indefinitely) provides a fillip; somebody may chance upon culture media that will protect *Euglena* chloroplasts from heat destruction or keep them from disappearing in dark cultures, and so permit inference about cytoplasmic prerequisites for maintaining chloroplasts and—why not?—cultivating them.

Unlike higher plants, *E. gracilis* has but a minute calcium requirement; fresh-water green algae with a high calcium requirement and so, more like land plants, are undescribed. The better research object for the future may be the duckweed *Wolffia*, a monocot flowering plant which is no more than a tiny thallus, and which is manageable by minor modifications of orthodox microbiological methods; pure cultures have been obtained (Landolt, 1955a, b). The small crucifer *Arabidopsis thaliana* appears to be a suitable dicot (Langridge, 1957). Friable plant tissue cultures may be even more convenient for temperature studies.

IV. Vitamin B$_{12}$, Cobalt, and Temperature Factors

A. *Generalities; Ochromonas, Euglena, and Vertebrates*

The varied interests converging on cobalt and vitamin B$_{12}$ deserve discussion because, here, microorganisms have made unique theoretical and methodological contributions to trace element research. Vitamin B$_{12}$ research is seductive enough to have inspired two excellent symposium volumes (Williams, 1955; Heinrich, 1957) and a review of its microbiology (Ford and Hutner, 1955). The present discussion centers on B$_{12}$ (and, by extension, cobalt) as temperature factors and raises points not dealt with by Hutner *et al.*, 1957a or the reviews just cited.

To outline the present situation: B$_{12}$ seems wholly lacking in green plants and fungi. Unexpectedly, many members of the Chlorophyceae need B$_{12}$; probably all the Eugleninae do too. They presumably transform the B$_{12}$ given them into something inert for higher animals and their fellow assay microorganisms. When thyroactive materials are given to rats and chicks, their B$_{12}$ requirement may go up 4-fold or more. Vitamin B$_{12}$ could, then, be regarded as a stress factor or, more narrowly, as a temperature factor. Had B$_{12}$ been unknown, it might first have been identified as an antithyrotoxic factor. If the B$_{12}$ requirement of *O. malhamensis* is identical with that of vertebrates, then its B$_{12}$ requirement should rise steeply as the incubation temperature is raised and, moreover, for the same unknown reason it does in metazoa. The B$_{12}$ requirement of *O. malhamensis* does increase 500- to 1000-fold between 32° and 36.5°C. This "thermal" B$_{12}$ requirement is spared by folic acid, and folic acid in turn by deoxyribosides and other products of 1-carbon metabolism (Hutner *et al.*, 1957a). Folic acid and the other sparing compounds do not affect the ordinary B$_{12}$ requirement. Unfortunately it is not known whether the thyroid-induced increment in B$_{12}$ requirement is similarly sparable in vertebrates, or how their need for folic acid varies under thyroxine stress. In any event, B$_{12}$ *could* first have been noticed as a temperature factor for *Ochromonas*.

Another attractive organism is *Ochromonas danica*, which does not need exogenous B$_{12}$ (Heinrich, 1955) and is more strongly photosynthetic than *O. malhamensis* (Pringsheim, 1955), whose photosynthesis supports only marginal growth (Myers and Graham, 1956). Our ranging experiments indicate that the temperature factors for *O. danica* are accessible and that culture media for it differ appreciably from those for *O. malhamensis*.

Metal requirements intervened before the B$_{12}$ pattern of *Euglena* as affected by temperature could be discerned (Table II).

TABLE II

Metals as Temperature Factors for *Euglena gracilis* z

	35.9°C.		36.3°C.		36.7°C.	
	No addition	HEDTA 0.02%	No addition	HEDTA 0.02%	No addition	HEDTA 0.02%
I. Medium[a]						
0.5×	++++[d]	++++	0	0	0	0
1.0×	++++	++++	0	0	0	0
1.5×	++++	++++	0.04	0.30	0	0
2.0×	++++	++++	0	0.04	0	0
II. Metals						
45A[b] 3.0 mg. %						
No addition	++++	++++	0	0	0	0
KCl 20.0 mg. %	++++	++++	0	0.54	0	0
KCl 40.0 mg. %	++++	++++	0	0.62	0	0
Fe 0.05 mg. %	++++	++++	0	0.76	0	0
Fe 0.2 mg. %	++++	++++	0	0.94	0	0
Zn 0.1 mg. %	++++	++++	0	0.82	0	0
Zn 0.4 mg. %	++++	++++	0	0.66	0	0
KCl 20.0 mg. %, Fe 0.05 mg. %	++++	++++	0	0.12	0	0
Zn 0.1 mg. %, KCl 20.0 mg. %, Fe 0.05 mg. %	++++	++++	0.5	1.46	0	0
Zn 0.1 mg. %, KCl 20.0 mg. %, Fe 0.05 mg. %, Purine and pyrimidine mix[c] 1.0 ml. %	++++	++++	1.98	1.98	0	0.04

[a] Medium modified from Hutner *et al.*, 1956a.

[b] Metals 45A: see Hutner *et al.*, 1957a.

[c] Purine and pyrimidine mix: 1.0 ml. contains (mg.): adenine 0.5, adenosine 1.0, yeast adenylic acid 1.2, hypoxanthine 0.5, guanine·HCl 0.5, guanosine 1.0, guanylic acid 1.2, inosine 1.0, xanthine 0.5, xanthosine 1.0, cytosine 0.5, cytidine 1.0, thymine 0.5, thymidine 1.0, uracil 0.5, uridine 1.0, orotic acid 0.4.

[d] ++++ = Full growth.

Final pH 3.4–3.6.

B. Crithidia fasciculata *and* Pneumococcus

The trypanosomid flagellate *Crithidia fasciculata* lives in the gut of mosquitoes; it probably has no vertebrate host. It is very different from flagellates such as *Ochromonas, Euglena,* and *Chlamydomonas.* Some of its temperature factors below 32°C. are trace metals (Table III),

TABLE III

Metals and Supplementary Substrates as Temperature Factors for *Crithidia fasciculata*
(Anopheles Strain)

Additions[a]	(mg./100 ml.)	24–26°C.	28–30°C.	32–32.3°C.
(1) None		1.20	0.16	0.03
(2) Ca (as Cl⁻),	1.5			
MgSO₄·7H₂O,	100			
Fe (as SO₄),	0.5			
Cu (as SO₄)	0.4	1.22	1.42	0.99
(3) L-Glutamic acid,	300			
Na₂ succinate·H₂O,	100			
DL-Lactate	200	1.21	1.28	1.13

[a] The unsupplemented medium is given in Nathan and Cowperthwaite, 1954.

which carries implications for the evolution of blood parasites. Notably, the combination glutamic acid, succinate, and lactate is interchangeable with a mixture of four metals at temperatures up to 32.3°C. It was impossible to tell whether the interchangeability of the organic with inorganic supplements below 32.3°C. was due to contamination of the organic compounds with metals. Later experiments, at higher temperatures, indicate that both the organic and inorganic components are necessary. Such pathogens as *Leishmania* have species living in mammals, i.e., at 37°C. or higher; grown *in vitro,* they revert to motile leptomonads much like *Crithidia.* Efforts to grow *Leishmania* above 32°C. or so in artificial media have failed. Very complex media, blood extracts plus other supplements, are required to keep *Leishmania donovani,* a parasite of mammals, alive at 37°C. for a few days (Trager, 1953). The question is, do the temperature factors for *C. fasciculata* and *L. donovani* overlap? An overlap would imply that the body fluids and tissues of mammals are (*a*) good sources of inorganic temperature factors or (*b*) that they are exceptionally rich in the metabolites for whose synthesis the metals are needed. It seems tacitly accepted that the barrier to the invasion of the blood stream of warm-blooded animals by parasites of invertebrates is mainly immunological. Perhaps temperature factors play a part too.

What seems to be a unique instance of a trace element determining infectivity is that of pneumococcus and mice, as recounted by Hitchings *et al.* (reviewed by Clark, 1950). White mice survived 100,000 lethal doses of Type 1 pneumococci when fed on a purified diet as compared with commercial stock diets. When certain crude supplements were added to the purified diet, the susceptibility of the mice increased with the manganese content of the diet. The effect was not simple; some strains markedly stimulated *in vitro* by manganese did not show the effect in mice.

C. Other Protists

A satisfactory theory of B_{12} function must explain the diverse nutritional patterns found in bacteria. About 4 per cent of soil bacteria isolated by nonselective procedures require B_{12} (Lochhead and Burton, 1956); some of them have the same molecular specificity as *Ochromonas* and higher animals; however, methionine is not sparing (Ford and Hutner, 1957) as it is in higher animals and *Ochromonas* (Johnson *et al.*, 1957). For lactobacilli which require B_{12}, the B_{12} is replaceable by deoxyribosides, and for *Escherichia coli* 113–3, by methionine.

If, as the temperatures of their non-B_{12}-requiring counterparts are pushed up, B_{12} emerges as a temperature factor, will these thermal B_{12} patterns resemble those of the B_{12}-requirers? In some thermophilic bacilli (Baker *et al.*, 1955), a B_{12} requirement emerges in some strains at certain temperatures; B_{12} here is interchangeable with folic acid, and folic acid in turn is spared by products of 1-carbon metabolism—a situation reminiscent of the thermal B_{12} requirement of *Ochromonas malhamensis* (Section II) and of the nutritional distortions induced in *Escherichia coli* by sulfanilamide (Section IV, *D*). Aerobic members of the Athiorhodaceae (photosynthetic purple nonsulfur bacteria) grow well in simple chemically-defined media, and so their B_{12} relations might be easy to study. In autotrophic bacteria such as these, the fundamental role of B_{12} might perhaps be seen more clearly—if B_{12} plays a part in them at all. We find that some strains of *Rhodopseudomonas palustris, R. gelatinosa,* and *Rhodospirillum rubrum* have their critical temperature at 35°C. or higher, and they appear sufficiently permeable to organic metabolites to invite temperature-factor studies.

Unpublished studies with thermophilic bacilli grown at 70°C. and higher indicate that the inorganic requirements for these elevated temperatures much exceed those for 45–55°C.; see Sobotka *et al.*, 1957.

As for protists that do not contain B_{12}—will a thermal B_{12} requirement emerge and so unmask a role for B_{12} in their metabolism? For the sake of direct comparison, it seems desirable to use, where possible, microorganisms whose critical temperature is about the same as that of *O. malhamensis* and *Euglena gracilis* z—which is like the rat and man but lower than the chick. Unpublished work by Dr. George Holz and R. J. Davis indicates that a thermophilic strain of the ciliate *Tetrahymena pyriformis* has accessible temperature factors. Ordinary mesophilic strains of *Tetrahymena* in conventional media stop growing at about 30°C.;

thermophilic strains stop at about 38°C. A comparison of the temperature factors for both ciliates might point to general principles.

A thermophilic intestinal yeast, *Saccharomycopsis guttulata,* has a temperature optimum at approximately 37°C., with growth falling off steeply on each side. Given appropriate nutritional supplements, its

TABLE IV

Metals as Temperature Factors for *Saccharomycopsis guttulata*[a]:

		37°C.	40°C.	41°C.
No addition		0.32	0.30	0
Fe	0.02 mg. %	0.26	0.30	0
Fe	0.1 mg. %	0.42	0.40	0
Fe	0.5 mg. %	0.31	0.40	0
Mn	0.03 mg. %	0.40	0.38	0
Mn	0.1 mg. %	0.30	0	0
Mn	0.3 mg. %	0	0	0
Zn	0.01 mg. %	0.33	0.34	0
Zn	0.05 mg. %	0.34	0.32	0
Zn	0.2 mg. %	0.33	0.29	0
Cu	0.002 mg. %	0.39	0.29	0
Cu	0.01 mg. %	0.33	0.06	0
Cu	0.05 mg. %	0.32	0.06	0
Ca	0.3 mg. %	0.33	0.18	0
Ca	1.0 mg. %	0.34	0.25	0
Ca	3.0 mg. %	0.56	0.30	0
$MgSO_4 \cdot 7H_2O$	0.01 g. %	0.48	0.28	0
$MgSO_4 \cdot 7H_2O$	0.03 g. %	0.49	0.36	0
$MgSO_4 \cdot 7H_2O$	0.1 g. %	0.59	0.50	0.40
Metals 45A	0.5 mg. %	0.35	0.10	0
Metals 45A	1.0 mg. %	0.15	0.10	0

[a] *Basal* medium (amounts per 100 ml. final volume): KH_2PO_4, 0.04 g; $MgSO_4 \cdot 7H_2O$, 0.05 g; DL-asparagine·H_2O, 0.2 g; $(NH_4)_2H$ citrate, 0.05 g; metals 45A, 0.5 mg; $ZnSO_4 \cdot 7H_2O$, 1.2 mg; $CaCO_3$, 2.5 mg; glucose, 2.0 g; casein hydrolyzate (GBI), 0.04 g; yeast autolyzate, 0.01 g; DL-tryptophan, 4.0 mg; L-cystine, 4.0 mg; inositol, 2.0 mg; nicotinic acid, 0.2 mg; Ca pantothenate, 0.4 mg; thiamine·HCl, 1.0 mg; pyridoxine·HCl, 0.1 mg; biotin, 4.0 µg; thymidine, 1.5 mg; adenine, 0.5 mg; "Tween 80," 0.02 g. Final pH 3.5–4.0.

temperature range can be extended up and down. It grows only in acid media, with a pH optimum of 3–4; by increasing the metal content of the medium, growth is possible at pH 5.0. A typical experiment is shown in Table IV; the effect of magnesium is almost certainly nonspecific (see Section V, *C*); magnesium here together with the high zinc in the basal medium are probably only crude approximations of a properly balanced metal supply.

Certainly no scarcity exists of attractive protists for temperature studies. Our hopes go beyond B_{12} and cobalt: Will some temperature factors be new to biochemistry, as B_{12} almost was? Perhaps some of the hoped-for new temperature factors will contain unfamiliar trace elements and so provide clues to their function, as B_{12} did for cobalt. The growth factors for most nonfastidious, hardy, easily accessible microorganisms have been identified; new growth factors are hard to come by directly. The phagotrophy of the protozoa makes available to them lipid and high-molecular materials hitherto largely neglected in microbiology and so makes them especially eligible to respond to new growth factors.

Exceedingly valuable material where microbiological methods apply are cultures of some mammalian cells. The temperature tolerances of three neoplastic cell lines were determined by Selawry *et al.* (1957), who found adaptive phenomena coming into play in the appearance of resistance to elevated temperatures. Culture media for vetebrate cells are still too poorly defined for ease in studying the effect of temperature on their already complicated nutritional requirements.

D. Cobalt as a B_{12} Tracer

If an organism made a great excess of a growth factor that integrally contained a trace element, then supplying the organism with a radioactive isotope of that element and following the fate of this tracer might lead directly to the growth factor. To our knowledge, experiments have not been published in which Co^{60} was given to the actinomycetes that are the commercial sources of B_{12}. Studies such as those of Garibaldi *et al.* (1953) on the proportionality between cobalt in the medium and B_{12} produced suggest that cobalt could be used to guide the isolation of B_{12} from fermentation beers. When Co^{60} was given to *Neurospora*, which like all fungi lacks B_{12}, 40 per cent of the cobalt was bound, apparently to protein fractions; in higher plants, cobalt was bound to rather nondescript protein fractions (Ballentine and Stephens, 1951). At least two laboratories are trying to trace the fate of Co^{60} in *Euglena*. Isotope technique seems not to have been extended to other trace elements, perhaps because the chances are slim for finding an organism making an excess of a growth factor containing the desired element. From a high B_{12}-producing *Streptomyces*, a mutant was produced that made no detectible B_{12} (Dulaney, 1954). One wonders how this mutation affects the fate of administered Co^{60} and whether the mutant still needs cobalt. The issue is, does cobalt have functions apart from B_{12}?

The occurrence of cobalt in B_{12} has a curious value in setting a goal for purifying nutrients. Thus, while trying to demonstrate a cobalt requirement, Arnon discovered the essentiality of vanadium for *Scenedes-mus*, and Broyer *et al.* (1954) the essentiality of chlorine for higher plants. The novel technique of freeing cobalt from both macronutrient elements and $MnSO_4$ employed by Bolle-Jones and Mallikarjuneswara (1957) permitted what may be the first demonstration of a cobalt require-ment in a B_{12}-free organism—in this instance, the rubber tree.

E. Vitamin B_{12} and Inhibition Analysis

Understanding of the function of a trace element obviously makes a giant stride forward when the element is found in an organic growth factor; analysis can go on to the next stage: is the growth factor part of the prosthetic group of an enzyme? The independent discovery of B_{12} through inhibition analysis (Shive, 1950) shows another way to find growth factors. Sulfanilamide inhibition of *E. coli* is relieved competi-tively by *p*-aminobenzoic acid; less and less *p*-aminobenzoic acid has to be used if products of the synthetic activity of *p*-aminobenzoic acid are supplied in succession. Liver extract, in the presence of methionine, purines, pyrimidines, and other amino acids concerned in 1-carbon metab-olism, lessened the concentration of *p*-aminobenzoic acid required. The exceedingly active constituent of liver was isolated; it was B_{12}.

In time, protists learn to circumvent the familiar antibiotics and syn-thetic chemotherapeutic agents; new agents must be found continually—nature abhors an ecological vacuum. As a by-product of this contest, bio-chemists have a splendid collection of tools for uncovering new metab-olites through their role in opposing biocidal activity. Success here de-mands delicate analytical work. For example, in Shive's study, in isolating B_{12} from liver, one supposes it was necessary to rule out in the various fractions the activity of *p*-aminobenzoic acid and the other compounds known to oppose sulfanilamide inhibition.

Not surprisingly, there are few penetrating studies of the reversal of toxicity of chemotherapeutic agents whose mode of action is not fairly obvious from their structural analogy to known metabolites. New, powerful, and selective antiprotozoal agents are becoming available. Some of their metabolic targets might well be new metabolites. The scarcity of antiprotozoal agents that are not impracticably toxic to higher animals contrasts with the profusion of safe antibacterial antibiotics; e.g., peni-cillin does not annoy protozoa. This accumulated chemotherapeutic in-formation strengthens the belief that protozoa (and to a lesser extent fungi and most algae) resemble metazoa more than they do bacteria; by implication, protozoal growth factors are likelier to be important in metazoan metabolism than are bacterial growth factors.

F. Vitamin B_{12} and Cobalt as Ecological Factors

The securing in pure culture of many important photosynthetic plankton organisms opens to analysis the determinants of their succession in fresh-water bodies and the ocean. All the photosynthetic dinoflagellates so far studied in pure culture require B_{12}. Such studies are being rapidly extended. An example is the finding that the algal symbionts ("zooxanthellae") of a sea anemone and a jellyfish are dinoflagellates (McLaughlin and Zahl, 1957), which heightens the probability that most symbionts of light-loving corals are dinoflagellates or else other brown-pigmented flagellates. There are indications in the literature that the zooxanthellae of such important planktonts as radiolaria are dinoflagellates.

Other phytoplanktonts found to need B_{12} include all the euglenoids, most chrysomonads, some cryptomonads and pinnate diatoms, and at least one common marine blue-green alga (Pintner and Provasoli, 1957)—in short, a substantial slice, if not the greater part, of the base of the food pyramid in fresh-water bodies and the ocean (for reviews see Hutner *et al.*, 1956b; Droop, 1957; Provasoli, in press). Are cobalt or B_{12} ever limiting factors for plankton production, as with ruminants on some soils? The seasonal fluctuations of cobalt and B_{12} in a fresh-water pond have been charted (Benoit, 1957), and B_{12} in estuarine muds (Starr, 1956; Burkholder and Burkholder, 1956) and the sea off England (Cowey, 1956). In the laboratory, the sensitivity of the resources to B_{12} of the assay organism is seldom pushed to the limit, but these very limits may decide the survival in nature of a growth-factor-requiring population. Heinrich and Lahann (1953) demonstrated a quantitative response of *Euglena* down to a 10^{-12} (1 $\mu\mu$g.) B_{12}. This should be compared with Lewin's calculations (1954) for a marine green alga, *Stichococcus*, which for *maximum* growth needs only approximately 0.2 mμg. B_{12} per ml. and was used to measure B_{12} in Halifax harbor water (content in winter: 0.01 μg./l.) and Cowey's values (1956) for North Sea and Norwegian waters which went as low as 0.1 mμg./l.

These are opening gambits in a vast research: why are the world's great fisheries along the shores of the continents rather than mid-ocean? This problem is related to enterprises such as learning how to use mass culture of marine phytoplanktonts as a dependable food for marine larvae —a prerequisite for artificial oyster breeding on a truly practical scale. The sensitivity of the B_{12} requirement of different plankton organisms might prove to vary through the temperature range of the winter-summer cycle. An appalling complexity would then be introduced into ecological prediction; one envisions multiple simultaneous differential equations, some for trace elements, others for vitamins, awaiting their turn at the electronic computers.

V. Design of Inorganic Portions of Culture Media for Temperature Experiments

A. General Techniques

Methods for compounding culture media for temperature studies have been previously outlined (Hutner *et al.*, 1957a) and are given in additional detail in a review being prepared on microbiological assays. This section recounts in operational fashion how the literature on trace elements influences the design of experiments.

B. Chelating Agents and Trace Elements

The constituents of culture media, including "C.P." chemicals, are significantly contaminated with essential or toxic trace elements; the two properties are not mutually exclusive. By adding a chelating agent, then compensating for its sequestering action by adding the essential metals, background fluctuations become much less disturbing. This widely applied procedure (Hutner *et al.*, 1950) has been used systematically for cultivating many fastidious marine protists (Provasoli *et al.*, 1957).

Ethylenediaminetetraacetic acid (EDTA), used in earlier experiments, has the disadvantage that its magnesium and calcium chelates are poorly soluble. Applying the data of Chaberek and Bersworth (1953), hydroxyl-ethylethylenediaminetriacetic acid (HEDTA) has been used for protists having high iron and calcium requirements, e.g., most marine forms and *O. malhamensis*. Nitrilotriacetic acid has also been useful.

We ordinarily grow *O. malhamensis* at pH 4.8–5.2. For studying the mode of action of basic drugs, where penetration is favored by high pH, less acid media are desirable. Iron and calcium must then be much increased, and concentrations and ratios of the other chelatable metals must be defined with exceptional precision. The difficulty in supplying *Ochromonas* with iron puts us on the side of those who reason that an acid gastric juice is an excellent device to speed absorption of the large amounts of iron needed to make the abundant heme pigments of warm-blooded animals (*cf.* Callender and O'Brien, 1957). Solutions of iron salts soon precipitate unless made strongly acid. A low concentration of sulfosalicylic acid, suggested by Schubert's studies (1954) of chelation of alkaline earth metals, is remarkably effective and does not upset metal balances in the final media.

1. Boron, Cobalt, and Vanadium. We have routinely used a trace element mixture containing iron, zinc, manganese, copper, molybdenum, boron, cobalt, and vanadium (composition in Hutner *et al.*, 1957a). There is no evidence that boron is needed for organisms besides green plants and blue-green algae. Use of borosilicate glassware almost surely precludes a deficiency. But, as boron chelates, it is added, as is cobalt. Because of the incidence of vanadium in tunicates (reviewed by Webb, 1956), we would include it even were it unknown as essential for *Scenedesmus*.

Storage of basal media in the form of dry mixes (Hutner *et al.*, 1957a) makes it far more convenient to assemble complicated media. Until recently our attention was fixed on organic nutrients, not on metals, as temperature factors. Previous experiments on organic factors must be redone with the aid of basal media which incorporate the present information on metals as temperature factors and are better supplemented with trace elements.

2. *Selenium.* Its essentiality for both the rat and chick means that greater weight attaches to Pinsent's report (1954) of its essentiality for formic dehydrogenase activity in *E. coli;* she calculated that 5,000 to 10,000 molecules per cell were necessary. Selenite was the active form; selenate was not. Prior fractional distillation of phosphate as the oxychloride (Hutner *et al.*, 1950) may perhaps eliminate what may be a major source of Se contamination of media.

3. *Sodium and Halides.* We have discussed elsewhere the evidence for strong electrolytes being essential for life, viewing such requirements as reflecting the origin of life in a primordially salty ocean (Hutner *et al.*, 1957b). The sodium requirement of nonmarine bacteria is probably so small as to be almost impossible to demonstrate, e.g., Shooter and Wyatt (1957) by means of ion exchange reduced the sodium content of media to <0.022 mg. per liter without diminishing growth. A requirement for halide in a marine bacterium (MacLeod and Onofrey, 1957) is not unexpected and may be interpreted as reinforcing the belief that chlorine is essential for life in general; the occurrence of chlorine in some antibiotics is another hint. Bromine may be an essential element; it helped overcome the growth inhibition in chicks (Bosshardt *et al.*, 1956) and rats (Huff *et al.*, 1956) induced by thyroactive materials and so is being watched as a potential temperature factor for *Ochromonas*. Ozanne *et al.* (1957), in confirming the essentiality of chlorine for higher plants, noted that bromine may antagonize the uptake of chlorine. Iodine is almost certainly necessary for all life, but there is no proof for nonvertebrates. Fluorine probably can safely be ignored, judging from the inability of Maurer and Day (1957) to demonstrate a requirement in rats fed a diet containing <0.007 p.p.m. utilizable fluorine.

4. Silicon. A silicon requirement can be demonstrated quantitatively (e.g., Lewin, 1957) in organisms such as diatoms having silicious skeletal structures. *Ochromonas* belongs to the vast array of brown-pigmented forms that includes diatoms. Many chrysomonads have silicious scales or walls; essentiality of silicon has not been studied in them. Demonstration of a silicon requirement in *Ochromonas,* necessarily with the help of non-glass equipment, would not be surprising, and would, for reasons already discussed, suggest tests on animals. Unfortunately there appears to have been no effort to confirm the results of Raleigh (1939) pointing to the essentiality of silicon for higher plants.

C. Nonspecific Effects

Increments of chelatable nontoxic metals such as magnesium and calcium at times stimulate growth. These increased concentrations may displace, by mass action, limiting elements from complexes, and so increase the effective concentration of these limiting elements. Lesser concentrations of more strongly chelating elements may also do this. Vitale *et al.* (1957) reported that rats kept at 12.8°C. needed twice as much magnesium as those at 23.9°C.; magnesium also counteracted a thyroxine-induced growth depression. One wonders whether the effect of magnesium is specific for magnesium itself, or whether the response to magnesium masks, as repeatedly happened in our studies of *Ochromonas* and *Euglena* temperature factors, responses to trace metals.

If trace elements (aside from cobalt) are indeed temperature factors for birds and mammals, failure to note this may contribute to the inability of workers in laboratories where thyrotoxicity is studied to agree upon the organic factors first coming into play. Natural ion exchange materials such as casein, which compose a large part of "synthetic" diets, might vary widely in trace element content. We find that most samples of hydrolyzed casein have an excess of essential trace metals. With assurance that the bulk of these elements came from the original casein and not from the reagents used for hydrolysis, a good beginning would have been made in devising procedures for purifying casein.

VI. Summary

One marvels that the essentiality of cobalt via B_{12} was not discovered sooner; it could have come about in so many ways. The mass unpreparedness for the advent of the near-ubiquitous B_{12} prompts us to add one more quotation to Pasteur's "chance favors the prepared mind" and Darwin's "How odd it is that anyone should not see that all observation must be for or against some view if it is to be of any service!"

"A Fact by itself is useless, impotent, phantasmal, as weak and wavering as the shades of the dead that Ulysses met in the underworld. And as the shades become strong enough to speak only by drinking the blood from Ulysses' sacrifices, so a Fact can acquire reality only by drinking the blood of theory, by becoming related to other Facts through some kind of assumption, hypothesis, generalization. Indeed, a Fact not thus fortified is usually too weak even to be perceived; as a rule one pays attention only to data that fit into some general idea of things one already has. The facts speak for themselves, we say, but this is just what they don't do" (MacDonald, 1957).

The history of chelation documents this thesis. A wealth of phenomena pointing to chelation as relevant to biology had long obtruded on biologists. From the chemical side, chelation theory was workably coherent, as shown by the writings of G. T. Morgan and his colleagues (e.g., Morgan and Burstall, 1937), by about 1924. In now discovering that chelation pervades dynamic biochemistry we are like Molière's gentleman who discovered he had been talking prose all his life.

If new metabolites and metabolic pathways were indeed uncovered through their roles as temperature factors, how to justify channeling the resources to identify them? The development of the biochemistry of chelation was accelerated by such applications as removing radioactive metals from the body, correcting ordinarily refractory trace-metal deficiencies in crop plants, and increasing the yields of mass cultures of algae in the hope of making them crop plants. The prodigious efforts reflected in the present knowledge of B_{12} were obviously justified in the light of its importance in animal and human nutrition. We cannot now assert that *Ochromonas* temperature factors are relevant to stress in higher animals; wondering about *Ochromonas*'s humanoidness merely poses the question concisely. Perhaps *Ochromonas* has misleading idiosyncrasies; if so, judgment rests on the common features discerned from comparative studies. The odds seem good that some microelements under usual circumstances are macroelements in point of importance in metabolic stress. Microbiology, as one views the costs of experimentation with crop plants and higher animals, is the poor man's experimental biology. It would be expensive to ascertain directly the heightened demands for trace elements in a crop plant bred for high yield through having a high optimum temperature. Hence the strategy of first working out the common denominator of temperature factors for, say *Euglena* and a duckweed.

The nutrients for our temperature experiments were ordinary reagent-grade chemicals. Amplifying trace element requirements by superimposing temperature stress upon chelation should permit better use of the chemicals, metals above all, that must be purified for knowledge of trace elements to be extended solidly.

To close this exposition of metaphytic and metazoan uses of microorganisms, let us sketch how one might economically find out whether vanadium is essential for man; we make the assumption that the concentration of vanadium satisfying the putative requirement lies under the sensitivity of chemical and spectroscopic analysis. To start: a repetition of Professor Arnon's experiments with *Scenedesmus* in order to be able to use *Scenedesmus* to measure vanadium. Then to see whether some pet photosynthetic organism having a higher temperature optimum and growing densely and rapidly with the aid of easily purified substrates might serve the purpose more conveniently. Then to use the chosen microorganism to guide the elimination of vanadium from media for *Ochromonas*.

If a medium satisfactorily vanadium-free for the assay organism still induced no vanadium deficiency in *Ochromonas*, one might increase the vanadium requirement of *Ochromonas* by: (*a*) raising the *p*H of the medium, intensifying sequestering of vanadium (a highly chelatable metal); (*b*) supplying more chelating agent; (*c*) raising the temperature —efficacious, of course, only if vanadium behaves as a temperature factor. Once *Ochromonas* is an assay organism for vanadium, chick and rat experiments (especially if *Ochromonas* remained in good standing as a humanoid). Other things being equal, the chick would be preferable because of the intense metabolism which goes with its higher body temperature. *Ochromonas* might be especially good for detecting vanadium in components of diets such as casein and lipids. Then, human experiments: blood levels, tissue localization, etc. (Whatever the outcome, vanadium would appear about this time in widely-advertised "stress-fortified" vitamin-mineral nostrums.) Afterwards, well-controlled experiments on quantitative requirements and the incidence of natural deficiencies; much later perhaps, mode-of-action studies.

Acknowledgments

The support of the following agencies is gratefully acknowledged: the Rockefeller Foundation, the Loomis Institute, the American Cancer Society (grant CP-57-30), the U.S. Public Health Service (grants E-1088 and B-1198), and the National Science Foundation (grant G-3984).

One of us (A.C.) is indebted to the Conselho Nacional de Pesquisas of Brazil for continuing grants-in-aid.

REFERENCES

Baker, H., Hutner, S. H., and Sobotka, H. 1955. *Ann. New York Acad. Sci.* **62**, 349–376.

Ballentine, R., and Stephens, D. G. 1951. *J. Cellular Comp. Physiol.* **37**, 369–388.

Benoit, R. J. 1957. *Limnol. and Oceanog.* **2**, 233–240.

Bolle-Jones, E. W., and Mallikarjuneswara, V. R. 1957. *Nature* **179**, 738–739.

Bosshardt, D. K., Huff, J. W., and Barnes, R. H. 1956. *Proc. Soc. Exptl. Biol. Med.* **92**, 219–221.

Broyer, T. C., Carlton, A. B., Johnson, C. M., and Stout, P. R. 1954. *Plant Physiol.* **29**, 526–532.

Burkholder, P. R., and Burkholder, L. M. 1956. *Limnol. and Oceanog.* **1**, 202–208.

Callender, S. T., and O'Brien, J. R. P. 1957. *In* "Biochemical Disorders in Human Disease" (R. H. S. Thompson and E. J. King, eds.), p. 105. Academic Press, New York.

Caughey, W. S., Smiley, J. D., and Hellerman, L. 1957. *J. Biol. Chem.* **224**, 591–607.

Chaberek, S., Jr., and Bersworth, F. C. 1953. *Science* **118**, 280.

Clark, P. F. 1950. *Ann. Rev. Microbiol.* **4**, 343–358.

Cowey, C. B. 1956. *J. Marine Biol. Assoc. United Kingdom* **35**, 609–620.

Droop, M. R. 1957. *J. Gen. Microbiol.* **16**, 286–293.

Dulaney, E. L. 1954. *Ann. New York Acad. Sci.* **60**, 155–163.

Ford, J. E., and Hutner, S. H. 1955. *Vitamins and Hormones* **13**, 101–136.

Ford, J. E., and Hutner, S. H. 1957. *Can. J. Microbiol.* **3**, 319–327.

Garibaldi, J. A., Ijichi, W., Snell, N. S., and Lewis, J. C. 1953. *Ind. Eng. Chem.* **45**, 838–846.

Heinrich, H. C. 1955. *Naturwissenschaften* **14**, 418.

Heinrich, H. C., ed. 1957 "Vitamin B_{12} und Intrinsic Factor. 1. Europäisches Symposion über Vitamin B_{12} und Intrinsic Factor. Hamburg 23.–26. Mai 1956." F. Enke, Stuttgart.

Heinrich, H. C., and Lahann, H. 1953. *Z. Naturforsch.* **86**, 589–598.

Huff, J. W., Bosshardt, D. K., Miller, O. P., and Barnes, R. H. 1956. *Proc. Soc. Exptl. Biol. Med.* **92**, 216–219.

Hutner, S. H., and Provasoli, L. 1951. *In* "Biochemistry and Physiology of Protozoa" (A. Lwoff, ed.), Vol. 1, pp. 27–128. Academic Press, New York.

Hutner, S. H., and Provasoli, L. 1954. *In* "Biochemistry and Physiology of Protozoa" (S. H. Hutner and A. Lwoff, eds.), Vol. 2, pp. 17–43. Academic Press, New York.

Hutner, S. H., Provasoli, L., Schatz, A., and Haskins, C. P. 1950. *Proc. Am. Phil. Soc.* **94**, 152–170.

Hutner, S. H., Bach, M. K., and Ross, G. I. M. 1956a. *J. Protozool.* **3**, 101–112.

Hutner, S. H., Provasoli, L., McLaughlin, J. J. A., and Pintner, I. J. 1956b. *Geograph. Rev.* **46**, 404-407.

Hutner, S. H., Baker, H., Aaronson, S., Nathan, H. A., Rodriguez, E., Lockwood, S., Sanders, M., and Petersen, R. A. 1957a. *J. Protozool.* **4**, 259-269.

Hutner, S. H., Sanders, M., McLaughlin, J. J. A., and Scher, S. 1957b. *Ann. New York Acad. Sci.* **69**, 286–291.

Johnson, B. C., Holdsworth, E. S., Porter, J. W. G., and Kon, S. K. 1957. *Brit. J. Nutrition* **11**, 313–323.

Landolt, E. 1955a. *Verhandl. schweiz. naturforsch. Ges.*, pp. 135–136.

Landolt, E. 1955b. *Carnegie Inst. Wash. Year Book* No. **54**, July 1954–June 1955, pp. 177–180.
Langridge, J. 1957. *Australian J. Biol. Sci.* **10**, 243–252.
Lewin, J. C. 1957. *Can. J. Microbiol.* **3**, 427–433.
Lewin, R. A. 1954. *J. Gen. Microbiol.* **10**, 93–96.
Lochhead, A. G., and Burton, M. O. 1956. *Nature* **178**, 144–145.
MacDonald, D. 1957. *The Anchor Rev.* **2**, 113–144.
McLaughlin, J. J. A., and Zahl, P. A. 1957. *Proc. Soc. Exptl. Biol. Med.* **95**, 115–120.
MacLeod, R. A., and Onofrey, E. 1957. *Can. J. Microbiol.* **3**, 753–760.
Maurer, R. L., and Day, H. G. 1957. *J. Nutrition* **62**, 561–573.
Morgan, G. T., and Burstall, F. H. 1937. "Inorganic Chemistry: A Survey of Modern Developments." Chem. Pub., New York.
Myers, J., and Graham, J. 1956. *J. Cellular Comp. Physiol.* **47**, 397–414.
Nathan, H. A., and Cowperthwaite, J. 1954. *Proc. Soc. Exptl. Biol. Med.* **85**, 117–119.
Ozanne, P. G., Wolley, J. T., and Broyer, T. C. 1957. *Australian J. Biol. Sci.* **10**, 66–79.
Pinsent, J. 1954. *Biochem. J.* **57**, 10–16.
Pintner, I. J., and Provasoli, L. 1957. *J. Gen. Microbiol.* **18**, 190–197.
Pringsheim, E. G. 1955. *Arch. Mikrobiol.* **23**, 181–192.
Provasoli, L. *In* "Perspectives in Marine Biology" (A. Buzzati-Traverso, ed.), Univ. California Press, Berkeley, California. In press.
Provasoli, L., McLaughlin, J. J. A., and Droop, M. R. 1957. *Arch. Mikrobiol.* **25**, 392–428.
Raleigh, G. J. 1939. *Plant Physiol.* **14**, 823–828.
Sager, R., and Palade, G. E. 1957. *J. Biophys. Biochem. Cytol.* **3**, 463–487.
Schubert, J. 1954. *In* "Chemical Specificity in Biological Interactions" (F. R. N. Gurd, ed.), pp. 114–163. Academic Press, New York.
Selawry, O. S., Goldstein, M. N., and McCormick, T. 1957. *Cancer Research* **17**, 785–791.
Shive, W. 1950. *Ann. New York Acad. Sci.* **52**, 1212–1234.
Shooter, R. A., and Wyatt, H. V. 1957. *Brit. J. Exptl. Pathol.* **38**, 473–477.
Sobotka, H., Baker, H., Luisada-Opper, A. V., and Hutner, S. H. 1957. *Rev. fermentations et inds. aliment.* **12**, 51–56.
Starr, T. J. 1956. *Ecology* **37**, 658–664.
Trager, W. 1953. *J. Exptl. Med.* **97**, 177–188.
Vitale, J. J., Hegsted, D. M., Nakamura, M., and Connors, P. 1957. *J. Biol. Chem.* **226**, 597–601.
Webb, D. A. 1956. *Pubbl. staz zool. Napoli* **28**, 273–288.
Williams, T. R., ed. 1955. "The Biochemistry of Vitamin B_{12}." *Biochem. Soc. Symposia* No. **13**.
Wolken, J. J. 1956. *J. Protozool.* **3**, 211–221.

CHAPTER 4

The Relation of Soils to the Micronutrient Element Content of Plants and to Animal Nutrition

KENNETH C. BEESON

United States Plant, Soil, & Nutrition Laboratory
Agricultural Research Service
Ithaca, New York

	Page
I. Introduction	67
II. Soil-Animal Nutrition Problems in the United States	68
III. Cobalt Deficiency in the Atlantic Coastal Plain	72
IV. Molybdenum Toxicity in the United States	76
V. Summary	77
References	78

I. INTRODUCTION

The interrelationship of soils to plant composition and animal nutrition has long been recognized and acknowledged. The historical background beginning with the description of bone diseases in cattle in the middle of the 19th century and continuing through the discoveries of cobalt as an essential nutrient and selenium and molybdenum as toxicity problems is a fascinating story. Of even greater interest are the older and sometimes colorful items—observations of farmers and herdsmen—of troubles with their cattle or other animals when they were permitted to graze certain areas. Although the nature of the troubles differs from place to place, there is no continent free of some disease, nutritional in nature and caused by an abnormality in some soil.

On the contrary, it is seldom true that any continuous area of great extent is involved. Typically, the deficiency or toxicity is spotty with good and poor areas following their characteristic soils in the apparently haphazard patterns so often evident in nature.

Although the suspected troubles of soil origin in animals are numerous, progress in their solution is slow. There are probably many reasons for this. The causative factors have not only been obscure and unsuspected but they were of minute quantity in their occurrence. All of the micronutrient elements are examples of this. The discovery of cobalt followed many years of intensive research by a number of scientists. It followed by at least 150 years the first observations of the undiagnosed malady by farmers in New Hampshire and Scotland. The troubles of this nature confronting us today are as obscure. Pressure for their solution is greater, however, and in our impatience to "explain" every ailment, imaginary or otherwise in man or animal, some are condemning, without a reasonable hearing, all kinds of soils, soil conditions, and management practices. This sort of activity tends to bring into disrepute the sound efforts being made to discover causes and interrelationships in a most complex field of agricultural research.

II. Soil-Animal Nutrition Problems in the United States

Of our total agricultural area, deficient and toxic soils are a proportionately smaller part than is probably true of many other countries. In terms of our total production of animal products, we could ignore those occurrences of poor performance. There was no great urge to expend the time and cost of solving such problems, and the principal effort went into better animals and larger crops on the soils where these goals could be achieved. Hence, our research in the area of soil-nutritional relationships lagged behind that in other countries.

However, we did, and still do, have problems and with the announcements from Australia (Marston, 1935; Underwood and Filmer, 1935) of the essentiality of cobalt and from the United States of the toxicity of selenium to animals (Byers, 1935), we began to take stock of the situation.

In Fig. 1 there are plotted those areas where nutritional problems have been reported in the United States. A deficiency of phosphorus in pasture and hay from some areas was early recognized, and it still is one of the more common ailments in cattle. However, as more and more phosphorus is applied to our soils, and as a greater effort is made to assure an ample supply to the animals of the mineral phosphate, this problem is no longer acute. Good management can prevent the deficiency, and most farmers are now following recommended practices.

It has already been mentioned that a trouble now known to be cobalt deficiency was described in New Hampshire in the latter part of the 18th century. Among the superstitious townfolk of Albany, New Hampshire, the disease was believed to be the result of an Indian curse (Coolidge and Mansfield, 1859). About 1830, Professor Dana, the famous geologist, was consulted, and he ascribed the cause as something toxic in the water of the region (Beals, 1916).

A little more than a century later, cobalt-deficient soils identified by the typical nutritional disturbance in ruminants were reported from nearly all of New Hampshire (Lyford *et al.*, 1946) and parts of the adjoining states, from Cape Cod, northern New York, northern Michigan and northeastern Wisconsin. Cobalt deficiency is also reported from much of the Atlantic Coastal Plain and Florida. Some of the implications of the Coastal Plain problem will be discussed in detail later. Only minor

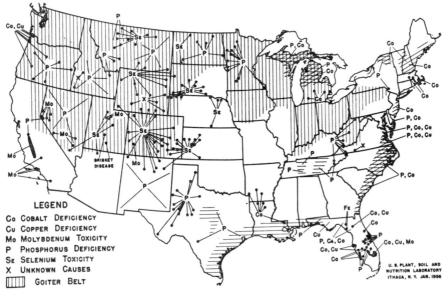

LEGEND
Co COBALT DEFICIENCY
Cu COPPER DEFICIENCY
Mo MOLYBDENUM TOXICITY
P   PHOSPHORUS DEFICIENCY
Se SELENIUM TOXICITY
X   UNKNOWN CAUSES
[||||] GOITER BELT

U. S. PLANT, SOIL AND
NUTRITION LABORATORY
ITHACA, N. Y. JAN. 1956

FIG. 1. Known areas in the United States where mineral-nutritional diseases of animals occur. The dots indicate approximate locations where troubles occur. The lines not terminating in dots indicate a generalized area or areas where specific locations have not been reported.

areas of cobalt-deficient soil are known south or west of these regions.

The reported occurrence in the United States of goiter in man and its relation to soils is a matter of interest but is little understood. The so-called goiter belt is very extensive, covering almost half of our total area. Although the iodine content of the waters of a region are an important factor in preventing goiter, it is evident that the soil should be the primary source for both waters and crops.

Iodine does not appear to be deficient in the humid regions, particularly along the coastal areas, although the soils here are highly leached and acid in reaction. There would seem to be little opportunity for iodine to be retained in these soils so as to be readily available to plant roots. On the contrary, iodine-deficient areas in the Northwest are associated with a semiarid climate, and a minimum of soil leaching under alkaline conditions occurs. Very little has been learned about the iodine content of these soils, but the work of Fraps and Fudge (1939) in the state of Texas shows that soils in many of the upland semiarid regions of that state are not different in total iodine from the Gulf of Mexico Coastal Plain.

Contrary to the popular conception, there seems to be no evidence of any particular relationship of iodine deficiency to the areas subjected to Pleistocene glaciation. It is true that some of these areas are involved, but it is also evident that others of this region are not associated with troubles caused by iodine deficiency. Furthermore, there is no particular reason other than coincidental location to suspect these areas because of glaciation. Although there was a vast mixing action of the rock material over the landscape, no quantity of recognizable material was transported for very great distances. Consequently, the nature of the rock material over the region as a whole should not have differed greatly from the original.

The possibility of rain water as a source of iodine has been suggested by a number of workers. Hercus et al. (1925) have calculated that from 22 to 50 mg. of iodine per acre will fall on the Atlantic Coastal Plain as compared to 0.7 mg. in the Great Lakes region. This is undoubtedly an important difference in the source of supply of iodine.

In contrast to the general situation in northern and western United States, there are many isolated sites where the iodine content of vegetation is very high. Typically these sites are poorly drained with a high water table. The sedges and juncus predominate, but these are excellent feeds and very palatable to cattle and sheep. There is no knowledge, at present, as to the frequence of occurrence of such areas nor as to their extent or importance in animal nutrition. They must, however, make a considerable contribution in this respect.

The only other micronutrient element deficiency causing malnutrition in animals now recognized as resulting from a soil deficiency is copper. A few areas of uncomplicated copper deficiency have been reported in Florida (Davis, 1950), and at least one is known in North Carolina. Other countries, particularly Australia, have reported much more extensive areas of uncomplicated copper deficiency (Russell and Duncan, 1956). It might be noted, however, that work in our laboratory indicates large areas in the Northeast where the forage is very low in copper. It is probable, however, that the feeding of grain by-products has adequately supplemented the ration with respect to this element. In any event, a deficiency of copper has apparently not been demonstrated in that region.

The molybdenum-copper interrelationship, i.e., a toxicity due to a combination of excessive levels of molybdenum and low levels of copper in forages, has been reported in Florida and California (Britton and Goss, 1946; Davis, 1950). Areas where molybdenum is unusually high in the forage have been observed in Utah, Nevada, and Colorado, and a probable relationship to nutritional trouble in cattle is suspected. The diagnosis of such troubles is difficult, particularly on the basis of forage composition. That is, there are no quantitative data for determining a molybdenum toxic area on the basis of the concentrations of molybdenum, copper, and sulfur in the plant or the soil. Hence, only frank cases of toxicity in the animal can be used as criteria, while borderline areas or chronic cases remain doubtful. Some details of the soil-plant relationships of molybdenum will be discussed later.

The situation with respect to selenium is somewhat better known. This widespread toxicity in our western states is clearly associated with specific geological formations and plant species that have enhanced the detection of the soils involved (Moxon *et al.*, 1950). Suffice it to say that new areas are continuously being discovered, and there is still much to be done in the delineation of both known and newly discovered areas.

Currently, there are several other problems, nutritional in nature, that are of concern. Two of these should be discussed briefly. In a rugged mountainous area of central Idaho there is a congenital anomaly in lambs, a "cyclopia" known locally as "monkey faces." Efforts to find a genetic clue to this trouble have been fruitless. In general its occurrence is patterned in such a manner as to strongly suggest that if the ewe, early in gestation, grazes in certain areas a deformed lamb is likely to result.

Geologically this area is a huge intrusion of granitic rock of light color. On first inspection of the area it might be assumed that a deficiency of some nature should exist. However, a careful examination of forages has failed to reveal any trouble of this kind. A characteristic of this area is the postconsolidation emanations relatively high in concentration of a number of elements (Anderson, 1942, 1951). Among the important ore deposits are lead, silver, zinc, copper, cobalt, antimony, and tungsten and lesser amounts of mercury, arsenic, molybdenum, bismuth, and selenium. Hence, it seems reasonable to assume that relatively large quantities of one or more such elements might be present in plants and influence their nutritional quality. No evidence of this has been discovered, however.

"Brisket disease" occurs in cattle in the high mountain grazing lands of Colorado, Utah, and Wyoming. The name refers to the outstanding clinical manifestation—a swollen brisket. It has been suspected that high altitudes were involved in the etiology of this disease, and it is almost invariably associated with altitudes of 6000 feet (Pearson and Jensen, 1956) or higher, and recovery appears only when the animal is taken to lower altitudes. On the other hand, cattle are successfully grazed at equally high altitudes in each of these states. "Brisket" is not infectious nor contagious, and if altitude is not the primary cause, we have another example of an animal disease problem with a close association to localized areas. This leads to a consideration of a possible nutritional cause, either as a deficiency or toxicity.

These and possibly other animal disease problems in our western range country carry a long history of association with particular geographical areas. To postulate that the etiology of these diseases is related to a soil and the composition of the plant seems to present a workable hypothesis.

III. Cobalt Deficiency in the Atlantic Coastal Plain

The extensive and careful investigations of workers in Australia and New Zealand not only clarified a puzzling nutritional problem in the United States but had an important impact on soil-nutrition research here. Although similar and possibly more extensive studies may have been carried on elsewhere, it may be appropriate to examine in some detail the soil-nutrition relationship existing in our Atlantic Coastal Plain with particular reference to that portion in eastern North Carolina and South Carolina.

A deficiency of cobalt as one cause of nutritional troubles in cattle in eastern North Carolina probably was first recognized about 1940 by Dr. Branch Moore, a veterinarian in Kinston, North Carolina. According to Dr. Moore (personal communication), this nutritional deficiency had been observed for many years to occur in cattle in the early spring. Affected animals had poor appetites that resulted in malnutrition, although feed was abundant. The trouble frequently terminated in the death of the animal. Dr. Moore could correct the trouble and obtain recovery of appetite within a week or less by administering small doses of an aqueous solution of a cobalt salt.

At about the same time, Professor John Foster of the North Carolina State College of Agriculture was conducting grazing experiments in cooperation with the U.S. Bureau of Animal Industry and the U.S. Forest Service in the Hoffman Forest in Jones County (personal communication, 1941). Cattle transferred to this area from the Blackland

Station at Wenona, North Carolina, rapidly developed an unthrifty condition, although the forage types available were the same in both areas. The first time a transfer was made, the animals became so unthrifty it was necessary to return them to Wenona to save them. Later, cobalt chloride was added to the mineral mixture supplied the animals in the Hoffman Forest area, and a significant improvement in their health resulted.

A sampling and analysis of native forages in this region showed that 60 per cent or more contained less than 0.08 p.p.m. of cobalt in the dry tissue and a fourth of all the samples contained less than 0.04 p.p.m. A detailed study of a selected area within the region revealed a correlation between the occurrence of cobalt deficiency in cattle, a low concentration of the element in the forage, and two of three marine terraces, The Talbot and the Penholoway (Beeson and Matrone, 1950). To investigate further this apparent relationship a sampling scheme was devised involving five of these marine terraces extending from the Pamlico at sea level to the Sunderland terrace about 170 feet in elevation. Native forage types were collected in specific soils in forested areas over the entire area from north to south.

The results of the analysis of two native forage types, *Andropogon glomeratus* (Walt.) BSP, and the leaves of *Arundenaria tecta,* showed that the mean cobalt concentration in vegetation from the Talbot terrace (elevation 25–40 feet) was 0.03 p.p.m. and was significantly lower (P = 0.01) than that on the Sunderland or Penholoway terraces. Furthermore, the concentrations of copper, iron, calcium, and phosphorus in vegetation from the Talbot terrace were all lower than in that from any other terrace. In general, the highest values in forage were found on the Sunderland terrace lying at the highest elevation (Beeson, 1955).

The reasons therefore would be of considerable interest, but they are obscure. Nutritional deficiencies are not common on the Sunderland terrace. This observation supports the forage composition studies. The soils on the Sunderland are older than those on the lower terraces. Cooke (1935) suggested that the exposure of the Sunderland terrace and the lower terraces was separated by the Illinoian glacial stage. This would make the Sunderland several hundred thousand years older than the lower terraces, and the time interval between it and the next younger terrace would probably be much greater than the interval between any of the younger terraces. Since sands are common on the Sunderland terrace, leaching, if it were an important factor, should have produced a much greater depletion of the mineral elements than on the lower terraces.

Obviously there are factors acting to retain these elements in the soil for the quantities present (2–50 p.p.m. of cobalt) are representative of a wide range of soil conditions. There is no information at present as to the mechanisms of retention, but at least three possibilities can be envisioned: (1) ionic exchange adsorption, (2) the formation of complexes and chelates with certain constituents of soil organic matter, and (3) the vegetative cycle of absorption and redeposition of the elements. While all of these factors operate to produce soluble as well as difficultly-soluble compounds of the elements, the less soluble forms must predominate if retention is accomplished. Under a natural environment an equilibrium is established, and the levels of concentration of the elements in the natural vegetation is not high on even the Sunderland terrace. What will be the effect of an intensive cultivation on these soils? Within recent years, these soils have been improved by the use of fertilizers and lime, the quality of the cattle has been improved, and the numbers increased. Greater quantities of legumes, high cobalt feeders, are planted for pasture. No clear answer is available, but assuming the concentration of cobalt in successive clover crops to be not less than 0.1 p.p.m. and the concentration in the top 6 inches of soil to be only 10 p.p.m., it would require 10,000 crops to remove all of the cobalt in that horizon.

Excessively sandy soils are also common on the Talbot terrace. However, the native vegetation on many of these soils does not contain sufficient copper and cobalt, and nutritional deficiencies in cattle are common where adequate mineral supplements are not provided. Much has been done on these soils to improve the pastures, and the introduction of clovers has resulted in a general increase in the cobalt content of the pasture herbage. The concentration of cobalt in these sandy soils ranges from about 0.2 to 0.4 p.p.m. in the surface or A horizon, as compared to 1.0 to 2.5 p.p.m. in the geographically associated heavier textured soils (Lazar and Beeson, 1956). Hence, the same clover crop could deplete the cobalt in this soil in about 200 years. Actually, of course, the soluble or available cobalt will disappear long before this.

There is an obvious difference in the soils on these terraces, and it is of importance to the livestock industry, as well as of basic interest to soil science. To study these problems further, a number of sites were selected in rather remote areas of the lower Coastal Plain and where vegetation and soils were relatively undisturbed. Each plot represented a discrete soil type. An intensive study of these sites, both soils and vegetation, revealed the clue that the deficient soils were Ground-Water Podsols and the good soils were Low Humic Gleys (Lazar and Beeson, 1956). An incidental fact was the discovery that the swamp black gum (*Nyssa sylvatica* Marsh. var. *biflora* (Walt.) Sarg.) was a prodigious feeder on cobalt, for the leaves of this tree often contained from 60 to 250 times as much cobalt as did the native grasses grown on the same soil (Beeson *et al.,* 1955). A relationship between the cobalt content of black gum and that of *Andropogon glomeratus* was established which permitted the use of the former as an indicator plant.

Using the black gum as a test plant, a study was made by Dr. J. Kubota of the cobalt supply in soils in five states in the Southeast. In support of the earlier work it was found that the cobalt concentration was highest in black gum from sites where the soils were formed on coastal plain clay deposits, on parent materials of stratified sands and clays and sands that have been intermixed with clay deposits during deposition, or on parent material that originated from clay areas further inland. In contrast, the cobalt concentrations in black gum were lower in samples obtained from the Ground-Water Podsols, the Leon, Ona, and St. Johns soils, than from either the Low Humic Gley or Humic-Gley soils of comparable texture (J. Kubota, unpublished date).

In general, it appears that the incidence of cobalt deficiency in cattle in southeastern United States is closely correlated to the occurrence of the Ground-Water Podsol. On the other hand, these soils do not occur to any appreciable extent in the Gulf Coastal Plain region of Alabama, Mississippi, and Texas. Cobalt deficiency in cattle there has not been reported.

While the generalizations presented here are based on the study of a relatively few sites, when one considers the very large number of soil types and the tremendous areas involved, they are being confirmed in each situation to which they are applied. Hence, it is felt that they are of sufficient reliability to be used as a basis for recommendations to farmers. There is much to be learned as to the basic causes for this important difference between Ground-Water Podsols and other soils. The answer to the practical problem does not assist us in understanding the mechanism of the processes involved.

Likewise, the general solution to the soil-animal relationship in the Southeast contributes little to the problem of cobalt-deficient soils in the Northeast. There has been some speculation based on work in New Zealand and elsewhere that the soils developed on granite material of New Hampshire are the deficient soils. While there may be a correlation here for a restricted region, no generalizations concerning such soils are valid. Soils of this type in Pennsylvania, an area free of nutritional problems of this nature, produce forage relatively high in cobalt. The soil relationships to cobalt deficiency in the entire area from Maine to Wisconsin need clarification, and the task promises to be a difficult one.

IV. Molybdenum Toxicity in the United States

Among the toxicity problems resulting from excessive concentrations of a mineral element in the soil and the forage growing thereon, the soil-plant-nutrition relationships of molybdenum are certainly the least understood. This element required in minute quantities by plants, microorganisms, and possibly the animal is readily absorbed and accumulated by most plants. Hence, where the reaction of the soil ranges from neutral to alkaline, an appreciable concentration of the element in the plant can be expected. In controlled culture solutions, levels of 1000 p.p.m. and more in dry plant tissue have been found.

Molybdenum toxicity in vegetation is usually highest in the legumes although sedges, juncus, and grasses occasionally carry appreciable quantities of the element. The clovers will normally accumulate up to 50 per cent more molybdenum than will alfalfa growing in the same soil. Except in unusual cases, the grasses will contain less than 2 or 3 p.p.m. while several hundred parts per million have been found in legumes.

It is now clear that the concentration of molybdenum alone is not the complete answer to the question of whether or not vegetation is toxic. The concentrations of copper and sulfur also appear to be of importance (Dick, 1953). Likewise selectivity in grazing will determine whether or not an animal will become poisoned. Barshad (1948) has noted that a high percentage of Ladino clover with succulent leaves may cause trouble at relatively low concentrations of molybdenum. Mature hay with relatively high levels of molybdenum appears to have a very limited toxic effect.

Some progress is being made, however, in associating soil conditions with the concentration of molybdenum in forages in several areas where cattle do not thrive. For purposes of study, several valleys in Nevada have been selected because certain soils in them are suspected of producing vegetation toxic to animals. The particular situation there offers an unusual opportunity to study the soil, geological and plant factors associated with such a trouble. Investigations carried out in cooperation with the Soil Conservation Service during the past two summers indicate the following soil relationships:

(1) Soils formed on fans derived from granites produce forages that contain more molybdenum than do those on fans derived from rocks other than granite.

(2) Soil drainage and organic matter are important soil factors related to the molybdenum content in forages in areas where granite is one of the dominant rocks.

Poorly drained soils with a high content of organic matter have been suspected in many regions. Davis (1950) in Florida, has been concerned with the alkaline peats of that state. In Utah several areas of suspected molybdenum toxicity are comprised largely of peat soils. These soils vary greatly in nature but all are neutral or alkaline in reaction. Characteristically, there are numerous springs in their vicinity, and the water tables are normally close to or at the surface. The vegetation on these soils in the West consists largely of the juncus and sedges, and these plants appear capable of absorbing relatively high quantities of molybdenum particularly as compared to the grasses.

In many of these peats, selenium is high, and the highest quantity found in one survey, 10.3 p.p.m., was also associated with the highest level of molybdenum, 28 p.p.m. Most of these peats contain more selenium than the surrounding mineral soil. It is interesting to note that the Morrison formation, which is the parent rock of most of the known seleniferous soils in this region, is high in organic matter and carbon. Selenium, molybdenum, vanadium, and uranium all occur in these Morrison shales. In the geological past, these elements may have been concentrated by plant growth, the origin of the organic matter of the shales. The plants now growing on the peats, however, are relatively low in selenium, and in most cases in molybdenum. On the whole, it seems more likely that the selenium and molybdenum are absorbed by the peats from very small concentrations of these elements in the alkaline percolating waters, possibly through coprecipitation of iron sulfides in the anaerobic peat layers.

In Nevada, the problem of malnutrition in cattle is not associated so much with peats as it is with poor drainage and a high organic matter content of mineral soils. Insufficient data are at hand to indicate the distribution of molybdenum in the profiles of these soils. Knowledge of this should be of great assistance in determining the reasons for the presence of sufficient amounts of this element to cause animal troubles.

V. Summary

What remedies are available in correcting the many troubles due either to deficiencies or toxicities of the trace elements? The animal husbandman has little patience with corrective soil measures. He prefers to supply the missing element or the antidote directly to the animal. Practically, he is probably correct. More recently, however, we are recognizing the importance of the organic nutrients in plants. There is evidence at hand that indicates an important effect of mineral nutrition on nutritional factors in plants that are of importance in the growth of animals. To by-pass the soil may result in the failure to provide a complete food for animals or man.

In the case of toxicities, controlled grazing is, of course, a recommended practice. Treatment of large soil areas seems impractical. However, here too, more knowledge of the basic facts involved in the release and absorption of these elements could lead to corrective soil measures and result in completely healthful feed and food. We are woefully lacking in such knowledge, largely because practical solutions seem not to require it.

Consideration is being given these problems. Barshad (1951) has suggested several possibilities for the control of molybdenum toxicity. For example, the molybdenum content of the plant appears to bear a direct relationship to the water-soluble molybdenum in the soil, but the quantity of this form of the element is influenced by a number of other ions: phosphate, carbonate, ammonium nitrogen, calcium, and hydrogen. Of these ions, phosphate appears to enhance availability and the ammonium ion to suppress it. A decrease of soluble soil carbonates and hydroxyl ions by treatment with gypsum, sulfuric acid, or sulfur resulted in an increase in molybdenum content of the plant. The practical aspects of such control are still to be established.

It is evident that there are many problems to be solved not only in the separate fields of soils, plant chemistry, and animal nutrition, but also with respect to the interrelationships involved. Expanding populations may require this knowledge to meet their food requirements. It is our present task to supply that knowledge before it is needed.

REFERENCES

Anderson, A. L. 1942. *Bull. Geol. Soc. Am.* **53**, 1099–1126.
Anderson, A. L. 1951. *Econ. Geol.* **46**, 592–607.
Barshad, I. 1948. *Soil Sci.* **66**, 187–195.
Barshad, I. 1951. *Soil Sci.* **71**, 387–398.
Beals, C. E., Jr. 1916. "Passaconaway in the White Mountains." Richard G. Badger, Boston, Massachusetts.
Beeson, K. C. 1955. *Soil Sci.* **80**, 211–220.
Beeson, K. C., and Matrone, G. 1950. *Symposium on Copper Metabolism* pp. 370–398.
Beeson, K. C., Lazar, V. A., and Boyce, S. G. 1955. *Ecology* **36**, 155–156.
Britton, J. W., and Goss, H. J. 1946. *J. Am. Vet. Med. Assoc.* **108**, 176–178.
Byers, H. G. 1935. *U.S. Dept. Agr. Tech. Bull.* **482**.
Cooke, C. W. 1935. *J. Wash. Acad. Sci.* **25**, 333.
Coolidge, A. J., and Mansfield, J. B. 1859. "History and Description of New England, General and Locale," Vol. 1. A. J. Coolidge, Boston, Massachusetts.
Davis, G. K. 1950. *Symposium on Copper Metabolism* pp. 216–229.

Dick, A. T. 1953. *Australian Vet. J.* **29,** 233–239.

Fraps, G. S., and Fudge, J. F. 1939. *Texas Agr. Expt. Sta. Bull.* **579.**

Hercus, C. H., Benson, W. N., and Carter, C. L. 1925. *J. Hyg.* **24,** 321–402.

Lazar, V. A., and Beeson, K. C. 1956. *J. Agr. Food Chem.* **4,** 439–444.

Lyford, W. H., Jr., Percival, G. P., Keener, H. A., and Morrow, K. S. 1946. *Soil Sci. Soc. Am. Proc.* **10,** 375–380.

Marston, H. R. 1935. *J. Council Sci. Ind. Research* **8,** 111–116.

Moxon, A. L., Olson, O. E., and Searight, W. V. 1950. *South Dakota Agr. Expt. Sta. Tech. Bull.* **2.**

Pearson, R. E., and Jensen, R. 1956. *In* "Diseases of Cattle" (M. G. Fincher, W. J. Gibbons, K. Mayer, and S. E. Park, eds.), pp. 717–723, American Veterinary Publ., Evanston, Illinois.

Russell, F. C., and Duncan, D. L. 1956. *Commonwealth Bur. Animal Nutrition, Tech. Commun.* **15,** 76–82.

Underwood, E. J., and Filmer, J. F. 1935. *Australian Vet. J.* **11,** 84–92.

CHAPTER 5

Manganese and Its Role in Photosynthesis

ANDRÉ PIRSON

Botanical Institute
University of Marburg, Marburg, Germany

It is natural in research on mineral nutrition that the opinions on the function of a single element should change from time to time corresponding to new, impressive, and often surprising experimental data. Looking backward, the reviewer is faced with a rather confusing pattern of findings and interpretations which seems to call for some precise and convincing evidence. There are several reasons for the difficulties that must be overcome in the analysis of the functions of an element; these can be illustrated by a simple scheme (Fig. 1).

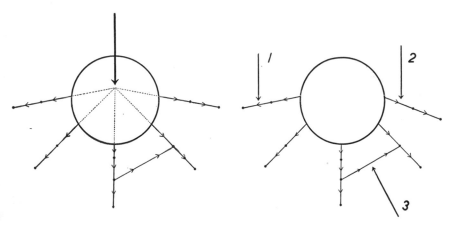

FIG. 1. Central or peripheral effects of mineral factors in nutrition.

If an element is involved in a major role in cell metabolism, especially in the carbon balance or in the energy transfer, then one has to expect that a large number of secondary reactions will be influenced too. The symptoms of deficiency, therefore, will necessarily cover a large spectrum of disturbances. On the other hand, a more peripheral reaction may be primarily governed by a minor element. But experience has shown that, often, more than one of these processes (e.g., 1, 2, 3) will be affected. Thus also in this case, an ambiguous situation can arise, and, in addition, the two principles may occur in combined form.

It is a biologist's task to find out physiological conditions by which a central and, even more, a peripheral action of a single element can be made a limiting process in the metabolism of the intact organism. I like to stress this point: we must ultimately study the living plant, and our work with dead cells or isolated systems can in many cases give only valuable indications, but no unequivocal proof, unless their correlation with the reaction *in vivo* has been established. If we turn then, to the living plant, this plant should be as simple as possible. This is also the reason for the increasing use of green algae of the *Chlorella* type in the field of mineral nutrition.

Let us now turn to our special minor element, manganese. It is an old concept that manganese is involved in the most important part of metabolism of the green plant, photosynthesis. Before it had become known that gray speck disease was connected with manganese deficiency, Hiltner (1924) had already observed that the outbreak and severity of this disease were markedly dependent on the conditions of illumination. Gerretsen (1937) later expressly used this fact in favor of the hypothesis of an influence of manganese on photosynthesis. More direct evidence for such a function of manganese has been gathered by several authors on higher plants and reviewed by Mulder and Gerretsen (1952).

According to these authors, various and partially divergent symptoms of manganese deficiency have been supposed to be produced as a consequence of a low carbohydrate level, resulting from low photosynthetic activity. Depressed rate of photosynthesis in manganese-deficient higher plants, however, has been measured directly only by a few workers, and in these cases evidence is lacking for a primary reaction of manganese (Reuther and Burrows, 1942; Ruck and Bolas, 1954). This holds true even in cases where special care had been taken not to use chlorotic leaves (Gerretsen, 1949). The immediate influence of manganese on photosynthesis could be convincingly demonstrated by the application of green algae in this special field of mineral nutrition (Pirson, 1937; Pirson *et al.*, 1952).

Photosynthesis, measured manometrically in three cultures of the unicellular alga *Ankistrodesmus* at different stages of manganese deficiency is shown in Fig. 2. The difference has been obtained simply by growing the algae in a nutrient solution without added manganese for different periods of time, i.e., 13 and 16 days and, in a second passage, to the nineteenth day of the culture. Depending on deficiency, photosynthesis drops to about one-fifth of its normal value, which is not shown in

Fig. 2 but runs at a level of about 250 mm.^{3}O$_2$/mg. per hour. Dry weight production and chlorophyll content are shown in the accompanying columns. While the former is markedly affected, chlorophyll per unit dry weight is comparatively less diminished. At an early stage of deficiency, there is not a real chlorosis, since only the lesser density of the suspension and its higher average light absorption must be considered responsible for the somewhat lower concentration of chlorophyll. This fact is re-

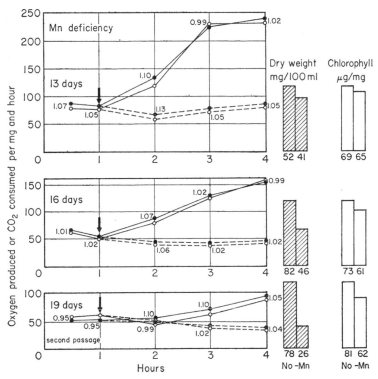

FIG. 2. Photosynthesis of manganese-deficient cultures of *Ankistrodesmus* at different stages of deficiency. Short term recovery after addition of manganese (cf. text). After Pirson *et al.* (1952).

markable since a chlorosis, in cases of manganese deficiency, has often been reported for higher plants (e.g., Martin, 1935; Haas, 1936; Friederichsen, 1944; Owen and Massey, 1953). Decrease of photosynthesis in algae at the beginning of manganese deficiency is clearly independent of any influence on the chlorophyll level.

After an addition of manganese, photosynthesis increases rapidly without any appreciable change in cell composition, and the normal activity is almost restored in the course of a few hours. The photosynthetic quotient remains practically constant at a value of unity during this time of recovery. Hence, the manometric effects are produced only by photosynthesis, without any change in other processes which could possibly influence the gas exchange. At the later stages of deficiency, the manganese effect is, in principle, the same, but recovery of photosynthesis is

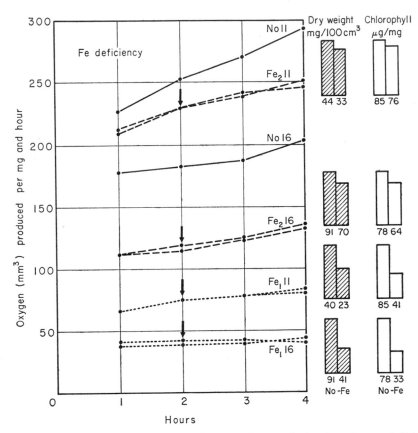

Fig. 3. Photosynthetic oxygen production of normal (No) and iron-deficient cultures of *Ankistrodesmus*. Two stages of deficiency (Fe₁, Fe₂ at the 11th and 16th day of culture). No short term recovery after the addition of Fe⁺⁺ (or Fe⁺⁺⁺) observable (cf. text). After Pirson *et al.* (1952).

no longer complete. However, even in these cases, the photosynthetic quotient remains normal in spite of unavoidable disturbances in the general metabolism of the deficient cells.

It is important to note in this connection that the behavior of iron-deficient algae grown in a similar way is quite different (Fig. 3). Iron deficiency inhibits photosynthesis but at the same time produces a distinct chlorosis. Recovery after addition of iron salts is not a matter of hours, but of days, and seems closely connected to the resumption of both growth and chlorophyll production. This shows that iron and manganese are acting in photosynthesis in a quite different way. There is particularly no indication of a redox system of these two elements, the maintenance of which has played a considerable part in the discussion of the function of manganese in the green plant for a long time (cf. p. 92).

It may be mentioned in passing that manganese is not unique so far as the quick recovery of photosynthesis following mineral deficiency is concerned. In the case of potassium and phosphorus deficiencies, we also found comparable reactions, but in these cases recovery was more or less superimposed by other reactions, which could be recognized by slight deviations of the photosynthetic quotient. Beyond this, potassium and

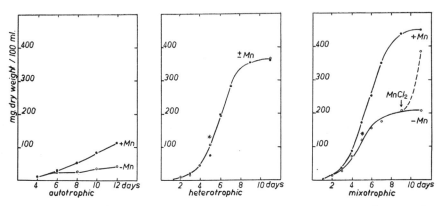

Fig. 4. Growth of *Chlorella vulgaris* in autotrophic, heterotrophic, and mixotrophic culture, with and without added manganese (cf. text). After Bergmann (1955).

phosphorus deficiencies have a marked and reversible influence on respiration which is not found to such a degree in manganese-deficient cells. This special point will be mentioned again later.

Further evidence for the function of manganese in photosynthesis can be derived from comparative experiments on algal growth under autotrophic, heterotrophic, and mixotrophic conditions. Such experiments have been performed with a *Chlorella* strain by Bergmann (1955) in our laboratory. As already shown, manganese deficiency appears very easily in a pure autotrophic culture of algae if we simply omit the metal from the usual nutrient solution without applying special methods of purification. If, by contrast, *Chlorella* grows in the same solution with added glucose in the dark, there appears no distinct difference between plus- and minus-manganese cultures, in spite of the fact that the dry-matter production of the cells is much greater under heterotrophic conditions than it is without glucose in the light (Fig. 4).

Growth of such cultures proceeds, under the experimental conditions used, until the supply of glucose is completely exhausted. It seems, therefore, to be independent of the presence or absence of manganese. It should be stressed that these apparently normal heterotrophic cultures have a masked manganese deficiency. If cells grown in the dark are used for a manometric determination of photosynthesis at the times marked in Fig. 4 by the asterisk, depression of photosynthesis and the typical sudden response to the addition of manganese can be observed. Thus,

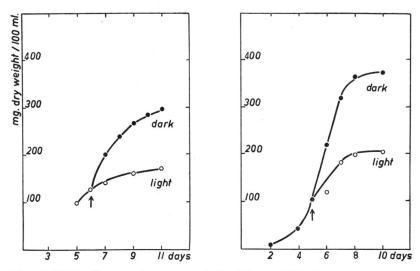

Fig. 5. Light effect on the growth of Mn-deficient *Chlorella* in the presence of glucose (1%). Mixotrophic cells transferred to dark (left side), heterotrophic cells transferred to light (right side). After Bergmann (1955).

the photosynthetic apparatus of the cells becomes manganese-defective in the dark, but this, of course, does not injure the cells as long as the defective mechanism remains out of use. As we compared these results with an experiment in which glucose had been added to the culture solution in the light, we were surprised to find that this mixotrophic culture developed a clear-cut manganese deficiency. The arrested growth of this culture, however, was instantly resumed when manganese was added.

If, furthermore, we take a glucose culture from light to dark and, conversely, from dark to light, we find a corresponding response of growth (Fig. 5). The deficient light culture resumes growth and glucose uptake in the dark, and the deficient dark culture soon stops growing and taking up glucose in the light.

In addition, we mention an experiment by Bergmann which starts from an observation made by Neish (1951). This author found that *Chlorella* can be grown in the light in the presence of glucose but without added carbon dioxide and oxygen. This apparently anaerobic utilization

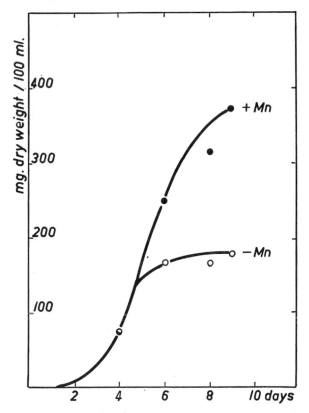

Fig. 6. Growth of *Chlorella* in anaerobic light culture with and without added manganese. Pure nitrogen flushed through the culture flasks. After Bergmann (1955).

of glucose as the sole carbon source in the light also depends on manganese (Fig. 6). From these results, we draw several conclusions:

(1) Glucose metabolism in the dark differs from that in the light. This is in agreement or can be reconciled with results of other authors (Neish, 1951; Simonis and Grube, 1953; Arnon *et al.*, 1954; Kandler, 1954).

(2) Manganese is strongly engaged in the consumption of glucose in the light.

(3) A pronounced requirement for manganese becomes apparent in all cases where the algae make use of their photosynthetic apparatus.

It must, however, be admitted that another explanation is possible for the inhibition of growth in mixotrophic algae. Reisner and Thompson (1956) recently reported that illuminated *Chlorella* cells in the presence of glucose show a reduced manganese content, which they believe to be responsible for the deficiency symptoms in this case. But the quantitative data of these authors available to us currently cannot convince us completely of the correctness of this conclusion. We will come back to this point somewhat later. But, apart from this, an inhibiting effect of light on the uptake of a minor element in growing cells seems to be a remarkable phenomenon since there is no comparable observation reported in the literature, as far as I know.

Since, in any case, the function of manganese in photosynthesis can be considered proven with sufficient clarity, the next step in the analysis of this function should be to find out its specific point of action within the mechanism of photosynthesis.

A primary indication is given by the fact that the inhibition of photosynthesis by manganese deficiency described above is independent of light intensity. This has been observed in our laboratory at a very low light intensity (Pirson *et al.*, 1952), at about 3 times compensation, and by Arnon (1954) about one-third of saturation. At first sight, the explanation would be that manganese acts on the photochemical part of photosynthesis, i.e., the photolysis of water, but a number of arguments and results point to another direction.

It must be considered that the old idea that an effect on photosynthesis at low light intensity reveals a specific influence on the photochemical step cannot be maintained in this narrow sense. We know today that some poisons, like hydroxylamine or *o*-phenanthroline, inhibit photosynthesis in weak and strong light exactly as manganese deficiency does, but at the same time do not inhibit photoreduction.

Photoreduction is the special type of photosynthesis that occurs in several species of algae containing the enzyme hydrogenase. In this case, after a period of adaptation to a hydrogen atmosphere in the dark, no oxygen is evolved upon illumination, but carbon dioxide and hydrogen are consumed simultaneously. This reaction is well known from investigations of Gaffron and others (Gaffron, 1940, 1944).

In order to understand the behavior of photoreducing algae, it must be mentioned that with increasing light intensity, consumption of hydrogen comes to an end and gives rise to a normal photosynthetic evolution of oxygen. This reversion from photoreduction to photosynthesis is called deadaptation (Fig. 7).

Photoreduction, then, offers an opportunity to check a possible function of manganese in photosynthetic oxygen evolution. If manganese-deficient algae showed a reduced rate of photosynthesis and, at the same time, a decreased photoreduction, then oxygen evolution could not be

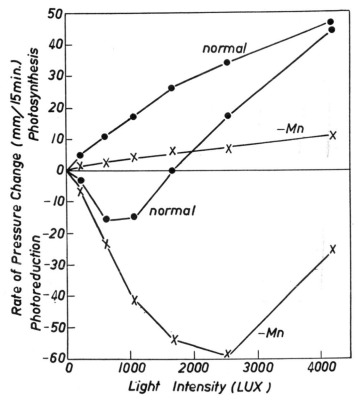

FIG. 7. Photoreduction and photosynthesis of *Ankistrodesmus* at increasing light intensities in normal and manganese-deficient cultures. After Kessler (1955, 1957a).

specifically influenced. If, conversely, photoreduction is independent of the manganese supply, oxygen evolution must be considered as the metal-requiring step. This would correspond exactly to the action of hydroxylamine on photosynthesis and photoreduction. This alternative has been studied by Kessler, (1955, 1957a) in Gaffron's laboratory.

As shown in Fig. 7, photoreduction with hydrogen, in contrast to photosynthesis, is not at all inhibited by manganese deficiency. In addition, there is a pronounced influence of manganese on deadaptation. Whereas in normal cells, the shift from photoreduction to photosynthesis with evolution of oxygen occurs at about 1000 lux, photoreduction is highly stabilized in manganese-deficient algae, so that even at 4000 lux, photoreduction is still preserved, although there are signs of beginning deadaptation at this light intensity. With increasing deficiency, photosynthesis is strongly (and reversibly) inhibited, but photoreduction is not affected even at rather high degrees of deficiency (Fig. 8). This seems to be important since in this way it can be shown that, in the entire range of the deficiency observed, only that part of photosynthesis is inhibited which is responsible for oxygen evolution.

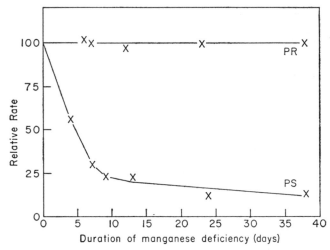

Fig. 8. Photosynthesis and photoreduction of *Ankistrodesmus* with increasing manganese deficiency. After Kessler (1957a).

Also in this case it is of interest to compare the corresponding behavior of cells deficient in iron (Fig. 9). Here photoreduction is inhibited, and deadaptation by no means prevented. Thus the effects of iron deficiency are completely different from those of manganese deficiency. To be brief, a scheme may be shown to explain these observations (Fig. 10). It assumes an action of manganese in a certain step between photolysis and oxygen evolution. The question as to why the function of manganese is supposed to be exactly at this step, between the somewhat hypothetical intermediates of the oxygen pathway, may only be touched upon in passing.

The first intermediate on the oxygen pathway is called $Y(OH)_2$. This is stabilized to some extent by the formation of peroxidelike substance

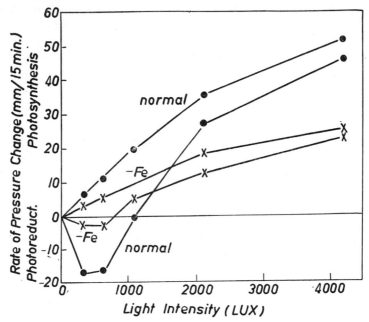

FIG. 9. Photoreduction (and photosynthesis) of *Ankistrodesmus* at increasing light intensities in normal and iron-deficient cultures. After Kessler (1957a).

$Z(OH)_2$ and from this, finally, oxygen will be released. $Z(OH)_2$ is assumed to be the component which is responsible for the deadaptation and inactivation of hydrogenase. In this respect, $Z(OH)_2$ is more active than free oxygen, since deadaptation in the light is much easier than deadap-

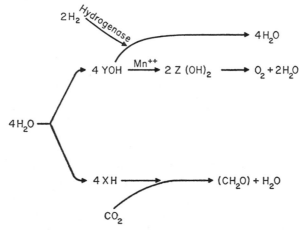

FIG. 10. Scheme showing the main action of manganese inside the photosynthetic apparatus. After Kessler (1957a).

tation with free oxygen in the dark. Therefore, the most convenient assumption is that Mn^{++} acts in the step which forms $Z(OH)_2$.

These conclusions concerning the role of manganese gain considerable support from experimental results obtained by other authors.

First, a paper of the Yellow Springs Group of the Kettering Foundation may be cited (Eyster *et al.*, 1956). This work provides additional evidence for the role of manganese in the oxygen-evolving system of photosynthesis. As Warburg (1948) and more explicitly Clendenning and Ehrmantraut (1950) found, unicellular algae, like chloroplasts, are able to give a Hill reaction with quinone. Therefore, the photosynthetic oxygen evolution of these algae can be examined independently of carbon dioxide fixation.

The Hill reaction in manganese-deficient algae is completely suppressed while photosynthesis is strongly inhibited. The specific function of manganese is impressively demonstrated in this case by the sudden recovery of both processes, complete photosynthesis and oxygen evolution, depending on the concentration of added manganese (cf. p. 145). Similar, in our opinion, but not as conclusive, are two earlier observations with isolated chloroplasts or leaf extracts from higher plants.

Mehler (1951) discovered a special type of Hill reaction with oxygen acting as a Hill reagent, i.e., as a substitute for carbon dioxide in the light reactions of chloroplasts.

This Mehler-type of the Hill reaction can be described in a somewhat simplified form by the following equations:

$$2H_2O \xrightarrow[\text{chloroplasts}]{\text{light}} 2\langle H\rangle + 2\langle OH\rangle$$
$$2\langle OH\rangle \longrightarrow H_2O + \tfrac{1}{2}O_2$$
$$2\langle H\rangle + O_2 \longrightarrow H_2O_2$$

In Mehler's experiments, H_2O_2 is not directly observed but caught indirectly by its stoichiometric reaction with ethanol and the formation of acetaldehyde. Mehler has already noted the fact that this sequence is dependent on the presence of manganese.

We mention this as a further indication for the proposed role of manganese in spite of the somewhat controversial opinions on the Mehler reaction as a regulating principle in natural photosynthesis. A comparable indication comes from Gerretsen's experiments (1950–51) on oxidation-reduction potentials in illuminated crude extracts from oat leaves. Addition of manganese to these extracts in the light produced such a high change in potential that the formation of a peroxide, presumably H_2O_2, according to the scheme of Mehler, must be assumed. In Gerretsen's experiments, however, iron produced the opposite effect, so that it is not clear whether his observations can be directly compared with our own iron-independent effects. It is possible that the phenomena observed by Gerretsen belong to a range of excess concentrations of manganese. And it is clear that we must carefully separate the effects of major or minor elements in the range between normal and deficiency concentrations from those produced in the range of supranormal doses.

Further, a paper by Kenten and Mann (1955) may be cited which considers the possible function of manganese in photosynthesis with respect to the properties of manganese itself. The Rothamsted authors observed an oxidation of bivalent manganese to the trivalent form by isolated chloroplasts in the light. This would at least show that manganese can be involved in the oxidative side of the photosynthetic apparatus. However, in this case the possibility must be taken into account that the oxidation of manganese is produced by the H_2O_2 coming from a previous Mehler reaction and would, therefore, not belong to the photosynthetic mechanism proper. Kenten and Mann tried to exclude this explanation by experiments with added peroxidase from horse-radish and, at the other side, by catalase preparations from ox liver. Catalase inhibits the manganese oxidation slightly, while—and this is the important point —peroxidase promotes it. Therefore, the authors suggest that the oxidation of manganese is due, at least in part, to the peroxidase system and that a manganese oxidation-reduction cycle may play a part in the reaction of photosynthesis. These experiments also deserve attention since they speak against a function of manganese comparable to that of magnesium. This similarity of the two bivalent ions, which play a considerable part in the activation of isolated enzymes, is also not supported by our own experience with living algae.

We come now to the question of whether we must consider the possibility of an additional point of attack of manganese in the photosynthetic mechanism. In this respect, an observation from Arnon's laboratory may be mentioned. Carbon dioxide fixation by isolated chloroplasts has been reported to be enhanced by manganese, but only in combination with ascorbate (Allen et al., 1955). Therefore it seems possible that manganese is also effective in a step of photosynthesis which uses ascorbic acid. Together with this fact, the observation may be recalled that manganese plays a part as an activating factor in the photochemically active combination of isolated chloroplasts with the reaction complex of the malic enzyme (Vishniac and Ochoa, 1951; Tolmach, 1951; Arnon 1951). Although this model system presumably is not a component of normal photosynthesis, the possibility should not be excluded a priori that manganese may also be involved, perhaps in a range of minute concentrations, in the reducing side of the photosynthetic apparatus.

If we now turn to some possible activities of manganese outside the photosynthétic mechanism, we are tempted to quote the immense material accumulated by the enzymologists. In fact, as we can see, for example, in a review by McElroy and Nason (1954), there are very numerous activations of enzymes by manganese. However, the same holds true in most cases for other bivalent ions, especially magnesium. In principle, all the double and multiple activations *in vitro* should not simply be transferred to corresponding enzymatic processes inside the living cell. If we were to proceed in this way, we would rarely discover any specificity, and perhaps comparatively few processes could be proved to be really uninfluenced by manganese. We, therefore, prefer to come back to physiological evidence for effects of manganese.

At first we mention the observation of Reisner and Thompson (1956) that heterotrophic growth in green algae is markedly decreased when all traces of manganese are carefully excluded. It becomes clear from these findings that even the dark metabolism of these algae cannot work without manganese. The very small requirement for manganese in heterotrophic algae, as compared to autotrophic ones, may also help to explain the behavior of mixotrophic cultures in the case of limiting manganese supply which we have already described. Photosynthesis, with its much higher demand, monopolizes for its own purpose all available traces of manganese in deficient cells. Hence, in these mixotrophic cells, no by-path into the heterotrophic mode of nutrition has been left open in the light.

The participation of manganese in some unknown step of dark metabolism recalls the somewhat obsolete claim raised, especially by Lundegårdh (1939), that manganese acts in the respiration of green plants as iron does in animal cells. Although this opinion may no longer be defended in its original sense, Lundegårdh's observation that manganese-deficient roots showed an increased oxygen uptake after the addition of manganese, should be kept in mind and certainly deserves further elucidation. It may be mentioned, too, that Eyster *et al.* (1956) report an influence of the manganese supply on endogenous respiration in algae changing from acceleration to inhibition, depending on the age of their cultures. Unfortunately, their data do not include any mention of a reversibility of these effects. Therefore, it is hard to decide whether these results can be simply explained as a consequence of changes in the carbohydrate level.

Finally, we should stress the experimental evidence which has been obtained by Burström (1939) to support his idea of a role of manganese in nitrate reduction by green plants. This much discussed conception has been put aside to a certain extent by the discovery of molybdenum as a component of nitrate reductase. However, since nitrate reduction contains a number of successive steps governed by different enzymes, an immediate role of manganese in this sequence cannot yet be ruled out. On the contrary, Burström's theory got recent support from the fact that hydroxylamine reductase from *Neurospora* and soybeans is specifically activated by manganese (Nason, 1956; Nicholas, 1957).

It may also be mentioned that Alberts-Dietert (1941) has already found a strain of *Chlorella* which, at limiting manganese supply, showed a transient preference for ammonia as compared to nitrate. We could not reproduce these findings with sufficient clarity with the algal strains now available in our laboratory, in spite of the precautions which are necessary in comparative cultures with ammonia and nitrate. Hence, in our opinion, this matter remains unsettled. A preference of ammonia vs. nitrate in cases of manganese deficiency has also been found by Kylin (1945) in nutritional experiments with the marine alga *Ulva lactuca*. In this connection, a recent observation of Kessler (1957b) should also be mentioned. He found that nitrite reduction with molecular hydrogen, performed in the dark by hydrogen-adapted green algae, is clearly dependent on manganese.

While we already have some starting points for further investigations on the physiological functions of manganese, we are still almost completely unaware of the mechanism by which manganese itself is acting inside the reaction systems concerned. In this respect, our knowledge is still inferior to that available for other minor elements, e.g., molybdenum or copper. In these cases we have well-known enzymes with a clear and sometimes even stoichiometric relation between the metal, the coenzymes, the proteins, and the substrates. In the case of manganese, it has not even been proved with certainty whether or not a change of valency is involved in its function. The hypothesis, particularly promoted by Somers and Shive (1942) and later by Gerretsen (1950–1951), that manganese cooperates with iron, presumably by maintaining a functional redox system, seems not to be based on sufficient and general evidence. This has been stressed repeatedly and again shown in a recent paper by Burghardt (1956), who reports extensively on this problem.

In any case, we have to consider manganese today as quite an autonomous minor element, as far as one can speak at all of independence in the system of the living cell. Concerning its role in photosynthetic oxygen evolution, an enzymological approach to the mechanism of action of manganese is rendered particularly difficult since neither the enzymes nor their substrates are known. Perhaps some stimulation may come from an examination of model reactions between manganese and peroxides. However, I would hesitate to compare flatly the function of manganese with that of a peroxidase or a catalase.

Since we are celebrating here the jubilee of an agricultural station, some concluding remarks should be made about the applicability of experiments with algae of the kind reported to the biology of higher plants and of crop plants.

If we were to try to transfer directly the techniques and results of algal physiology to investigations on higher plants, we would certainly be soon disappointed. For example, Reuther and Burrows (1942), and recently also Burghardt (1956), did not succeed in getting an immediate response of photosynthesis to the addition of manganese solution to manganese-deficient leaves. These differences and similar ones, however, should not discourage us in our efforts in the field of comparative physiology. To this comparative physiology, belongs, in the first place, a careful examination of the morphological differentiation and its physiological consequences. In any case, it seems unjustified to cut off any discussion with the argument that higher and lower plants would have developed an essentially different requirement for minor elements.

Until now, it has not been sufficiently proved that differences in qualitative requirements exist in the cells of growing green plants, which depend on their taxonomical position alone. Therefore, we have to look for another principle from which the observed differences can be derived. We intentionally put aside all the obvious methodological complications which arise from the use of higher plants as experimental organisms. Apart from these, one important point is that in green algae, deficiency symptoms develop in the course of continued growth in all cells, while in higher plants a deficiency can initially be avoided by translocation. If, then, this possibility has been exhausted, the speed at which deficiency sets in can be so high that early stages, which are so well accessible with algae, will practically be skipped.

Another point may also be mentioned which, in my opinion, deserves particular attention. It should be noticed that with the transition from the unicellular organization to the growth on a tissue level and to cell elongation, additional demands for mineral factors may appear. As an example, it may be mentioned that comparatively little data is available on the boron requirement of lower green plants (Eyster, 1952, cf. p. 229), while in many higher plants boron deficiency has been well known for a long time. The same holds true, to a certain degree, for the calcium requirement. This case is particularly interesting because Burström (1952, 1954) has worked out a kind of fractionated, tripartite activity of calcium in wheat roots: High doses are used for the detoxication of H^+ ions; lower doses are required for cell elongation, and the lowest concentrations at about 10^{-6} M must be available for normal cell division.

With unicellular algae, however, we, as well as others, have found that the requirement for calcium is restricted to the range of a minor element (Pirson, 1937; Stegmann, 1940; Walker, 1953). In this range, detoxication of H^+ ions apparently plays the main role. But if we change only from *Chlorella* to the green alga *Hydrodictyon* which belongs to the same taxonomical group but shows a higher differentiation and a marked cell elongation, the amount of calcium necessary for growth increases considerably (unpublished observation in the author's laboratory).

Thus also, in the case of manganese requirement of higher and lower plants, a quantitative factor and perhaps a shift in the concentrations necessary for different functions may be responsible for the varying symptoms which become apparent in the course of increasing deficiency.

Lastly, the whole problem evidently emphasizes the old demand of biology that physiological findings should never be considered as isolated phenomena but should be closely correlated to the morphological system to which they intimately belong.

REFERENCES

Alberts-Dietert, F. 1941. *Planta* 32, 88–117.

Allen, M. B., Arnon, D. I., Capindale, J. B., Whatley, F. R., and Durham, L. J. 1955. *J. Am. Chem. Soc.* 77, 4149–4155.

Arnon, D. I. 1951. *Nature* 167, 1008.

Arnon, D. I. 1954. *Congr. intern. botan. 8ᵉ Congr., Paris, Sects.* 11–12, 73–80.

Arnon, D. I., Whatley, F. R., and Allen, M. B. 1954. *J. Am. Chem. Soc.* 76, 6324–6329.

Bergmann, L. 1955. *Flora (Jena)* 142, 493–539. 1955. cf. Pirson, A., and Bergmann, L. *Nature* 176, 209.

Burghardt, H. 1956. *Flora (Jena)* 143, 1–30.

Burström, H. 1939. *Planta* 29, 292–305; 30, 129–150.

Burström, H. 1952. *Physiol. Plantarum* 5, 391–402.

Burström, H. 1954. *Physiol. Plantarum* 7, 332–342.

Clendenning, K. A., and Ehrmantraut, H. C. 1950. *Arch. Biochem.* 29, 387–403.

Eyster, C. 1952. *Nature* 170, 755.

Eyster, C., Brown, T. E., and Tanner, H. A. 1956. *Arch. Biochem. Biophys.* 64, 240–241.

Friederichsen, I. 1944. *Planta* 34, 67–87.

Gaffron, H. 1940. *Am. J. Botany* 27, 273–283.

Gaffron, H. 1944. *Biol. Revs. Cambridge Phil. Soc.* 19, 1–20.

Gerretsen, F. C. 1937. *Ann. Botany (London)* 1, 207–230.

Gerretsen, F. C. 1949. *Plant and Soil* 1, 346–358.

Gerretsen, F. C. 1950–1951. *Plant and Soil* 2, 159–193; 321–343.

Haas, A. R. C. 1936. *Soil Sci.* 42, 435–443.

Hiltner, E. 1924. *Landwirtsch. Jahrb.* 60, 689–769.

Kandler, O. 1954. *Z. Naturforsch.* 9b, 625–644.

Kenten, R. H., and Mann, P. J. G. 1955. *Biochem. J.* 61, 279–286.

Kessler, E. 1955. *Arch. Biochem. Biophys.* 59, 527–529.

Kessler, E. 1957a. *Planta* 49, 435–454.

Kessler, E. 1957b. *Arch. Mikrobiol.* **27**, 166–181.

Kylin, A. 1945. *Kgl. Fysiograf. Sällskap. Lund, Förh.* **15**, 27–35.

Lundegårdh, H. G. 1939. *Planta* **29**, 419–426.

McElroy, W. D., and Nason, A. 1954. *Ann. Rev. Plant Physiol.* **5**, 1–30.

Martin, J. P. 1935. *Hawaiian Planters' Record* **39**, 79–96.

Mehler, A. H. 1951. *Arch. Biochem. Biophys.* **33**, 65–77; **34**, 339–351.

Mulder, E. G., and Gerretsen, F. C. 1952. *Advances in Agron.* **4**, 221–277.

Nason, A. 1956. *Symposium on Inorg. Nitrogen Metabolism, Baltimore,* p. 130. Cf. Nason, A., Abraham, R. G., and Averbach, B. C. 1954. *Biochim. et Biophys. Acta* **15**, 160–161.

Neish, A. C. 1951. *Can. J. Botany* **29**, 68–78.

Nicholas, D. J. D. 1957. *Nature* **179**, 800–804.

Owen, O., and Massey, D. M. 1953. *Plant and Soil* **5**, 81–86.

Pirson, A. 1937. *Z. Botan.* **31**, 193–267.

Pirson, A., Tichy, C., and Wilhelmi, G. 1952. *Planta* **40**, 199–253.

Reisner, G. S., and Thompson, J. F. 1956. *Nature* **178**, 1473–1474.

Reuther, W., and Burrows, F. W. 1942. *Proc. Am. Soc. Hort. Sci.* **40**, 73–76.

Ruck, H. C., and Bolas, B. D. 1954. *Ann. Botany (London)* **18**, 267–297.

Simonis, W., and Grube, K. 1953. *Z. Naturforsch.* **8b**, 312–317.

Somers, I. I., and Shive, W. 1942. *Plant Physiol.* **17**, 582–602.

Stegmann, G. 1940. *Z. Botan.* **35**, 385–422.

Tolmach, L. J. 1951. *Nature* **167**, 946.

Vishniac, W., and Ochoa, S. 1951. *Nature* **167**, 768–769.

Walker, J. B. 1953. *Arch. Biochem. Biophys.* **46**, 1–11.

Warburg, O. 1948. "Schwermetalle als Wirkungsgruppen von Fermenten." 2 Aufl., pp. 183–184. Verlag Dr. W. Sänger, Berlin.

Chapter 6

Manganese Deficiency in Soybeans

H. J. Mederski and D. J. Hoff

Ohio Agricultural Experiment Station
Wooster, Ohio

	Page
I. Introduction	99
II. Correction of Manganese Deficiencies by Foliar Application	100
A. Rate of Absorption	100
B. Effect of Temperature and Vapor Pressure Gradient on Absorption	101
C. Manganese Rates and Solution Volumes	103
III. Correction of Manganese Deficiency with Soil Applications	104
IV. Manganese Deficiency in Relation to Soil Moisture and Soil Temperature	106
V. Summary	107
References	107

I. Introduction

The numerous reports of field studies showing the response of plants to manganese application, studies (McHargue, 1922; McHargue and Calfee, 1932; Haas, 1932; Hopkins, 1934) showing the essentiality of manganese to plants, and recent reviews (McElroy and Nason, 1954; Hewitt, 1951) on the mechanism of action of manganese in plants exemplify the importance of this element in plant growth.

All soils do not contain optimum quantities of manganese. Not only is there a considerable variation of from a trace to 1 per cent or more in total manganese present in different soils, but, also, the amount of manganese that is available to plants varies with soil type and is seldom related to total manganese. The wide range of available soil manganese is responsible for plants that may be manganese deficient when grown in one soil or may contain toxic quantities of manganese when grown in another. In either case, the plant growth and yield may be seriously reduced unless remedial measures are applied to correct the condition.

We will not attempt to review the chemistry of soil manganese and its relation to plants since Mulder and Gerretsen (1952) have reviewed this subject in considerable detail. Instead, we will restrict ourselves to

99

various aspects of manganese deficiency in soybeans and its control with frequent reference to our recent, but unpublished, work which was undertaken to enable us to enlarge our knowledge of the problem.

II. Correction of Manganese Deficiencies by Foliar Application

Manganese deficiency in soybeans manifests itself as a chlorotic mottling of the leaves with islets of light green tissue scattered between dark green leaf veins. As the condition progresses, the light green areas turn yellow, and in many cases necrosis sets in as small brown pin points eventually expanding to large dead areas.

Soybean plants that exhibit severe deficiency symptoms usually contain less than 15 p.p.m. manganese and may be expected to respond to applied manganese. Moderately deficient soybean plants may contain from 15 to 30 p.p.m. manganese, and although the deficiency may be prevented or corrected by manganese fertilization, a significant yield response may not be obtained.

Although foliar sprays of manganese salts are commonly used as a means of correcting manganese deficiencies in plants, only in a few instances have rates of foliar absorption and transport of this element been reported (Bukovac and Wittwer, 1957; Romney and Toth, 1954). As a consequence, the junior author initiated additional studies of the problem.

A. Rate of Absorption

Hoff (1955) studied the rate of manganese absorption by applying a 1 and 5 per cent manganese sulfate solution to the leaves and stems of 5-week old intact soybean plants. After allowing the manganese to contact the plant for varying intervals of time, the above-ground portion of the plant was harvested, washed immediately, and rinsed several times in distilled water to remove the surplus surface manganese, and analyzed for manganese. The increase in manganese content over the nontreated but washed control plants is considered as absorbed manganese. The result of the study, shown in Table I, indicates a very marked and physiologically significant increase in manganese concentration in a relatively short time with the maximum rate of absorption during the first 30 minutes. Although these experiments were conducted in a greenhouse, the conditions of light, temperature, and humidity were similar to those prevailing under field conditions. The instantaneous manganese absorption by plants that were harvested and washed immediately after treatment (0 min.) indicates that some of the so-called absorbed manganese may have been adsorbed on the surface of the leaves and stems. In similar

TABLE I

Increased Concentration of Manganese in Soybean Plants at Various Time Intervals after Momentary Dipping in 1 and in 5 per cent Manganese Sulfate Solutions

Manganese sulfate solution concentration (%)	Accumulative increase in plant manganese concentration after:						
	0 min.[a] (p.p.m.)	15 min. (p.p.m.)	30 min. (p.p.m.)	1 hr. (p.p.m.)	2 hr. (p.p.m.)	6 hr. (p.p.m.)	24 hr. (p.p.m.)
1	84	230	434	538	683	—	754
5	255	—	—	—	3300	3940	4860

[a] Plant samples harvested and washed immediately after dipping but actually in contact with solution for 15–20 seconds. Nondipped control plants contained approximately 30 p.p.m. manganese.

subsequent experiments, plants washed in a dilute $NaNO_3$ solution retained about 30 per cent less manganese than plants washed in distilled water. These results were interpreted as an indication of the presence of surface-adsorbed manganese that was displaced by the sodium ion in the wash water. A similar reversible adsorption of divalent manganese by yeast cell surfaces was observed by Rothstein and Hayes (1956). To our knowledge, this very rapid absorption of foliar-applied manganese has not been observed by other investigators who allowed at least several hours for absorption to occur.

B. Effect of Temperature and Vapor Pressure Gradient on Absorption

Either leaf temperature or vapor pressure gradient between leaf surface and atmosphere could have an effect on the rate of manganese entry into leaves from the applied solution. Leaf temperature may have a more or less direct effect on absorption, while vapor pressure gradient would affect the rate of drying of the solution film, presumably essential for absorption. Cook and Boynton (1952) found that an increase in either leaf temperature or vapor pressure gradient will reduce the rate of urea absorption by apple leaves. Their study of the effect of leaf temperature was confounded, however, by a concomitant change of vapor pressure gradient and leaf temperature that obscured the independent effect of leaf temperature.

In our studies of the effect of leaf temperature, the stems and leaves of intact living soybean plants were immersed in a 0.1 per cent manganese sulfate solution maintained at 2° and 22°C., respectively. This unorthodox technique circumvented the problem of changes in the rate of film-drying with a change in temperature. The results of the experiment show that during a 45-minute absorption period, the plants in solution at 22°C.

increased by 132 p.p.m. manganese, while those at 2°C. increased only 44 p.p.m. These results indicate that absorption proceeds over a wide range of temperature; however, the most rapid rates of absorption probably occur at the optimum plant growth temperature. Since the daily field temperature during the early development of soybeans in Ohio is seldom below 13°C., temperature conditions are not likely to be a factor limiting manganese absorption by leaves.

In studies of the effect of vapor pressure gradient on absorption of foliar-applied manganese, the leaves and stems of intact soybean plants were momentarily dipped in a 0.5 per cent manganese sulfate solution, then respective groups of plants were subjected to the environmental conditions shown in Table II. Immediate drying of the leaf surfaces was

TABLE II

Increase in Plant Manganese as Affected by Maintaining Leaf Surfaces Moist for Various Periods of Time after Dipping Plants in a Manganese Sulfate Solution

Treatment	Increase[a] in plant manganese at:	
	30 min. after dipping (p.p.m.)	60 min. after dipping (p.p.m.)
Dried immediately after dipping	70	70
Moist leaf surface for 10 min. (dry thereafter)	100	120
Moist leaf surface for 20 min. (dry thereafter)	105	120
Moist leaf surface for 30 min. (dry thereafter)	180	180
Leaf surface continuously moist	—	260

[a] Control or nondipped plants contained 40 p.p.m. Mn.

accomplished by placing the plants in a moving current of air having a 40 to 50 per cent relative humidity. The moist leaf condition followed by drying was accomplished by placing the plants in a humid chamber (95 to 98 per cent relative humidity) for the designated time, then placing them in the low-humidity air current for the remainder of the absorption period. The data in Table II show a marked increase in plant manganese with an increase in the length of time the leaf surface remained moist. Plant samples taken at 60 minutes show only a slight increase over corresponding samples taken at 30 minutes. These results indicate that little, if any, manganese absorption occurred during the time the leaf surfaces were dry. Under some field conditions, transpired water vapor may be sufficient to maintain a moisture film, and absorption may continue even though the leaf surface appears dry. The data in Table I, showing continued absorption after the leaves appeared to be dry (15 minutes), indicate this may be the case. The condensation of moisture on leaf surfaces, under field conditions, during the hours of darkness probably favors the rapid absorption of manganese.

C. Manganese Rates and Solution Volumes

The most desirable rate of foliar-applied manganese is one which is neither so large as to cause "burning" by excessive manganese salt accumulation on the leaf surface, nor so small as to correct only partially the deficiency. Very little information appears to have been published on appropriate quantities of manganese and water to use for effective control of deficiencies.

Recently Hoff (1955) conducted studies with soybeans under field conditions. Manganese sulfate was applied at 5 and 10 pounds per acre with each rate applied in 5, 10, and 25 gallons of water per acre. The beans were sprayed 5 weeks after planting or when they were approximately 15 to 18 inches high. The data shown in Table III indicate

TABLE III

Effect of Rate and Solution Volume of Foliar-Applied Manganese Sulfate on Plant Manganese Content and Yield of Soybeans

Pounds of $MnSO_4$ (per acre)	Gallons solution (per acre)	Mn concentration (p.p.m.)	Total Mn[a] (mg.)	Yield bu./acre
0	0	14	3.4	23
5	5	31	8.5	27
5	10	36	10.5	27
5	25	35	10.5	29
10	5	39	11.5	29
10	10	48	13.3	27
10	25	43	13.2	26

[a] Milligrams manganese in 15 plants.

that the manganese concentration in plants (harvested at flowering) tended to increase with rate of manganese and the volume of water applied. Of the two variables, rate of manganese appeared to have more effect on manganese content than the water volume applied per acre. This is to be expected since dilution does not alter the actual amount of manganese applied. The only justification for using large volumes of solution is to secure a more uniform and thorough coverage of the plant surface. This did not appear important under the conditions of this experiment. Quantities of manganese sulfate in excess of 10 pounds per acre have resulted in some injury to the leaf tissue when applied in 10 to 25 gallons of water per acre.

Continuous absorption of manganese throughout the development of the soybean plant does not appear to be essential for normal plant growth. Small soybean plants sprayed during the early stage of development absorb sufficient manganese through the leaves to increase their manganese concentration in excess of 150 p.p.m. This concentration decreases with an increase in dry matter as the plant continues to grow. Normal growth will continue until the manganese concentration in the tissue falls below the approximate threshold level of 20 p.p.m. Thus the accumulation of quantities of manganese in excess of the plant's requirement and the translocation of this accumulated manganese during growth are probable reasons for the effectiveness of single foliar applications.

In practice, we have recommended that the soybean producer apply manganese sprays only when a foliar deficiency is apparent. We have never found that normally appearing plants respond to manganese, and very often even slightly chlorotic plants fail to show a yield response when the symptoms are corrected. In contrast, yields may be increased by phosphorus and potassium when foliar deficiencies of these elements are not apparent.

III. Correction of Manganese Deficiency with Soil Applications

Applications of manganese to deficient soils are usually effective; however, the degree of effectiveness and cost of treatment will vary with method of application. For example, Steckel *et al.* (1949) have shown that mixing one increment of $MnSO_4$ with superphosphate and applying the mixture in a band near the oat or soybean seed was more effective than "band" placement of two increments of $MnSO_4$ applied alone. Mixing either one or both materials throughout was less effective than row placement near the seed. Others (Carlyle, 1931; Cook and Millar, 1941) have observed a similar beneficial effect of phosphorus on the uptake of applied manganese. In recent, but unpublished studies, Hoff banded $MnSO_4$ near the seed at rates equivalent to 0, 5, and 10 pounds of manganese per acre. Each rate of manganese occurred in combination with and without 200 pounds per acre of 0–20–20 fertilizer mixed with the manganese and banded near the seed. The data in Table IV show that 0–20–20 fertilizer used alone produced a yield increase of 14 bushels of soybeans per acre. However, in the presence of the high manganese rate, yields were at a maximum but were not increased by 0–20–20 fertilizer. the beans grown without either manganese or 0–20–20 were very chlorotic, while those grown with 0–20–20 but without manganese were as normal in appearance as those fertilized with manganese. The data and observations indicate that the 0–20–20 increased the availability not only of the applied manganese but that of the native soil manganese as well.

TABLE IV

Manganese Absorption and Soybean Yields as Affected by Manganese Sulfate Applied in the Row in Combination with and without 200 pounds per acre of 0–20–20 Fertilizer

Pounds of Mn per acre	Soybean yield		Total manganese absorbed	
	With 0–20–20 (bu./acre)	Without 0–20–20 (bu./acre)	With 0–20–20 (mg./24 plants)	Without 0–20–20 (mg./24 plants)
0	31	17	9.9	5.2
5	32	25	33.8	9.0
10	31	30	49.3	11.3

In this case, the application of manganese was not necessary when the soybeans were fertilized with 0–20–20.

Over a period of years, we have observed that superphosphate cannot always be relied upon to increase the availability of native soil manganese to the extent that manganese fertilization of deficient soils may be eliminated. The beneficial effect of superphosphate varies from season to season. Now, although fertilization of soybeans with nitrogen is unnecessary because of its symbiotic relation with nitrogen-fixing bacteria, ammonia fertilization has been shown to increase available soil manganese by reducing soil pH. Since both ammonium and phosphate ions increase the availability of soil manganese, we compared the effectiveness of diammonium phosphate fertilization with superphosphate fertilization of soybeans under field conditions. Both materials were applied near the seed at the rates equivalent to 20 and 40 pounds of P_2O_5, respectively. The data from the experiment shown in Table V indicate that at the time of sampling (6 weeks after planting) ammonium phosphate did, but superphosphate did not, increase the manganese content of the soybean plants. The higher yield of beans also indicates the superiority of ammonium phosphate. Since soybeans are usually fertilized with phosphorus

TABLE V

Soybean Yield and Manganese Concentration in Flowering Soybean Plants as Affected by Source of Phosphorus Fertilizer

Phosphorus source	Rate of application (pounds P_2O_5/acre)	Bean yield (bu./acre)	Plant Mn concentration (p.p.m.)
0	0	16	11
Superphosphate	20	19	11
Superphosphate	40	18	11
Diammonium phosphate	20	21	16
Diammonium phosphate	40	22	19

fertilizers of some kind, the use of ammonium phosphate may either reduce or, in less severe cases, eliminate the need for applied manganese more effectively than superphosphate.

IV. MANGANESE DEFICIENCY IN RELATION TO SOIL MOISTURE AND SOIL TEMPERATURE

The occurrence and severity of manganese deficiency in soybeans grown on the poorly drained lake bed soils of Ohio appear to be associated with seasonal weather changes. In the spring, when the soils are cool and moist, the soybean plant may show pronounced symptoms of manganese deficiency. As the development of the plant continues, the leaves formed during late spring and early summer may not show deficiency symptoms. Willis (1929) made similar observations of manganese deficiency in wet soils. Reuther and Crawford (1946) reported an analogous condition of increasingly severe iron chlorosis in citrus with increasing soil moisture and decreasing soil temperature. Mulder and Gerretsen (1952) have reported that flooding soils may increase the manganese supply, presumably by reduction of manganic oxides to available manganese, or may have the reverse effect of increasing manganese deficiency.

The assumption that manganese availability is related to soil temperature and soil moisture arose from field observations rather than experiments under controlled conditions. Recently, Mederski and Wilson (1955) grew soybeans in pots containing a manganese-deficient soil. Pots were placed in three constant-temperature water baths maintained at 15°, 27°C., and a third bath maintained at 15°C. for the first 7 weeks of plant growth and increased to 27°C. for the remaining 5 weeks of plant development. Two soil moistures were provided for plants at each temperature. At the high-moisture level, the soil was maintained near field capacity by surface irrigation, while at the low-moisture level only enough water was added to maintain growth and prevent wilting. The data in Table VI show that both total manganese per plant and manganese concentration in the tissue were greater at the high than low soil temperature at both levels of moisture. Manganese concentration, but not total manganese, increased with decreasing moisture at the highest temperature. Approximately 2 per cent of the plant's leaves were chlorotic at the low moisture–high temperature combination while 35 per cent of the leaves were chlorotic at the high moisture–low temperature combination. Further experimentation with solution cultures showed that plants grown in solutions maintained at 15°C. contained 18 p.p.m. manganese while cultures raised to 27°C. during the last 5 days of development

TABLE VI

Manganese Content of Soybean Plants as Affected by Soil Temperature and Soil Moisture

	Mn concentration		Total manganese	
Soil temperature	Low soil moisture (p.p.m.)	High soil moisture (p.p.m.)	Low soil moisture (mg.)	High soil moisture (mg.)
Constant 27°C.	22	15	0.22	0.28
15° to 27°C.	16	16	0.11	0.14
Constant 15°C.	10	9	0.07	0.09

contained 23 p.p.m. manganese. This result indicates that the increased absorption in soils having the higher temperature may have been due, in whole or in part, to more rapid ion accumulation at the higher root temperature. Just how soil moisture level affects manganese availability and absorption by plants is not understood.

V. SUMMARY

Manganese deficiency in soybeans is easily detected by the characteristic foliar symptoms exhibited. The small quantity of manganese required, the rapid absorption of foliar-applied manganese, and the rapid recovery by the plant are factors conducive to correction by foliar application. Our research indicates the deficiency can be satisfactorily corrected by spraying the plants with 5 to 10 pounds of manganese sulfate per acre applied in a solution volume of 5 to 25 gallons.

The correction by row application at planting time of manganese or a manganese fertilizer mixture may be desirable where a manganese deficiency is known to exist. Under Ohio conditions, 30 pounds per acre of manganese sulfate in the row at planting has been found adequate. The application of fertilizer increases the effectiveness of the applied manganese and enhances the availability of native soil manganese.

While the supply of available manganese in soils is affected by a large number of factors, it is probable that the seasonal fluctuation of manganese deficiency in field-grown soybeans, in Ohio, is largely a result of seasonal variations in soil moisture and soil temperature.

REFERENCES

Bukovac, M. J., and Whittwer, S. H. 1957. *Plant Physiol.* **32**, 428–434.
Carlyle, F. C. 1931. *Texas Agr. Expt. Sta. Bull.* **432**.
Cook, J. A., and Boynton, D. 1952. *Proc. Am. Soc. Hort. Sci.* **59**, 82–90.

Cook, R. L., and Millar, C. E. 1941. *Soil Sci. Soc. Am. Proc.* **6**, 224–227.

Haas, A. R. C. 1932. *Hilgardia* **7**, 181–206.

Hewitt, E. J. 1951. *Ann. Rev. Plant Physiol.* **2**, 25–52.

Hoff, D. J. 1955. Soil and plant manganese studies with soybeans. Ph.D. Dissertation. Ohio State University, Columbus, Ohio.

Hopkins, E. F. 1934. *Cornell Univ. Agr. Expt. Sta. Mem.* **151**.

McElroy, W. D., and Nason, A. 1954. *Ann. Rev. Plant Physiol.* **5**, 1–30.

McHargue, J. S. 1922. *J. Am. Chem. Soc.* **44**, 1592–1598.

McHargue, J. S., and Calfee, R. K. 1932. *Plant Physiol.* **7**, 697–703.

Mederski, H. J., and Wilson, J. H. 1955. *Soil Sci. Soc. Am. Proc.* **19**, 461–464.

Mulder, E. G., and Gerretsen, F. C. 1952. *Advances in Agron.* **4**, 222–272.

Reuther, W., and Crawford, C. L. 1946. *Soil Sci.* **62**, 477–491.

Romney, E. M., and Toth, S. J. 1954. *Soil Sci.* **77**, 107–117.

Rothstein, A., and Hayes, A. 1956. *Arch. Biochem. Biophys.* **63**, 87–99.

Steckel, J. E., Bertramson, B. R., and Ohlrogge, A. J. 1949. *Soil Sci. Soc. Am. Proc.* **13**, 108–111.

Willis, L. G. 1929. *Am. Fertilizer* **71** (7), 17.

CHAPTER 7

Chemical Methods of Estimating Available Soil Manganese

D. J. HOFF AND H. J. MEDERSKI

Ohio Agricultural Experiment Station
Wooster, Ohio

		Page
I.	Introduction	109
II.	Literature Review	110
III.	Chemical Extraction Methods	111
	A. Extraction with Ammonium Dihydrogen Phosphate	111
	B. Extraction with Alcoholic Hydroquinone	111
	C. Extraction with Hydroquinone in Ammonium Acetate	111
	D. Extraction with Phosphoric Acid	111
	E. Extraction with Sodium Acetate	112
	F. Extraction with Ammonium Acetate (Exchangeable Manganese)	112
IV.	Evaluation of Methods	112
V.	Summary	115
	References	116

I. INTRODUCTION

Manganese exists in the soil in various states of oxidation having widely different solubilities. The various forms of soil manganese may be grouped into four categories:

(1) Divalent manganese which may exist as an ion in the soil solution or in exchangeable or nonexchangeable forms.

(2) Highly reactive trivalent manganese oxides—$Mn_2O_3 \cdot XH_2O$.

(3) Less active oxides containing manganese in both the divalent and trivalent states—Mn_3O_4.

(4) Relatively inert oxides composed of manganese in the tetravalent state—MnO_4.

Due to the various forms in which manganese can occur in the soil, it is difficult to distinguish plant available and unavailable soil manganese by chemical procedures. Investigations concerned with differentiating by chemical methods, manganese-deficient and nondeficient soils have indicated that plant-available or active manganese in the soil consists of the water-soluble, exchangeable, and those forms of manganese oxide that are easily reduced. While not always satisfactory, estimates of easily reducible manganese have shown most promise in differentiating between manganese-deficient and nondeficient soils.

The favorable effect of phosphate fertilization on manganese uptake by various crops (Snider, 1943; Steckel *et al.*, 1949) indicates that some form of phosphate extraction may be a reliable estimate of plant available manganese. Preliminary investigations by the authors have indicated that extractions with ammonium dihydrogen phosphate or phosphoric acid are as good as and probably superior to extraction methods using easily reducible manganese as an estimate of availability.

II. LITERATURE REVIEW

Within the past decade, several investigations (Finck, 1954; Coppenet and Calvez, 1952; Jones and Leeper, 1950, 1951a,b; Dion *et al.*, 1947; Heintze, 1946) concerned with the chemical estimation of plant-available soil manganese have been recorded. Most authors have been concerned with differentiating by chemical methods manganese-deficient and non-deficient soils.

Heintze (1938, 1946) in an extensive study of "marsh spot" in peas, using exchangeable and easily reducible manganese to estimate availability, was unable to differentiate adequately between contrasted pairs of manganese-deficient and nondeficient soils.

Jones and Leeper (1950, 1951a,b) were unable to correlate the response of oats and peas obtained in pot experiments with the quantities of soil manganese extracted using a solution of hydroquinone in neutral, normal ammonium acetate. More satisfactory results were obtained when the hydroquinone was removed before extraction. The method finally adopted consisted of shaking the soils with 50 per cent aqueous alcohol containing 0.05 per cent hydroquinone. The hydroquinone was removed by washing with water, and the reduced manganese presumably present on the exchange complex was displaced with a neutral semimolar calcium nitrate solution.

Recently Finck (1954), working with gray speck disease in oats, compared eight methods for estimating plant-available soil manganese. Only those methods involving a measure of easily reducible manganese were of any value in differentiating between manganese-deficient and non-deficient soils. He concluded that the pH value of the soils with which he was working was a better indication of whether gray speck disease would develop.

In investigations conducted in 1955 (Hoff and Mederski, 1958), soil manganese from 25 deficient and nondeficient soybean fields in widely separated areas of northwestern Ohio was extracted by several chemical methods. The extracted manganese was compared with the manganese concentration in the uppermost leaf of the soybean plants growing on the selected sites and the degree of correlation determined. Although chemical methods of estimating plant nutrient availability should ultimately be evaluated on the basis of crop response to applied nutrient, the widely accepted comparison of chemical soil test values with plant analysis offers a simple and rapid method of preliminary evaluation under a wide variety of conditions.

III. CHEMICAL EXTRACTION METHODS

The chemical extraction methods evaluated and procedures employed were:

A. *Extraction with Ammonium Dihydrogen Phosphate*

Ten-gram samples of soil were shaken with 100 ml. of 1.0 *M* ammonium dihydrogen phosphate, filtered without washing, and manganese determined in the extract.

B. *Extraction with Alcoholic Hydroquinone*

The procedure used was the same as that recently proposed by Jones and Leeper (1951a,b). Ten-gram samples of soil were shaken for one hour with a 50 per cent aqueous alcohol solution containing 0.05 per cent hydroquinone, filtered and washed with five 20-ml. portions of 50 per cent aqueous alcohol to remove the hydroquinone. The reduced manganese presumably present on the exchange complex was removed by shaking the soil for one hour with a neutral semimolar solution of calcium nitrate, filtering and washing with five 20-ml. portions of calcium nitrate.

C. *Extraction with Hydroquinone in Ammonium Acetate*

Ten-gram samples of soil were shaken with 100 ml. of neutral, normal ammonium acetate containing 0.05 per cent hydroquinone filtered and washed with five 20-ml. portions of neutral, normal ammonium acetate.

D. *Extraction with Phosphoric Acid*

Ten-gram samples of soil were shaken with 100 ml. of 0.1 *N* phosphoric acid and filtered without washing.

E. Extraction with Sodium Acetate

This procedure employs the reagent in the widely used Morgan (1935) soil-testing systems. Ten-gram samples of soil were shaken with 20 ml. of a solution containing 100 grams of sodium acetate and 30 ml. of glacial acetic acid per liter, filtered and washed with five 10-ml. portions of sodium acetate solution.

F. Extraction with Ammonium Acetate (Exchangeable Manganese)

Twenty-gram samples of soil were shaken with 200 ml. of neutral, normal ammonium acetate, filtered and washed with five 20-ml. portions of neutral, normal ammonium acetate.

A common extraction procedure was used for the different methods. Soil samples were shaken for one hour at maximum speed on a Burrell wrist-action shaker. Organic matter in the extracts was destroyed by nitric acid oxidation and manganese determined colorimetrically. Estimates of the appropriate concentrations and extraction times for phosphoric acid and ammonium dihydrogen phosphate were established in preliminary investigations.

IV. EVALUATION OF METHODS

The methods were evaluated 1), by determining the degree of correlation between the manganese concentration in the uppermost leaf of the soybean plants and the amount of soil manganese extracted by the various methods; and 2), by determining the variance of deviations from regression, in terms of the independent variate (plant manganese), and testing for statistical difference between methods using the variance ratio. The correlation and regression coefficients, and the variance of deviations from regression for each of the methods including total soil manganese, are summarized in Table I. The correlation coefficients for all methods except total soil manganese are significant at the 1 per cent level.

Of the methods investigated, ammonium dihydrogen phosphate had the highest correlation coefficient and the smallest variance. The application of the variance ratio as a test for significant difference indicates that ammonium dihydrogen phosphate, while not significantly different from alcoholic hydroquinone and phosphoric acid, may be considered statistically superior to all other methods tested in estimating available manganese. This evaluation indicates that of the methods tested, three: ammonium dihydrogen phosphate, alcoholic hydroquinone, and phosphoric acid, merit further consideration and evaluation. Of these methods, ammonium dihydrogen phosphate and phosphoric acid are preferable to

TABLE I

Correlation Coefficients, Regression Coefficients, and Variance of Deviations from Regression for Mn Extraction Methods

Extraction method	Ammonium dihydrogen phosphate	Alcoholic hydroquinone	Phosphoric acid	Hydroquinone ammonium acetate	Exchangeable	Sodium acetate	Total
Correlation coefficient	0.899	0.860	0.856	0.771	0.686	0.671	0.487
Regression coefficient	0.78	0.24	0.63	0.12	5.5	1.40	0.018
Variance[a]	128	174	178	270	352	366	508

[a] For statistical difference at the 5 per cent level the variance ratio must exceed 2.

alcoholic hydroquinone. The alcoholic hydroquinone method is tedious and time-consuming and for these reasons does not offer promise as a routine quick test. Total soil manganese, ammonium acetate, and sodium acetate extractable manganese provided the poorest estimate of available soil manganese.

In 1957, an additional 17 soybean fields were sampled, and ammonium dihydrogen phosphate, phosphoric acid, and alcoholic hydroquinone extraction methods further evaluated. Correlation coefficients, regression coefficients, and variance of deviation from regression for the combined 1955 and 1957 data have been computed; these are shown in Table II.

TABLE II

Correlation Coefficients, Regression Coefficients, and Variance of Deviation from Regression for Mn Extraction Methods (1955 and 1957 Samples)

Extraction method	Ammonium dihydrogen phosphate	Phosphoric acid	Alcoholic hydroquinone
Correlation coefficient	0.900	0.846	0.808
Regression coefficient	0.83	0.52	0.22
Variance[a]	132	199	241

[a] For statistical difference at the 5 per cent level the variance ratio must exceed 1.7.

The new estimates of correlation and regression coefficients have not changed appreciably, indicating that these methods have performed similarly in 1955 and 1957. The larger number of samples provided a more sensitive statistical evaluation. Using the variance ratio as a test of

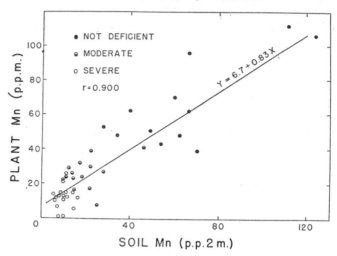

FIG. 1. Relationship between soil manganese extracted with 1 *M* ammonium dihydrogen phosphate and manganese concentration in the upper soybean leaf.

significant difference indicates that ammonium dihydrogen phosphate may be considered to predict available soil manganese with a greater degree of precision than alcoholic hydroquinone, while phosphoric acid and ammonium dihydrogen phosphate may be considered to predict plant-available manganese with the same degree of precision.

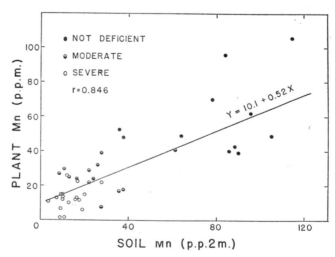

FIG. 2. Relationship between soil manganese extracted with 0.1 *N* phosphoric acid and manganese concentration in the upper soybean leaf. One sample (112 p.p.m. plant Mn and 228 p.p.2m. soil Mn) not shown.

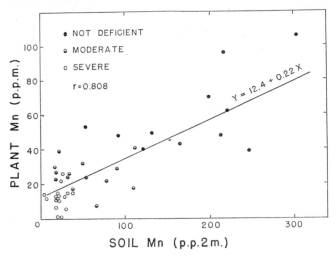

FIG. 3. Relationship between soil manganese extracted with alcoholic hydro-quinone and manganese concentration in the upper soybean leaf. One sample (112 p.p.m. plant Mn and 460 p.p.2m. soil Mn) not shown.

The scatter diagrams and regressions shown in Figs. 1, 2, and 3 indicate that manganese deficiency in soybeans may be expected if the manganese extracted with ammonium dihydrogen phosphate or phosphoric acid is less than 40 p.p.2m. With alcoholic hydroquinone, manganese deficiency may be expected if the manganese extracted is less than 125 p.p.2m.

V. SUMMARY

For estimating available manganese, phosphate extraction appears to be as reliable as, and probably superior to, methods involving a measure of easily reducible manganese. Results reported here indicate they are much superior to sodium acetate extractable and exchangeable manganese in estimating availability. In addition they are less tedious and time-consuming than alcoholic hydroquinone extraction and consequently lend themselves to routine soil testing.

The inverse relationship between soil pH and exchangeable manganese or plant manganese so often reported by other workers was not evident in these data. However, the soils in this study represented a number of soil types, and one might logically expect the inverse relationship between soil pH and exchangeable manganese to be less evident where several soil types are represented.

References

Coppenet, M., and Calvez, J. 1952. *Ann. inst. natl. recherche agron. Sér. A.* **3**, 351–358.
Dion, H. G., Mann, P. J. G., and Heintze, S. G. 1947a. *J. Agr. Sci.* **37**, 17–22.
Finck, V. A. 1954. *Z. Pflanzenernähr. Düng. u. Bodenk.* **67**, 198–211.
Heintze, S. G. 1938. *J. Agr. Sci.* **28**, 175–186.
Heintze, S. G. 1946. *J. Agr. Sci.* **36**, 227–238.
Hoff, D. J., and Mederski, H. J. 1958. *Soil Sci. Soc. Am. Proc.* **22**, 129–132.
Jones, L. H. P., and Leeper, G. W. 1950. *Science* **111**, 463–464.
Jones, L. H. P., and Leeper, G. W. 1951a. *Plant and Soil* **3**, 141–153.
Jones, L. H. P., and Leeper, G. W. 1951b. *Plant and Soil* **3**, 154–159.
Morgan, M. F. 1935. *Conn. Agr. Expt. Sta. Bull.* **372**.
Snider, H. J. 1943. *Soil Sci.* **56**, 187–195.
Steckel, J. E., Bertramson, B. R., and Ahlrogge, A. J. 1949. *Soil Sci. Soc. Am. Proc.* **13**, 108–111.

CHAPTER 8

Manganese Problems in the Production of Concord Grapes

JAMES M. BEATTIE

Ohio Agricultural Experiment Station
Wooster, Ohio

Manganese deficiency in grapes in Ohio was first identified during the summer of 1952. At that time commercial vineyards representing the important production areas of the State were visited for the purpose of obtaining leaf samples for chemical analysis. In seven of the eighty-three vineyards visited, manganese was found to be deficient as evidenced by visual symptoms appearing on the foliage. Chemical analysis of the leaf petioles from these vines showed that when the deficiency symptoms were present their manganese content was 30 p.p.m. or less on the dry weight basis. Leaf petiole samples from vineyards with normal foliage invariably contained more than this amount. The deficiency symptoms occurred most frequently on leaves at the second, third, or fourth node from the base of current season's fruit-bearing shoots. Symptoms were expressed by an interveinal chlorosis, the veins and tissues immediately adjacent to them remaining green. On the basis of the chemical and yield data obtained from the survey, a tentative lower limit for manganese was set for the Concord grape. This limit of 30 p.p.m. on the dry basis was for an early July sample of leaf petioles from the first mature leaf nearest the tip of fruiting shoots.

One of the vineyards which showed severe symptoms of manganese deficiency in 1952 was selected for further work. This vineyard was located on a Bennington silt loam soil with an acid soil reaction, pH 5.31. In 1952, an early July composite leaf petiole sample from this location was found to contain 3 p.p.m. of manganese and 0.39 per cent potassium on the dry basis. Since both manganese and potassium appeared to be limiting in this vineyard, fertilizer trials involving the application of both elements were planned. In the spring of 1953, a test was begun in which replicated three vine plots were treated with potassium and manganese fertilizers. A total of eleven treatments of manganese and potassium fertilizers applied separately and in combination were employed and compared with unfertilized check plots. The experiment was continued through 1953 and 1954. The various treatments employed and a summary of the results for early July leaf petiole potassium and manganese, average yield per vine, and average number of fruit clusters per vine are presented in Table I.

The data presented in Table I show that potassium was available to

TABLE I

The Effect of Various Soil and Foliar Treatments with Potassium and Manganese on the Leaf Petiole Contents of Potassium and Manganese, Average Yield per Vine, and Average Number of Fruit Clusters per Vine of Concord Grape (1953 and 1954)

	1953				1954			
Treatment	K (% dry wt.)	Mn (p.p.m. dry wt.)	Yield (lb./ vine)	No. clus- ters per vine	K (% dry wt.)	Mn (p.p.m. dry wt.)	Yield (lb./ vine)	No. clus- ters per vine
¼ lb. diNa Mn versenate/vine	1.11	12.4	18.3	101	0.70	10.4	14.0	79
1 lb. MnSO₄/vine	1.25	21.6	17.2	106	0.97	30.9	11.5	59
2 lb. K₂SO₄/vine	1.60	12.4	18.1	104	1.37	18.3	16.1	85
3 Foliage sprays K₂SO₄ (16 lb./100 gal.)	1.38	12.5	13.9	93	0.94	10.8	10.6	63
3 Foliage sprays MnSO₄ (6 lb./100 gal.)	1.14	41.0	13.0	98	0.85	32.6	17.5	93
2 lb. K₂SO₄ plus ¼ lb. diNa Mn versenate/vine	1.50	18.4	21.5	113	1.29	28.4	20.2	94
3 Foliage sprays K₂SO₄ plus ¼ lb. diNa Mn versenate per vine	1.46	8.5	15.0	101	1.06	9.1	12.4	72
2 lb. K₂SO₄ plus 3 foliage sprays MnSO₄	1.50	44.7	11.0	81	1.34	26.5	18.2	91
3 Foliage sprays K₂SO₄ plus 3 foliage sprays MnSO₄	1.22	50.2	9.0	76	1.01	29.5	11.0	62
2 lb. K₂SO₄ plus 1 lb. MnSO₄ per vine	1.60	42.5	20.7	116	1.41	90.8	21.7	110
3 Foliage sprays K₂SO₄ plus 1 lb. MnSO₄/vine	1.34	20.8	14.4	86	1.22	30.4	12.1	70
Check	1.10	10.0	16.6	100	0.86	11.4	14.3	76

these vines from both foliar and soil applications of potassium sulfate as indicated by the July leaf petiole contents of potassium. In 1953, the average petiole concentration of potassium resulting from soil applications of potassium sulfate was 1.55 per cent while that from foliar-applied potassium sulfate was 1.37 per cent. Leaf petioles from untreated check vines contained 1.10 per cent potassium. In 1954, the average petiole content of potassium on the dry weight basis from the soil potassium-treated vines was 1.37 per cent, from foliar-applied potassium vines it was 1.06 per cent, and from the unfertilized check vines it was 0.86 per cent

Manganese was applied as a soil application of disodium manganese versenate, as a soil application of manganese sulfate, and as foliar applications of manganese sulfate (Table I). In 1953, these treatments resulted in average leaf petiole concentrations of 13.1, 28.3, and 45.3 p.p.m., respectively, as compared with 10.0 p.p.m. of manganese in the petioles of untreated check vines. During 1954, comparable values for manganese given in the same order with respect to treatment were 15.0, 50.7, and 29.5 p.p.m. as compared with 11.4 p.p.m. for the checks. Neither the chelated manganese material nor the soil-applied manganese sulfate was highly effective in increasing leaf petiole concentrations of manganese unless they were applied in combination with soil applications of potassium sulfate. Foliar applications of manganese sulfate were equally effective whether applied alone or in combination with soil or foliage applications of potassium sulfate. In 1953, the foliage applications of manganese sulfate resulted in the highest average petiole concentrations of manganese, but the following year soil applications of manganese sulfate gave the highest leaf petiole concentrations of manganese.

The vines in two of the eleven treatments consistently produced the largest number of clusters and highest yields per vine during both years of the experiment. These were the 2-pound potassium sulfate plus ¼ pound disodium manganese versenate and the 2-pound potassium sulfate plus 1-pound manganese sulfate treatments. The yields resulting from these two treatments were equivalent to 6 tons per acre during each of the two years. In view of these high yields and the leaf petiole contents of manganese associated with them, it was possible to revise downward the previously set lower limit for manganese from 30 to 20 p.p.m. of the dry weight of grape leaf petioles sampled during early July.

The existence of a relationship between potassium and manganese nutrition of the Concord grape was indicated by the 1953–54 results, but the exact nature of the relationship remained unknown. Moreover, it was necessary to learn if good response in terms of leaf petiole composition and yield could be obtained with lower rates of potassium and manganese fertilizer application than had been used previously. Thus in April of 1955, a potassium-manganese factorial experiment was initiated in an adjacent portion of this same vineyard. Four levels of application of potassium and of manganese in all possible combinations were established in randomized blocks replicated three times. Each plot within a block consisted of 3 vines similarly treated and was separated from adjacent plots by a buffer vine within the row and by guard rows between rows. Manganese sulfate was applied in April of each year at 0, ¼, ½, and 1 pound per vine. Potassium sulfate was applied at the same time at rates of 0, ½, 1, and 2 pounds per vine.

All vines included in the experiment were pruned uniformly according to the weight of 1-year-old cane growth on the vine at pruning time. Thirty buds were left for the first pound of 1-year canes removed plus 10 additional buds for each additional pound of prunings removed. During 1955, the vines were allowed to come to equilibrium with the newly established treatments, and no data are presented for that year. In 1956, data were accumulated of leaf petiole composition, yield per vine, and number of clusters per vine.

A frost which occurred in late May of 1956 killed the developing shoots and flowers originating from the primary bud, and all subsequent growth and fruit were produced from the development of the secondary bud. These secondary buds are less productive than the primary bud, and this accounts for the relatively low yields during that year.

The results are presented in Table II. Considering the main effects of potassium and manganese fertilization, these data show the following:

(1) As the potassium sulfate application rate increased, leaf petiole contents of potassium *and manganese* increased.

(2) As the manganese sulfate application rate increased, leaf petiole contents of manganese increased but petiole potassium was unaffected.

(3) Increasing the potassium sulfate application up to 1 pound per vine resulted in increased number of clusters and yield, but further increase to 2 pounds per vine was associated with a decrease in yield and number of clusters.

(4) As the manganese sulfate application rate increased, average yield and number of clusters increased up to the ½ pound per vine rate and then decreased as the manganese rate was further increased to 1 pound per vine.

Average yield was significantly influenced by the interaction of potassium and manganese (Table II). When no potassium was applied, increasing the manganese sulfate application above ¼ pound per vine resulted in a depression in yield. At the ½ pound per vine rate of potassium sulfate, increasing the manganese application rate did not significantly affect yield. At the 1 pound per vine rate of potassium sulfate, yields in-

TABLE II

The Effect of Varying Quantities and Combinations of Potassium and Manganese Fertilizer Applications on the Average Leaf Petiole Composition, Yield, and Number of Clusters per Vine of Concord Grapes (1956)

Treatment[a]		K (0)	K (½)	K (1)	K (2)	Mn Treatment means
Mn (0)	Per cent K	1.71	1.66	1.35	1.94	1.67
	p.p.m. Mn	9.7	17.9	12.3	16.3	14.2
	Yield (lb./vine)	4.3	3.5	3.8	3.8	3.9
	No. clusters/vine	39	33	34	33	35
Mn (¼)	Per cent K	1.26	1.48	1.51	2.11	1.60
	p.p.m. Mn	16.2	19.4	25.4	14.5	18.9
	Yield (lb./vine)	7.4	2.8	4.2	4.7	4.8
	No. clusters/vine	59	26	37	41	41
Mn (½)	Per cent K	1.19	1.60	1.99	2.16	1.74
	p.p.m. Mn	17.8	26.4	17.4	27.2	22.2
	Yield (lb./vine)	2.7	3.8	8.7	6.1	5.3
	No. clusters/vine	29	34	59	46	42
Mn (1)	Per cent K	1.52	1.43	1.25	2.56	1.69
	p.p.m. Mn	54.8	30.9	53.2	72.3	52.8
	Yield (lb./vine)	4.3	2.6	6.0	4.8	4.4
	No. clusters/vine	35	26	46	40	37
	K Treatment means:					
	Per cent K	1.42	1.55	1.53	2.19	—
	p.p.m. Mn	24.6	23.6	27.1	32.7	—
	Yield (lb./vine)	4.7	3.2	5.7	4.8	—
	No. clusters/vine	41	30	44	40	—

[a] Treatment designations refer to pounds per vine of potassium sulfate and manganese sulfate.

creased as the manganese rate increased up to the ½ pound per vine of manganese sulfate but were depressed with a further increase to the 1 pound per vine rate. When potassium sulfate was applied at 2 pounds per vine, the rate of manganese fertilization did not significantly affect yield. The highest yields were obtained from vines receiving the combination treatment of 1 pound per vine of potassium sulfate plus ½ pound per vine of manganese sulfate. These vines produced leaf petioles containing 1.99 per cent potassium, 17.4 p.p.m. of manganese, and gave an average yield of 8.7 pounds of fruit per vine.

The experimental work described was undertaken primarily to help establish the cause of a nutritional disorder which had been observed and to attempt to find methods for its correction. In this connection, the grape plant presented problems differing from those which one might encounter in certain other crops. Grape plantings in Ohio are for the most part located on acid rather than alkaline soils. For this reason, methods of correcting manganese deficiency which are found most effective under alkaline soil conditions could not be assumed to work best here. Such was found to be the case, for the best response was obtained with soil applications of manganese sulfate. On alkaline soils, foliar sprays are often preferred because manganese sulfate applied to the soil soon becomes fixed and is not available to the plant.

In contrast to annual crops, grape vineyards are established in a given location and remain there for many years. The correction of manganese deficiency under such circumstances calls for long term corrective measures. Under such circumstances, large per acre rates of manganese application which are feasible with soil additions of manganese sulfate offer a more logical solution to the problem than foliar applications of manganese. Since the trunk and roots of the grape are retained year after year, these organs may serve in the storage of reserve supplies of essential nutrients such as manganese. In this respect, this species differs from species of annual plants which are grown during a single season and then often are removed from the soil on which they are grown. All of these factors and many others must be considered in attempting to compare these findings with those reported by other workers dealing with different species.

The findings presented in this paper serve to identify the particular nutritional disorder described as manganese deficiency. Its occurrence in the Concord grape has been found to be associated with a minimal concentration of total manganese in the leaf petiole of certain leaves of a particular physiological age. This lower limit for manganese is believed to be approximately 17.5 to 20 p.p.m. of the dry weight. It was established that potassium deficiency also existed in the same vineyard where the work was undertaken and that maximum response to either potassium or manganese fertilization could be obtained only when both elements were supplied at optimum levels.

Under the conditions of this experiment, optimum response as measured by leaf petiole analysis, yield, and number of clusters per vine was obtained with application rates of potassium sulfate, approximately 600 pounds per acre, plus manganese sulfate rates, approximately 300 pounds per acre.

Much remains to be done on the effects of manganese deficiency on the grape. The influence of the deficiency and of the correction of the disorder by additions of manganese fertilizers upon the quality of the fruit is of great importance to the grape industry. Studies of these effects are currently in progress. These investigations may reveal that manganese deficiency symptoms are associated with indices other than visual symptoms, petiole composition, and yield for the definite possibility exists that factors such as fruit quality may be affected deleteriously long before an influence on yield can be detected.

CHAPTER 9

Manganese Toxicity: a Possible Cause of Internal Bark Necrosis of Apple

H. F. WINTER
Ohio Agricultural Experiment Station
Wooster, Ohio

		Page
I.	Introduction	125
II.	History	126
III.	Experimental Procedure	128
IV.	Results	129
V.	Discussion and Summary	132
	References	134

I. INTRODUCTION

Internal bark necrosis is now the accepted name for a bark disorder or disease occurring principally on the Red Delicious apple variety and its red bud sports. The disease has been referred to frequently as "apple measles," and it is perhaps best known to fruit growers by this name. However, the term "apple measles" also has been used to designate several other types of abnormal apple bark conditions, and thus the use of this name has led to considerable confusion. Several apple varieties, other than Red Delicious and its bud sports, are occasionally affected by internal bark necrosis, but only in orchards where the disease would be of extreme severity on adjacent Red Delicious trees.

Internal bark necrosis is best described as a necrotic spotting in the inner apple bark tissues, accompanied by a "pimply," rough-bark surface condition of the twigs and branches of the tree. Other symptoms are severe stunting of growth, dieback of severely affected branches, and prolific production of water-sprouts, the bark of which also soon becomes necrotic (see Fig. 1).

In all cases, the productivity of affected trees is reduced in proportion to the severity of the disorder. Very severely diseased trees frequently die. Young Red Delicious trees planted in soil from which diseased trees

125

Fig. 1. Red Delicious apple tree severely affected by internal bark necrosis.

have been removed almost invariably become severely affected and usually die within two years.

II. History

The first reference to "apple measles" in the literature was by Hewitt and Truax (1912) who observed the disease in Arkansas. They were unable to associate the disease with any parasitic organism and ascribed it to some "physiological derangement." Rose (1914) reported a disease of apple which he termed "pimple canker," and which he considered the same as the "measles" disease described by Hewitt and Truax. He also stated that the disease had been known to exist in Missouri since 1904. In the years immediately following Hewitt and Truax's first reference to "Measles," many reports of similar troubles on apple appeared.

It is now evident that these troubles, while somewhat similar in symptom expression, were not all identical with the Red Delicious disease now called "internal bark necrosis." Rhoades (1924) published a report in which he classified the "measles" diseases into three more or less distinct types. One of these, while described on the Jonathan apple variety, appears to fit the description of internal bark necrosis as it is now known. Berg (1934) published a very comprehensive bulletin in West Virginia, in which he classified the "measles" diseases into three distinct types. One of these he termed "black pox" which he demonstrated was caused by the fungus *Helminthosporium papulosum* n. sp. A second type was termed "measles" as originally described by Hewitt and Truax (1912).

The third type of "measles" was the one occurring principally on the Red Delicious variety, and this Berg called "internal bark necrosis." It is this disorder which has been of greatest concern in Ohio and is the one under discussion in this paper. Berg (1934) and numerous other plant pathologists, in many attempts, were unable to isolate a causal organism from diseased bark or from other tissues of diseased trees. They were likewise unable to transmit internal bark necrosis from diseased to healthy trees by budding or grafting. Berg concluded simply that the disease was of unknown cause.

Young and Winter (1937) reported in Ohio the results of a sand culture experiment designed to determine the possible relationship of minor element deficiencies to internal bark necrosis of apple. What appeared to be typical bark symptoms of this disease were induced during this experiment by growing young Red Delicious apple trees for two seasons in boron-free sand culture solutions. It thus appeared possible that soil boron deficiency could, in some situations, be a cause of internal bark necrosis. Hildebrand (1939) published evidence supporting this view.

The writer (unpublished work), during 1938 and 1939 made extensive analyses of bark and leaves from diseased and healthy trees but failed to establish any correlation between the boron content of these tissues and the incidence of internal bark necrosis. Applications of boric acid and borax were made in 1938 to the soil around numerous diseased Red Delicious apple trees in several Ohio orchards. Subsequent applications of these compounds were made to the soil around the trees at two-year intervals. Annual examinations of these trees and comparable controls, over a period of six years, failed to reveal any significant improvement of the boron-treated trees as compared with the controls. Analyses of tissues of boron-treated trees revealed a much higher boron content than that of tissues from untreated trees. In many instances badly diseased bark of boron-treated trees contained much more boron than healthy bark of adjacent untreated trees. Berg and Clulo (1943) published a report of similar experiments in which they obtained essentially the same results. They further reported that they were unable to induce symptoms of bark necrosis in boron-free sand cultures. It was concluded by the writer at this time, that boron deficiency certainly was not a major cause of internal bark necrosis in Ohio.

Berg and Clulo (1946) reported the results of experiments which strongly indicated that an excess of manganese, and possibly an excess of iron, were responsible for the development of internal bark necrosis in West Virginia. They made analyses of diseased bark and found it to be much higher in both manganese and iron content than healthy bark. They were able also to induce internal bark necrosis in soil potted trees and in trees grown in sand culture, by adding iron tartrate, manganous sulfate, or combinations of these two compounds to the soil or to culture solutions. Further, they were able to prevent the development of this disease in young potted trees by liming the disease-inducing soil to decrease its acidity from pH 4.2 to pH 6.5.

III. EXPERIMENTAL PROCEDURE

The work of Berg and Clulo (1946) in West Virginia had clearly shown that a manganese or iron excess, possibly brought about by a highly acid condition of the soil, was largely responsible for the occurrence of internal bark necrosis in that State. Experiments were started at Wooster during the fall of 1946 to determine the relationship of manganese excess to the occurrence of the disease in Ohio.

Numerous bark samples were collected in the late fall of 1946 from both diseased and from apparently healthy trees in many Ohio orchards where internal bark necrosis incidence was high. Other samples of bark were taken from trees in orchards where the disease incidence was low. All plant tissue samples were dried, ground, wet digested with nitric, perchloric, and sulfuric acid, and then analyzed for manganese according to the potassium periodate method of Willard and Greathouse (1917). Additional samples of both bark and leaves were collected in July of 1948 and analyzed during the winter of 1948–49 by the same methods.

During the fall of 1948, soil samples were collected to a depth of 15 inches from around the bases of diseased and apparently healthy trees in orchards where the disease incidence was high, where disease incidence was low, and from some orchards where internal bark necrosis did not occur. Analyses were made to determine the exchangeable calcium, magnesium, and manganese in these soils. Extraction of the soil samples was carried out in accordance with the neutral ammonium acetate method of Schollenberger and Simon (1945), and determinations of the three cations in question were made in accordance with the methods published by Peech et al. (1947). Bark samples were collected from the same trees from around which the soil samples were taken. The bark samples were analyzed for manganese only.

Soil was brought to the greenhouse at the Ohio Agricultural Experiment Station in the spring of 1948 from two orchards where the internal bark necrosis disease had been especially severe. Soil A was from an orchard at Wooster, and Soil B was from an orchard near Gallipolis, in southeastern Ohio. Each of these orchard soils was divided into two lots. One lot of each was limed with dolomitic hydrated lime to bring the pH above the neutral point; the other lot of each soil was untreated. The liming treatment was intended to reduce the availability of manganese in the soil. The original pH readings before treatment were 4.2 and 4.3 for soils A and B, respectively. Four 1-year-old healthy Red Delicious apple trees were potted in each of the resulting four lots of soil. All of the trees were given a moderate application of ammonium sulfate at the time of potting and again the following spring. The potted trees were placed out of doors and watered with distilled water throughout the course of the experiment. The trees were examined periodically during the two seasons they were grown and notes taken as to their condition.

At the close of the experiment, after two seasons of tree growth, the soil from each lot of four trees was analyzed for exchangeable calcium, magnesium, and manganese. Composite samples of bark and composite samples of leaves from each lot of four trees were analyzed for manganese. The same chemical methods described earlier in this paper were used for these analyses. Where bark samples were taken, the bark from the 1948 and 1949 growth increments were composited.

IV. Results

The results of the initial analyses of apple bark from apparently healthy and from diseased trees, growing in four different orchards where internal bark necrosis occurred in various degrees, disclosed that the bark of fourteen apparently healthy trees contained an average of 54 p.p.m. manganese, with a range for individual trees of from 20 to 138 p.p.m. However, the bark from a like number of diseased trees in the same orchards contained an average of 144 p.p.m. manganese, ranging from 52 to 339 p.p.m. for individual trees. Similar analyses of both bark and leaves of healthy and diseased trees collected in July 1948, disclosed an even greater difference in the manganese content of tissues of healthy versus those of diseased trees (see Table I).

In this case the samples were all collected from two orchards near Wooster where the disease incidence was high and where the diseased trees were, in most cases, very severely affected. It should in all fairness be stated here that the bark and leaves of some apparently healthy trees in these two orchards contained more manganese than the bark and leaves of some diseased trees in other orchards where internal bark

TABLE I

Manganese (p.p.m.) in Red Delicious Apple Bark and Leaves from Apparently Healthy and from Diseased Trees in Two Wooster Area Orchards where Internal Bark Necrosis Incidence was High (1948)

	Apparently healthy trees		Diseased trees	
	Bark	Leaves	Bark	Leaves
	93	125	259	471
	82	99	245	498
	119	180	208	434
	83	151	260	448
	143	271	172	292
	93	136	312	500
	68	116	416	600
	91	154	231	416
	100	150	220	325
	68	109	330	554
Averages	94	149	265	454

necrosis was less prevalent. However, it should also be borne in mind that some of these apparently healthy trees could conceivably have been on the verge of showing disease symptoms.

The results of analyses of the soil and bark samples collected in the

TABLE II

Soil pH, Exchangeable Bases (Ca, Mg, Mn) in Soil, and Manganese in Bark of Red Delicious Apple Trees in Several Orchards where Internal Bark Necrosis was Absent

	Exchangeable bases in soil (p.p.m.)				Mn in bark (p.p.m.)
	pH	Ca	Mg	Mn	
	4.8	780	75	2.5	43
	4.5	415	65	2.6	49
	5.1	1447	167	1.2	59
	5.2	1512	175	1.2	62
	6.3	3128	759	Trace	23
	6.3	4059	560	Trace	25
	7.1	4128	613	Trace	14
	4.5	452	110	12.0	100
	4.3	351	85	14.5	68
	—	770	125	1.0	63
	—	701	149	3.0	90
Averages	—	1613	262	3.5	54

TABLE III

Exchangeable Bases (Ca, Mg, Mn) in Soil and Manganese in Apple Bark from Orchards
where Internal Bark Necrosis was Prevalent (Bark Samples Taken from Diseased Trees
and Soil Samples from around Bases of Diseased Trees)

	Exchangeable bases (p.p.m.)			Mn in bark
pH	Ca	Mg	Mn	p.p.m.
4.2	446	108	17.5	259
4.1	347	94	42.5	245
4.4	370	101	70.0	208
4.4	400	90	60.0	260
3.8	121	28	33.0	172
3.7	104	30	20.0	312
4.1	116	55	26.5	416
3.9	169	42	21.0	231
3.7	218	35	38.0	220
3.8	365	29	25.0	330
4.2	161	52	18.0	195
4.3	284	66	43.0	332
4.3	204	53	20.0	341
Averages —	254	60	33.4	271

autumn of 1948 are shown in Tables II and III. It will be noted in these
two tables that while the average soil pH in orchards where internal bark
necrosis did not occur was higher than that in orchards where the disease
was prevalent, there was a great variation in pH between individual
samples from orchards where the disease was absent (Table II). This
variation was enhanced by the fact that the three samples of soil showing
the highest pH were from northwestern Ohio, a limestone region where
soil pH is naturally high. These three soil samples were also high in exchangeable calcium and magnesium, but as might be expected, were very
low in exchangeable manganese. It is significant to note here that internal
bark necrosis of apple does not occur in this region of Ohio. Table III,
which presents the results of analyses of soil and bark from orchards
where the disease was prevalent, shows that soil pH was extremely low
in such orchards, that calcium and magnesuim were low, and that manganese in the soil and in the bark was very high.

Table IV presents the results of the experiment designed to determine
the effect of liming of certain soils upon the development of internal bark
necrosis in healthy young Red Delicious apple trees. The data given in
Table IV were taken at the close of the experiment after the trees had
been growing in pots for two seasons. All of the trees growing in the un-

TABLE IV

The Effect of Liming of Certain Internal Bark Necrosis-Inducing Soils on the Exchangeable Manganese in those Soils, and on the Manganese Content and the Incidence
of Internal Bark Necrosis of Young Red Delicious Apple Trees

	Soil A		Soil B	
	Untreated (pH 3.8)	Limed (pH 6.7)	Untreated (pH 3.9)	Limed (pH 7.8)
Exchangeable Ca (p.p.m.)	175	1108	165	1218
Exchangeable Mg (p.p.m.)	84	471	73	493
Exchangeable Mn (p.p.m.)	37	2	44	2
Mn in bark (p.p.m.)	891	58	594	50
Mn in leaves (p.p.m.)	1474	122	709	149
Mn in roots (p.p.m.)	—	—	291	62
Condition of trees	All severely diseased	All healthy	All severely diseased	All healthy

limed soil (four in Soil A and four in Soil B) were moderately diseased by
the end of the first season and showed very severe symptoms of internal
bark necrosis before the end of the second season (see Fig. 2).

On the other hand, the eight trees growing in the limed soils were
entirely free of internal bark necrosis and were healthy in every respect.
The liming of these soils had obviously brought about a change in the
soil which prevented the development of internal bark necrosis. Data
presented in Table IV show the soil pH, the exchangeable calcium, magnesium, and manganese in the several soil lots, and the manganese in the
tree tissues at the close of the experiment. It is obvious that the liming
treatment resulted in a very greatly reduced amount of exchangeable
manganese in the soil and that manganese uptake was greatly reduced
as a result of the liming treatment.

V. Discussion and Summary

The work reported in this paper was undertaken primarily to determine whether the findings of Berg and Clulo (1946) in West Virginia
applied to internal bark necrosis of apple in Ohio. Young and Winter
(1937) had found that typical bark symptoms of the disorder could be
induced in young Red Delicious apple trees by growing them in boron-
free sand culture. Following this work, however, this writer had failed to
establish any correlation between the boron content of apple tissues and
the occurrence of the disorder in Ohio orchards. He likewise failed, in
all efforts, to correct the condition in orchards by soil boron treatments.

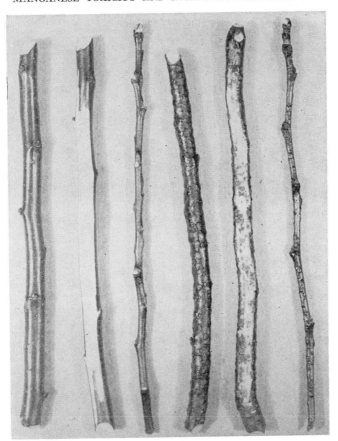

Fig. 2. The effect of liming of acid soils on the development of internal bark necrosis on potted young Red Delicious apple trees. Healthy twigs grown in limed soil on left. Diseased twigs grown in unlimed soil on right.

It could only be concluded that boron deficiency was not a major cause of the disorder in Ohio.

The results of manganese analyses of apple bark and leaves, initiated in 1947 and continued through 1948 and 1949 in Ohio, have consistently revealed a positive correlation between the occurrence of internal bark necrosis and a high manganese content of the bark and leaves of apple trees. The results of soil analyses, made during this same period, have shown a similar correlation between the occurrence of the disorder and a high exchangeable manganese content of the soil in which diseased trees were growing.

Since it was well known that the liming of acid soils reduced the availability to plants of such elements as manganese and iron, this procedure was followed in a soil pot experiment at Wooster. The results of this experiment clearly indicate that the development of internal bark necrosis can be prevented by liming disease-inducing soils of low pH.

While the analyses carried out in the soil-liming experiment clearly showed that manganese availability and uptake had been greatly reduced by the liming treatment and that development of symptoms of the disorder had been prevented, they do not alone prove that manganese excess is a cause of internal bark necrosis. The work of Berg and Clulo in West Virginia showed, however, that the addition of manganese salts to soil or to sand culture solutions induced symptoms of the disorder in apple trees. This fact, coupled with the correlation found between the occurrence of the disorder and high manganese content of diseased trees and soil in which diseased trees were growing, is considered to be strong evidence that manganese toxicity is the major cause of internal bark necrosis of apple in Ohio and West Virginia.

REFERENCES

Berg, A. 1934. *West Virginia Agr. Expt. Sta. Bull.* **260**, 1–31.
Berg, A., and Clulo, G. 1943. *Phytopathology* **33**, 1 (Abstract).
Berg, A., and Clulo, G. 1946. *Science* **104**, 265–266.
Hewitt, J. L., and Truax, H. E. 1912. *Arkansas Agr. Expt. Sta. Bull.* **112**, 481–491.
Hildebrand, E. M. 1939. *Phytopathology* **29**, 10 (Abstract).
Peech, M., Alexander, L. T., Dean, L. A., and Reed, J. F. 1947. *U.S. Dept. Agr. Circ.* **757**, 1–25.
Rhoades, A. S. 1924. *Phytopathology* **14**, 289–314.
Rose, D. H. 1914. *Missouri Agr. Expt. Sta. Bull.* **24**, 30.
Schollenberger, C. J., and Simon, R. H. 1945. *Soil Sci.* **59**, 13–24.
Willard, H. H., and Greathouse, L. H. 1917. *J. Am. Chem. Soc.* **39**, 2366–2377.
Young, H. C., and Winter, H. F. 1937. *Ohio Agr. Expt. Sta. Bimonthly Bull.* **22**, 147–152.

Chapter 10

Physiological Effects of Manganese Deficiency

Thomas E. Brown, H. Clyde Eyster, and
Howard A. Tanner
Charles F. Kettering Foundation
Yellow Springs, Ohio

	Page
I. Introduction	135
II. Materials and Methods	135
III. Results and Discussion	139
A. Effect of Manganese Deficiency upon Respiration	139
B. Effect of Glucose and Manganese Deficiency	140
C. Effect of Manganese Deficiency upon the Hill Reaction and Photosynthesis	145
D. Visible and General Effects of Manganese Deficiency	148
E. Effect of Manganese Deficiency on Carbon Dioxide Fixation	151
Acknowledgments	154
References	154

I. Introduction

In a recent paper, Kessler (1957) reviewed the metabolic effects of manganese on plants. The work is impressive if only to suggest that manganese is without a doubt one of the key essential elements. This was strongly pointed out to us also as we became interested in differences in growth requirement by *Chlorella* for this element in light and dark (Fig. 1). There is evident here a 100- to 1000-fold difference in manganese requirement. We feel that some of the key problems facing us in the field of photosynthesis can be solved by elucidation of the roles of this element.

II. Materials and Methods

Unless otherwise stated, the described work involved the Emerson strain of *Chlorella pyrenoidosa*. General methods of growth in use at the

Kettering Foundation have been previously described and illustrated (Brown, 1954). Three physiological cell types were grown:

(*1*) Autotrophic—grown in light with a completely inorganic medium.

(*2*) Mixotrophic—grown in light with autotrophic medium supplemented by 1 per cent glucose.

(*3*) Heterotrophic—grown in complete darkness with mixotrophic medium.

Heterotrophic cultures were started from a loop inoculum (1 loopful = 1/186 ml. and contains 4×10^6 cells) from a previous autotrophic bacteria-free culture as concentrated to 14 μl./ml. These cultures required from 14 to 20 days of growth. The mixotrophic cultures were started in the same fashion and grown heterotrophically for 14 to 20 days and then

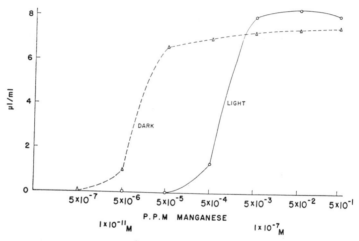

Fig. 1. Manganese requirement for *Chlorella pyrenoidosa* in light and dark.

exposed to light for 1 day. This procedure afforded sufficient cells at all levels of manganese for the desired measurements. Autotrophic cultures were likewise begun as heterotrophic cultures, except that only minus-manganese cultures were used. Cultures were centrifuged, decanted, washed with fresh minus-manganese medium, and resuspended in additional media such that 1 ml. suspension contained 10 μl. packed cells. The manganese concentration series were set up using a minimum of 50 μl. cells per 100 ml. culture. Techniques for maintaining sterility were used throughout with the exception of the final autotrophic series. Bacterial or fungal contamination in this case was not sufficient to create any problem. Heterotrophic or dark-grown algae were handled in complete darkness as far as possible. Samples were removed under dim green light and all vessels used in the handling procedures were sprayed externally with flat black plastic lacquer (Krylon).

Determinations of photosynthesis, respiration, and Hill reaction were made manometrically, using a modified Warburg apparatus (Brown, 1954; Clendenning et al., 1956a; Clendenning and Ehrmantraut, 1950). The method of chloroplast preparation followed that of Clendenning and co-workers (1956b). Chlorophyll determinations were made according to MacKinney (1941) from extractions with absolute methanol.

Fig. 2. Apparatus for the simultaneous fixation of $C^{14}O_2$ in light and dark.

Determinations of dry weight were made by drying a known packed cell volume of cells to constant weight at 105°C. in tared sintered glass crucibles of "fine" porosity. Packed cell volumes were determined by centrifugation to constant volume in 3 ml. Blue-line Exax hematocrit tubes disregarding any white layer of dead cells which may appear.

Carbon dioxide fixation work involved fixation of radioactive $C^{14}O_2$ under varying conditions with subsequent extraction and chromatogramming of the products. Techniques of fixation, chromatography, and autoradiography, as developed by Benson and co-workers (1950), were adapted to our particular needs. Gaseous $C^{14}O_2$ was used as the radioactive carbon source. A known volume and activity of the gas was injected through serum bottle caps into 50-ml. round-bottom flasks containing the algal cells. The flasks were vigorously shaken (top amplitude on a Burrell Wrist-Action shaker) in 3500 f.c. (foot candles) of light and in complete darkness at constant room temperature as illustrated (Fig. 2). Upon termination of fixation, the cells were killed and extracted in the usual fashion (Benson *et al.*, 1950). Water-insoluble fractions were hydrolyzed with 6 N HCl under 15 lb. pressure for 6 hours. Two-dimensional chromatograms were run with neutralized water-saturated phenol

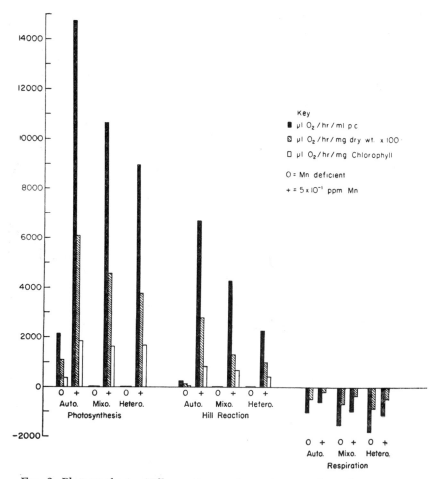

Fɪɢ. 3. Photosynthesis, Hill reaction, and respiration of aerobic, autotrophic, mixotrophic, and heterotrophic manganese-deficient and normal *Chlorella pyrenoidosa.*

and *n*-butanol, propionic acid, water as the two solvent systems according to Block *et al.* 1958). Identification of compounds was achieved by co-chromatography and autoradiography.

III. RESULTS AND DISCUSSION

Figure 3 provides an overall summation of physiological work with the three cell types of *Chlorella*. Photosynthesis, Hill reaction, and respiration measurements are summarized. The data have been calculated on the basis of μl.O_2/hr./ml. packed cells, per mg. dry weight and per mg. chlorophyll. The relationships are similar regardless of the method of calculation. Note specifically the absence of Hill activity with manganese-deficient cells. It can be seen further that respiration of manganese-deficient cells is, in this case, greater than that of normal cells.

A. *Effect of Manganese Deficiency upon Respiration*

Pirson and co-workers (1952) found essentially unaltered respiration during manganese deficiency. Kessler (1957) found a generally reduced respiratory oxygen consumption with manganese deficiency. In our earlier paper (Eyster *et al.*, 1956), we noted that the dark respiration relation between manganese-deficient and normal *Chlorella* varied with the time of harvesting. Results would provide respiration values for manganese-

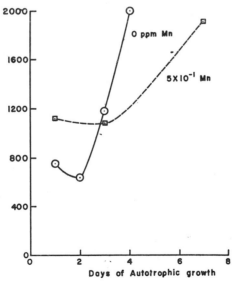

FIG. 4. Respiration of normal and manganese-deficient *Chlorella pyrenoidosa* with respect to time of autotrophic growth.

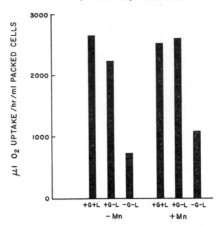

Fig. 5. The effect of glucose and light upon the respiration of normal and manganese-deficient *Chlorella pyrenoidosa*.

deficient cells lower, equal to, or higher than such values for normal cells. Within three days of autotrophic growth, respiration nearly doubled in manganese-deficient cells, while not significantly changing in normal cells (Fig. 4). If normal and manganese-deficient cells are exposed to 1 per cent glucose in the presence and absence of light for 3 hours, it can be shown that respiration of deficient cells is significantly increased by light over any change in normal cells (Fig. 5). The possible significance of these results will be discussed later.

B. Effect of Glucose and Manganese Deficiency

There is a considerable lag period in the growth of manganese-deficient mixotrophic *Chlorella* compared to normal mixotrophic cells or

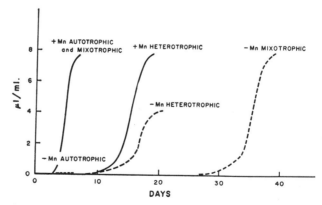

Fig. 6. The growth of three physiological types of *Chlorella pyrenoidosa* from autotrophic inoculum.

TABLE I

Growth Inhibition of *Chlorella pyrenoidosa* by Glucose

p.p.m. Mn	1% glucose	Yield μl./ml.	% Reduction by glucose
5×10^{-1}	—	4.5	
5×10^{-1}	+	4.0	11
5×10^{-2}	—	4.4	
5×10^{-2}	+	3.1	30
5×10^{-3}	—	2.9	
5×10^{-3}	+	1.15	60
5×10^{-4}	—	None	
5×10^{-4}	+	None	—

deficient heterotrophic cells (Fig. 6). It was found that with increasing manganese deficiency an increasing growth inhibition occurred (Table I). These results are from a 7-day growth period. If, however, 1 per cent glucose is added to media which contains a manganese concentration so low that no growth can occur, growth will then commence after a 4- to 4-week lag period. These cells seem to be completely heterotrophic, and Hill reaction capacity is below the range of manometric measurements. Under these same conditions, except with the absence of light, growth would readily occur. A possible explanation is that light inhibits the formation of necessary growth substances from glucose in manganese-free media, or perhaps the cells require adaptation in some other way. The former seems more logical since it has been shown that with the use of old heterotrophic media and with heterotrophic cells as inocula, the lag period in light can be reduced.

Upon further investigation of this lag period, a strong (up to 50 per cent) inhibition of the Hill reaction with manganese-deficient *Chlorella*

TABLE II

Rate of Hill Reaction vs. Total Yield as a Function of Glucose Concentration

Glucose molarity	μl.O_2/20μl. packed cells	
	10 min.	Total yield
0	31	85
1×10^{-4}	26	86
1×10^{-3}	24	86
1×10^{-2}	21	83
1×10^{-1}	19	82
1	13	83

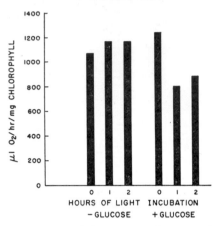

FIG. 7. Effect of contact time of 1 per cent glucose with partially manganese-deficient *Chlorella pyrenoidosa* on the Hill reaction.

was found upon adding the same glucose concentration as that used for growth (1 per cent). This inhibition is upon rate of oxygen evolution and not upon the total yield of oxygen (Table II). Since at very low concentrations of manganese, Hill reaction rates are so low as to make manometric determinations with inhibitor studies questionable, a manganese content of 1×10^{-3} p.p.m. in the growth medium was chosen for this

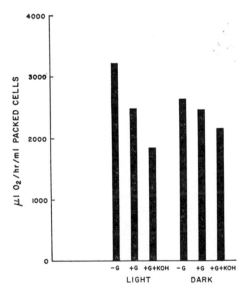

FIG. 8. Effect of 1-hour incubation with glucose and the presence of KOH in light and dark on the Hill reaction with partially manganese-deficient *Chlorella pyrenoidosa*.

work. It should be noted, however, that glucose inhibition of the Hill reaction increases with decreasing manganese content.

The effect of contact time between cells and glucose was studied (Fig. 7). Incubation or contact with glucose prior to manometric determinations of Hill reaction capacity was accomplished by shaking on a wrist-action shaker in 1500 f.c. of light or in the dark at room temperature. Cells were maintained in the original growth medium to which the glucose was added. Incubation for 1 hour in light provided maximum inhibi-

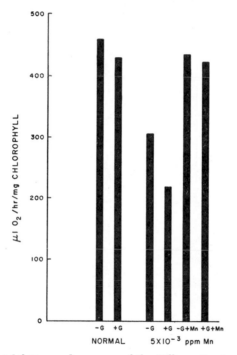

FIG. 9. Glucose inhibition and recovery of the Hill reaction in manganese-deficient *Chlorella pyrenoidosa*.

tion. Light incubation as opposed to dark gave a 2- to 3-fold greater inhibition. The presence of KOH, by absorbing CO_2, increased the magnitude of inhibition 2-fold (Fig. 8). After incubation, removal of glucose, by washing with either glucose-free media or buffer eliminated the inhibition. This inhibition of the Hill reaction with manganese-deficient *Chlorella* is consistently attained and can be completely reversed or eliminated by the addition of a normal complement of manganese (5×10^{-1} p.p.m.), as shown in Fig. 9.

As was expected, increasing glucose concentration increased the inhibition (Fig. 10). Since it was thought possible that the inhibition could be due to an artifact created by physical factors, viscosity, specific gravity, and effect on cell permeability to quinone were studied. The results indicate that such factors can be ruled out as contributing in any way measurable by manometric means to the inhibitory effect. In addition, it was shown that there is no direct reaction of glucose with or effect on quinone itself.

Bergmann (1955) and Pirson and Bergmann (1955) also noted retarded growth in the presence of glucose with manganese-deficient *Chlorella* in light as opposed to growth in dark. According to Pirson, manganese deficiency interferes with the assimilation of glucose, therefore

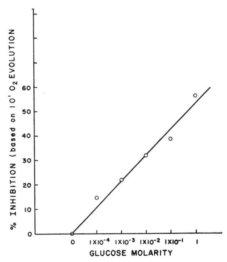

Fig. 10. Inhibition of the Hill reaction as a function of glucose concentration in partially manganese-deficient *Chlorella pyrenoidosa*.

retarding growth. Matsushima (1954), in working with *Bacillus mesentericus,* found a glucose inhibition of nitrogen metabolism which was eliminated by the addition of manganese. Seven other trace elements had no effect. Myers (1957) recently described an effect of glucose on *Chlorella,* under light-saturating conditions, whereby glucose actually suppressed photosynthetic assimilation of carbon dioxide. According to Kessler (1957), photochemical hydrogen formation of hydrogenase-containing algae, which is greatly enhanced by the addition of glucose, is strongly inhibited by manganese deficiency. The presence of glucose is not, however, essential for this inhibition to occur. Holm-Hansen (1957) has recently added confirmatory evidence in that manganese-deficient

Scenedesmus was not able to utilize glucose efficiently in the light. We have some evidence that other monosaccharides provide the same or similar inhibitory effects as glucose. This has not, however, been thoroughly investigated as yet.

It is separately observed that incubation of manganese-deficient *Chlorella* with glucose in the presence of KOH and light increases the glucose inhibition of Hill reaction rate. In addition, from the data of Fig. 5, it is shown that respiration of similarly deficient material is significantly increased in the presence of light and glucose. Therefore, inhibition of the Hill reaction by glucose with manganese-deficient *Chlorella* is, in part, a reflection of a stimulated respiratory rate in the light.

C. Effect of Manganese Deficiency upon the Hill Reaction and Photosynthesis

In order to rule out the possibility that this manganese effect on the Hill reaction could be unique to quinone as Hill reaction oxidant, other oxidants were tested. Hill's reagent (Holt and French, 1948) and benzaldehyde (Fan *et al.*, 1943) were used in comparison with quinone.

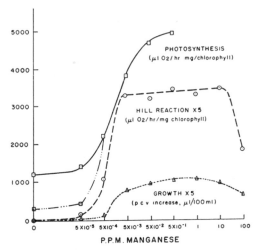

FIG. 11. Autotrophic *Chlorella pyrenoidosa*. Photosynthesis, Hill reaction, and growth at various levels of manganese.

Similar results were obtained in all cases with both manganese-deficient and normal *Chlorella*. Differences in Hill reaction capacity between manganese-deficient and normal cells with the different oxidants were as follows: benzaldehyde > quinone > Hill's reagent.

Figures 11, 12, and 13 demonstrate the data which we have obtained

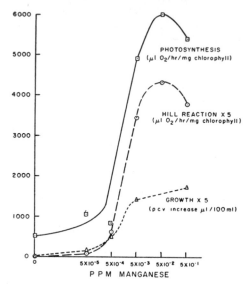

FIG. 12. Mixotrophic *Chlorella pyrenoidosa*. Photosynthesis, Hill reaction, and growth at various levels of manganese.

in respect to growth, Hill reaction, and photosynthesis with autotrophic, mixotrophic, and heterotrophic *Chlorella* respectively under varying levels of manganese. The two photosynthesis curves in Fig. 11 at lower levels of manganese represent initial data which are comparable to that of the entire figure and the decrease brought about by purification of reagents with respect to manganese contamination. Similarity between the three

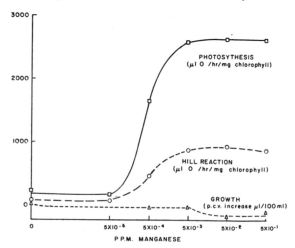

FIG. 13. Heterotrophic *Chlorella pyrenoidosa*. Photosynthesis, Hill reaction, and growth at various levels of manganese.

processes for each of the cell types can be seen. The main difference again is the growth pattern between light and dark culture in relation to Hill reaction and photosynthesis capacities. Previously reported results (Eyster and co-workers, 1956), and our own main emphasis as well, have been on *Chlorella*. Recently the work has expanded to include other algae and chloroplasts from higher plants. Growth, Hill reaction, and photosynthesis capacities with various levels of manganese were determined using the blue-green alga *Nostoc muscorum* and the green alga *Scenedesmus quadricauda*. Figures 14 and 15 present the findings with autotrophic cells of *Nostoc* and *Scenedesmus* respectively. *Nostoc* responds to a somewhat lower concentration of manganese than *Chlorella*, while

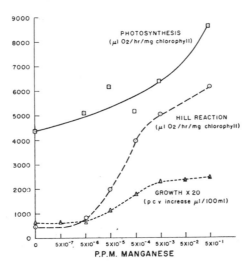

Fig. 14. Autotrophic *Nostoc muscorum*. Photosynthesis, Hill reaction, and growth at various levels of manganese.

Scenedesmus seems to require a higher concentration for maximum growth and Hill reaction activity. The substantial difference in photosynthetic capacities at low manganese levels between *Nostoc* and either *Chlorella* or *Scenedesmus* may be a reflection of either the difference in pigment systems between blue-green and green algae or differences in metabolism due to differing essential element requirements (see Clendenning *et al.*, 1956a). The latter possibility, as well as expansion to additional organisms with differing pigment systems, is currently under investigation.

Chloroplast preparations were made from *Phytolacca americana* (pokeweed), *Gleditsia tricanthos* (honey locust), and fresh and frozen *Spinacea oleracea* (market spinach). Capacity of these preparations for

Hill reaction was decreased both by treatment with Versene and by re-peated distilled water washes. Up to 40 per cent recovery of reaction capacity could be obtained by adding manganese. We now assume that these observed effects of manganese deficiency are probably universal among chlorophyll containing plants.

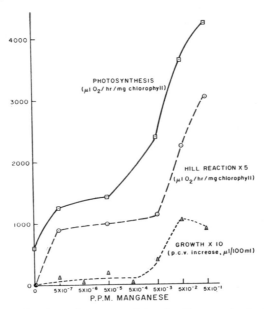

FIG. 15. Autotrophic *Scenedesmus quadricauda*. Photosynthesis, Hill reaction, and growth at various levels of manganese.

In studying Hill reaction recovery through the addition of manganese to manganese-deficient material, two valence states of manganese were tested ($+2$ as $MnSO_4$ and $+7$ as $KMnO_4$). No differences were evident. As could be expected, the greater the state of manganese deficiency, the higher the per cent of recovery. Preincubation times with manganese of ½ and 1 hour brought about Hill reaction capacity increases of 15- and 20-fold respectively in extremely deficient cultures (1×10^{-5} p.p.m. Mn). Similar preincubation with partially deficient cultures (1×10^{-3} p.p.m. Mn) would bring about only a 2- and 3-fold reaction capacity increase.

D. *Visible and General Effects of Manganese Deficiency*

There are effects of manganese deficiency on *Chlorella* visible under the light microscope. Irregular and abnormal clumping of unusually large cells can be readily seen during conditions of severe manganese defi-ciency (Fig. 16). Rather than a simple clumping of cells, our evidence indicates that this effect may come about due to an incompletion of

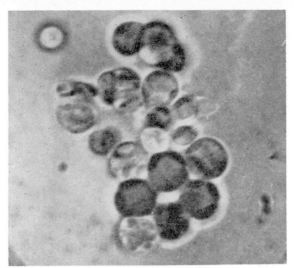

5×10^{-6} p.p.m. Mn

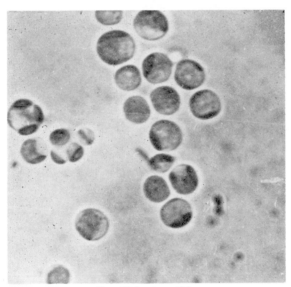

5×10^{-1} p.p.m. Mn

FIG. 16. Normal and manganese-deficient *Chlorella pyrenoidosa* as seen under the light microscope.

normal cell division through manganese deficiency. This is exhibited even more strikingly with chloroplasts of *Elodea* and *Lemna minor* (duck-weed). Within the living cells of these two higher plants, when under a state of manganese deficiency, many pairs and tetrads of chloroplasts can be seen. Normally these are very rarely seen. Since chloroplasts may increase by division (Granick, 1949) in a manner rougly similar to that of *Chlorella* it would seem, therefore, that the effect of manganese deficiency is not generalized throughout the cell. *Chlorella*, which exhibits this clumping effect, contains a single chloroplast approximating the total cell size. It therefore seems that manganese may be directly or indirectly involved in chloroplast multiplication. Eltinge (1941) found a similar effect with the plastids of palisade cells in manganese-deficient *Lycopersicum* (tomato). According to her, plastids of palisade cells were the first part of the leaf to show injury. They became indistinct in outline, coagulated, and vacuolated with eventual dissolution occurring as manganese deficiency progressed. We are planning to continue the study of these effects.

With respect to general differences between normal and manganese-deficient cells, Table III provides comparison of cell number (for a given

TABLE III

Size and Cell Number Comparison between Normal and Manganese-Deficient Heterotrophic *Chlorella pyrenoidosa*

	−Mn	+Mn
Cell no./μl. p.c.	21.4×10^6	43.5×10^6
Cell volume	$46.7 \ \mu^3$	$23 \ \mu^3$
Cell diameter	$4.5 \ \mu$	$3.5 \ \mu$

packed cell volume), cell volume, and cell diameter. Table IV provides comparison, with the three physiological cell types, of cell count, dry weight, and chlorophyll content between normal and manganese-deficient *Chlorella*. Although cell count differences are about the same between

TABLE IV

Cell Number, Dry Weight and Chlorophyll Comparisons between Normal and Manganese-Deficient Physiological Cell Types of *Chlorella pyrenoidosa*

Cell type		Cell no./μl. p.c. ($\times 10^7$)	Dry wt. (g./ml. p.c.)	Chlorophyll (g./ml. p.c.)
Autotrophic	−Mn	26.6	0.199	0.0658
	+Mn	42.0	0.242	0.0742
Mixotrophic	−Mn	16.4	0.218	0.0729
	+Mn	34.6	0.234	0.0646
Heterotrophic	−Mn	21.4	0.228	0.0732
	+Mn	44.2	0.240	0.0539

normal and deficient cells of the three types, the dry weights of manganese-deficient mixotrophic and heterotrophic cells more nearly approximates that of comparable normal cells than autotrophic material. Note that chlorophyll content of mixotrophic and heterotrophic manganese-deficient *Chlorella* is substantially higher than that of normal cells while the reverse is true with respect to autotrophic material. Manganese effect on chlorophyll content has been more fully described by Eyster and co-workers (1957).

E. Effect of Manganese Deficiency on Carbon Dioxide Fixation

Preliminary aspects of this work were reported at the 1957 meeting of the Midwest section of The American Society of Plant Physiologists.

Since we have shown that the Hill reaction requires 100 to 1000 times the amount of manganese as does growth and/or carbon dioxide fixation, it was felt that it would be of value to study the differences in product patterns of carbon dioxide fixation between normal and manganese-deficient materials. This would be an attempt to eventually pin point both the effect of manganese deficiency and the specific metabolic background of photolysis. Since this variance in requirement for manganese seems to be largely a result of light dependence, such studies could help to determine factors responsible for differences in carbon metabolism in light and dark (Rabinowitch, 1956). Holm-Hansen, in a recent report (1957), presented some initial data along a similar line of research.

Some expected and unexpected results have appeared. The data in Table V is a selected summary of our results. It should be pointed out that in every experiment on which these data are based manganese de-

TABLE V

$C^{14}O_2$ Fixation with Manganese-Deficient and Normal *Chlorella pyrenoidosa*
(c.p.m./mg. chlorophyll)

Compound	Conditions	$-Mn$	$+Mn$
Malic acid	1 hr. dark	340	4,190
	10 min. light	2,400	26,900
	1 hr. light	10,200	100,300
	24 hr. light		16,500
Isoleucine	1 hr. dark	14,500	<300
	10 min. light	32,000	
	1 hr. light		
Sucrose	10 min. light	151,000	244,000
	1 hr. light	222,000	339,500
	24 hr. light	1,188,600	68,600

ficiency was such that Hill reaction activity, as measured manometrically, did not occur. The identical data calculated on the basis of dry weight instead of chlorophyll content presents the same picture. Table VI summarizes the overall fixation of $C^{14}O_2$ with respect to autotrophic and heterotrophic *Chlorella*. Heterotrophic manganese-deficient cells seem better able to fix $C^{14}O_2$ than normal cells under the tested conditions of light and dark, except for 24 hours of light. After this length of time in light, heterotrophic cells evidently revert to autotrophic metabolism. In general, manganese-deficient *Chlorella* fix $C^{14}O_2$ on the average of 25 per cent of that fixed by normal cells. The patterns of overall fixation into water-soluble and insoluble fractions with manganese-deficient and normal cells do not indicate any significant differences. However, deficient autotrophic cells initially fix a greater percentage of $C^{14}O_2$ in light into water-soluble products than normal cells, decreasing to below

TABLE VI

The Relation between Manganese-Deficient and Normal *Chlorella pyrenoidosa* with Respect to Total Fixation of CO_2

$+Mn/-Mn$ (Based on c.p.m./mg. chlorophyll)

	Autotrophic	Heterotrophic
10 min. light	4.3	—
1 hr. light	4.4	0.55
24 hr. light	1.2	7.8
1 hr. dark	1.8	0.075
24 hr. dark	—	0.67

normal fixation by 24 hours. The reverse trend then applies with respect to water-insoluble products. These same cells have a higher dark fixation than normal cells into water insoluble products. Heterotrophic *Chlorella* does not differ significantly from autotrophic in the above instances.

In regard to the overall group of phosphorylated compounds, manganese-deficient *Chlorella* provide a 12-fold greater fixation of $C^{14}O_2$ into this group than normal cells, after 10 minutes of light (based on c.p.m./mg. chlorophyll). In *Nostoc muscorum*, the opposite seems to be the case (Holm-Hansen, 1957).

There is a striking decrease of 10- to 12-fold with manganese-deficient *Chlorella* in regard to fixation into malic acid. All other Krebs cycle intermediates which were found were lower in radioactivity with manganese-deficient cells than with normal ones, but none by more than 2-fold. In addition, there is a 12-fold decrease in fixation into glycolic acid with manganese-deficient *Chlorella* as opposed to normal. The glycolic acid and malic acid differences are probably linked, with the difference in one case being a reflection of the effect of manganese deficiency on the production of the other.

The difference in fixation into isoleucine, as shown in Table VI, is the most significant difference occurring in dark fixation. Very little is known about isoleucine metabolism. We believe that our data provides evidence that further metabolism or breakdown of isoleucine is blocked during manganese deficiency by the nonfunctioning of a manganese-requiring enzyme in either light or dark.

Differences between manganese deficient and normal *Chlorella* with respect to $C^{14}O_2$ fixation into sucrose were the most apparent and least expected of the differences found. This difference is strikingly visible on the autoradiographs and has been confirmed by repeated experiments. There is either an abnormal increase in sucrose formation or prevention of sucrose utilization, under a state of manganese deficiency. There is evidence for both.

Eltinge (1941) found, during her work with manganese-deficient tomato, that one of the earliest signs of such deficiency was an abnormal decrease in the number of starch granules as seen with the light microscope. This could, either directly or indirectly, provide for a large increase in sucrose content. As the state of manganese deficiency increases, and with subsequent decreasing photosynthesis, stored starch would be remetabolized by the plant as an energy source. If enzymes involved in the synthesis of starch required manganese, a deficiency in this element would then cause the observation of both starch decrease and sucrose increase. Since phosphorylated compounds build up during short-term fixation with manganese-deficient *Chlorella*, while Krebs cycle intermediates are sharply decreased upon continued fixation, it would seem that further normal metabolism of the phosphorylated compounds was blocked by malfunctioning of known manganese-requiring enzymes operating at the entrance to and within the Krebs cycle. Sucrose would subsequently build up due to both the unusual increase of intermediate compounds and blocking of further sucrose metabolism, again due to manganese deficiency. With normal cells, sucrose would be metabolized as a carbon and energy source as CO_2 starvation set in. Differences in overall levels of $C^{14}O_2$ fixation between manganese-deficient and normal *Chlorella* can account for only a small part of the 18-fold difference in sucrose accumulation.

The level of manganese which is essential for normal metabolism is at the level of required concentration for enzyme activity. We know that magnesium can take the place of manganese to some extent in all enzymes which have so far shown a requirement for manganese. However, evidence has been presented here that either an unknown manganese-specific enzyme is involved with photolysis or that magnesium cannot replace manganese to nearly the extent *in vivo* as it does *in vitro,* or both.

Light, as an essential contributing factor, enters into every major effect of manganese deficiency. With manganese deficiency, the presence of glucose in light apparently suppresses photosynthetic assimilation of carbon dioxide and/or stimulates uptake of oxygen. When the normal complement of manganese is present with or without glucose, autotrophic metabolism is supreme. Under conditions of manganese deficiency, the presence of glucose brings about domination of heterotrophic metabolism and suppression of normal autotrophic processes. It is therefore suggested that the functioning or nonfunctioning of manganese-specific processes creates the differences between light and dark metabolism in green plants.

In conclusion, the views of Possingham (1956) should be mentioned. He points out that the interplay between essential elements is certainly interfered with when working with any specific deficiency. We plan to follow this line of study in the near future. Because of this interplay of elements, a given nutrient deficiency usually does not involve the complete suppression of any system. Further, the absence of any product does not necessarily mean that the enzyme system for its production is not available, but is indicative of its nonfunction.

ACKNOWLEDGMENTS

Grateful acknowledgment is given to the advice of Doctors S. L. Hood and G. Zweig. Technical assistance for various aspects of this work was supplied by Mrs. D. Burris, Miss G. L. Norris, Miss R. Prather, Mrs. A. C. Thompson, and Mr. D. E. Wilson.

This work is being conducted at the laboratories of the Charles F. Kettering Foundation.

REFERENCES

Benson, A. A., Bassham, J. A., Calvin, M., Goodale, T. C., Haas, V. A., and Stepka, W. 1950. *J. Am. Chem. Soc.* **72,** 1710–1718.

Bergmann, L. 1955. *Flora (Jena)* **142,** 493–539.

Block, R. J., Durrum, E. L., and Zweig, G. 1958. "A Manual of Paper Chromatography and Paper Electrophoresis," 2nd ed. Academic Press, New York. 1958.

Brown, T. E. 1954. Ph.D. Dissertation, Ohio State University, Columbus, Ohio.

Clendenning, K. A., and Ehrmantraut, H. C. 1950. *Arch. Biochem* **29,** 387–403.

Clendenning, K. A., Brown, T. E., and Eyster, H. C. 1956a. *Can. J. Botany* **34,** 943–966.

Clendenning, K. A., Brown, T. E., and Walldov, E. E. 1956b. *Physiol. Plantarum* **9,** 519–532.

Eltinge, E. T. 1941. *Plant Physiol.* **16**, 189–195.

Eyster, H. C., Brown, T. E., and Tanner, H. A. 1956. *Arch. Biochem. Biophys.* **64**, 240–241.

Eyster, H. C., Brown, T. E., and Tanner, H. A. 1957. This volume, Chapter 11.

Fan, C. S., Stauffer, J. F., and Umbreit, W. W. 1943. *J. Gen. Physiol.* **27**, 15–28.

Granick, S. 1949. *In* "Photosynthesis in Plants" (J. Franck and W. E. Loomis, eds.), pp. 113–132. Iowa State College Press, Ames, Iowa.

Holm-Hansen, O. 1957. *Chem. Div. Quart. Rept.* **UCRL-3710**, 25–27. Univ. California, Berkeley, California.

Holt, A. S., and French, C. S. 1948. *Arch. Biochem.* **19**, 368–378.

Kessler, E. 1957. *Planta* **49**, 435–454.

MacKinney, G. 1941. *J. Biol. Chem.* **140**, 315–322.

Matsushima, K. 1954. *J. Agr. Chem. Soc. Japan* **28**, 646–649.

Myers, J. 1957. *Plant Physiol. Suppl.* **32**, xvi-xvii.

Pirson, A., and Bergmann, L. 1955. *Nature* **176**, 209–210.

Pirson, A., Tichy, C., and Wilhelmi, G. 1952. *Planta* **40**, 199–253.

Possingham, J. V. 1956. *Australian J. Biol. Sci.* **9**, 539–551.

Rabinowitch, E. I. 1956. "Photosynthesis and Related Processes," Vol. II, Part 2, Chapter 36, pp. 1630–1702. Interscience, New York.

CHAPTER 11

Mineral Requirements for *Chlorella pyrenoidosa* under Autotrophic and Heterotrophic Conditions

H. CLYDE EYSTER, THOMAS E. BROWN, AND
HOWARD A. TANNER
Charles F. Kettering Foundation
Yellow Springs, Ohio

		Page
I.	Introduction	157
II.	Culture Methods and Procedure	158
III.	Autotrophic and Heterotrophic Mineral Requirements	160
IV.	Manganese and Growth Response	163
	A. Rate of Growth	163
	B. Chlorophyll Content	167
	C. The Chlorophyll Unit in Photosynthesis	169
V.	Chloride and Growth Response	170
VI.	Recommended Autotrophic Medium	173
	References	173

I. INTRODUCTION

Minerals are required by plants for various functions. It is well known that biological reactions are enzymatic, and that most enzymes have a metal as an important constituent (Mahler, 1956; Hewitt, 1951; Lehninger, 1950). There are physiological processes which are entirely autotrophic, such as photosynthesis, and there are physiological processes which prevail under both autotrophic and heterotrophic conditions. A comparison between the mineral requirements for autotrophic and heterotrophic growth has already been fruitful with respect to manganese (Bergmann, 1955; Pirson and Bergmann, 1955). The requirements for manganese are centered around two types of functions: (1) a comparatively high concentration requirement for photosynthesis, and (2) a much lower concentration requirement for heterotrophic growth. Careful studies may resolve the essentiality of additional minerals for photosynthesis. Since an element may have roles in both autotrophic and heterotrophic processes, visible growth. Pirson and Bergmann (1955) and Bergmann (1955) reported a reduction to about 50 per cent for the minus-manganese autotrophic cultures. It would appear that their nutrient salts were contaminated with manganese. No measurable autotrophic growth resulted in the minus-manganese purified nutrient cultures which were set up by Reisner and Thompson (1956). Originally, Hopkins (1930) reported that he was able to reduce autotrophic growth in culture solutions from which the manganese had been removed by adsorption on calcium phosphate. These reductions varied all the way from 10- to 600-fold.

In our experiments, minus-manganese heterotrophic cultures consistently showed about 15 per cent less growth than heterotrophic plus-manganese cultures. By purifying the glucose as previously mentioned

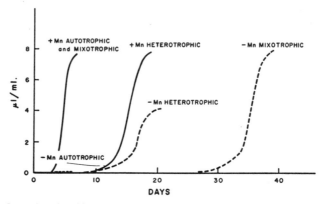

FIG. 9. Growth of *Chlorella pyrenoidosa* autotrophically, mixotrophically, and heterotrophically, both with and without manganese in the culture medium. Growth from 1 loopful cells.

and by using Specpure $MgSO_4$, the growth in the minus-manganese heterotrophic cultures was reduced from 50 to 70 per cent of that in plus-manganese heterotrophic control cultures. Used minus-manganese medium which previously supported abundant heterotrophic growth of *Chlorella* and thereby caused the removal of some of the contaminating manganese resulted in a reduction in heterotrophic growth to 34 per cent as compared with a paired "used medium" culture to which manganese had been added.

Complete elimination of growth heterotrophically in minus-manganese cultures was demonstrated by reducing the concentration of the nutrients 100-fold for the macronutrients, 10-fold for the iron and micronutrients, and by using purified glucose and a minus-manganese heterotrophic inoculum. Diluting the nutrients also diluted the contaminating man-

NaOH prepared from special reagent grade sodium, iron and trace elements as for *Chlorella,* except that molybdenum was increased from 0.01 p.p.m. to 0.1 p.p.m.

The water was redistilled in a Pyrex glass distillation apparatus. The glassware was supercleaned by the method of Waring and Werkman (1942). The culture flasks for autotrophic cultures and bubbled heterotrophic cultures were 300 ml. side-armed Pyrex flasks which were covered with cotton plugs and 1½″ Sani-Tab caps and which were connected with Aloe-Tex surgical rubber tubing (3/16″ I.D.–1/16″ wall). Static heterotrophic cultures were grown in regular 250 ml. Erlenmeyer Pyrex flasks which were plugged with cotton, and the cotton plugs covered with heavy paper, held in place by a rubber band. Usually 100 ml. of medium were cultured in each flask.

The sugar was reagent grade dextrose which was dissolved double-strength in water, autoclaved, and, when cool, added to double-strength inorganic medium. In other words, the dextrose and inorganic medium were made up separately double-strength and autoclaved separately; when combined, the inorganic nutrients were regular strength. The final concentration of dextrose in the medium was 1 per cent for all of the heterotrophic and mixotrophic cultures. In experiments designed to lower the growth in minus-manganese heterotrophic cultures, the glucose was purified by two passages through a cation resin. A 10 per cent solution of glucose (C. P. Baker's Analyzed) in redistilled water was passed successively through two Pyrex columns (1.1 × 25 cm.) containing Dowex 50-X^2 cation exchange resin (50–100 mesh, high porosity, styrene type, sulfonic acid) operating in the hydrogen cycle.

The autotrophic and mixotrophic cultures and the bubbled heterotrophic cultures were bubbled with 5 per cent CO_2 in air (about 35 ml./min.) and were continuously agitated on a shaker. The temperature of the bubbled cultures and of the static heterotrophic cultures was maintained at about 25°C. by air conditioning the culture room. The autotrophic and mixotrophic cultures were exposed to a light intensity of about 1000 foot-candles (ft.-c.).

Growth was measured by packed cell volumes which were determined by centrifuging 10 ml. of *Chlorella* culture suspension, pouring off most of the supernatant and then transferring the algae and remaining supernatant to an Exax hematocrit tube (Cenco) by the use of a dropper syringe pipette. A constant packed cell volume was obtained by centrifuging the tubes for 30 minutes at 3300 r.p.m. at a radius of 22 cm.

The procedure for chlorophyll determination of *Chlorella* extracts was based on the work of MacKinney (1941), who measured the absorption of light by methanol extracts of chlorophyll. The *Chlorella* cells were extracted two or three times with methanol, after previously boiling the cells for 3 minutes, centrifuging the cells down between each extraction. The concentration of chlorophyll was determined by measuring in a 10 mm. cuvette the density of methanol-chlorophyll extracts with a Beckman spectrophotometer at 665 mμ. Setting up simultaneous equations (Arnon, 1949) using the specific absorption coefficients for chlorophyll a and b as given by MacKinney (1941), it followed that total chlorophyll could be calculated by this equation:

$$C_T mg./ml. = (4.03 D_{665} + 25.4 D_{650}) \times \text{dilution factor} \times 1/1000$$

Chlorophyll determinations for *Nostoc* were based on Arnon's (1949) method for chloroplasts. Unboiled, centrifuged cells were extracted with 80 per cent acetone. Absorption readings were made at 663 mμ (with Beckman model D) multiplying by the coefficient 8.02. Chlorophyll determinations for *Scenedesmus* were based on MacKinney (1941). Unboiled, centrifuged cells were slurried with 2 drops of distilled water. Approximately 4 ml. of boiling absolute methanol were added for the initial extraction. This was repeated if necessary. Absorption readings were made as for *Chlorella.*

III. Autotrophic and Heterotrophic Mineral Requirements

The unicellular green alga *Chlorella pyrenoidosa* can be grown in the light by its own photosynthesis, or in the dark on a sugar substrate. Critical and minimum concentration requirements for the Emerson strain

TABLE I

Mineral Requirements for the Autotrophic Growth of *Chlorella pyrenoidosa*

Mineral	Critical concentration (M)	Minimum concentration (M)
NO_3	2.5×10^{-2}	2.5×10^{-5}
Mg	$2. \times 10^{-3}$	$2. \times 10^{-6}$
K	4.3×10^{-4}	4.3×10^{-6}
P	1.8×10^{-4}	1.8×10^{-6}
S	$2. \times 10^{-4}$	$2. \times 10^{-6}$
Fe	1.8×10^{-5}	1.8×10^{-7}
Zn	0.77×10^{-6}	0.77×10^{-9}
Mn	$1. \times 10^{-7}$	$1. \times 10^{-9}$

of *Chlorella pyrenoidosa* have been determined. Table I gives these mineral requirements for autotrophic growth. The critical concentration of an element in a nutrient medium, is the lowest concentration which will give maximum growth, and the minimum concentration is the highest concentration which will support no growth (Ulrich, 1945; Macy, 1936; Ramig and Vandecaveye, 1950).

The mineral requirements for heterotrophic growth are given in Table II. The values in Table I and Table II were derived from a careful study

TABLE II

Mineral Requirements for the Heterotrophic Growth of *Chlorella pyrenoidosa*

Mineral	Critical concentration (M)	Minimum concentration (M)
NO$_3$	2.5×10^{-3}	2.5×10^{-5}
Mg	$2. \times 10^{-2}$	$2. \times 10^{-4}$
K	4.3×10^{-3}	4.3×10^{-6}
P	1.8×10^{-4}	1.8×10^{-7}
S	$2. \times 10^{-4}$	$2. \times 10^{-6}$
Mn	$1. \times 10^{-9}$	$1. \times 10^{-11}$
Fe	$<1 \times 10^{-9}$	$<1. \times 10^{-9}$
Zn	$<0.77 \times 10^{-10}$	$<0.77 \times 10^{-10}$

of the growth of *Chlorella pyrenoidosa* at various concentrations of each element in the nutrient medium. Separate figures (Figs. 1–8) for each element graphically present these data.

Iron and zinc did not seem to be required for heterotrophic growth. It may be that sufficient iron and zinc contaminated the medium so that their expected heterotrophic requirements were not made evident. These

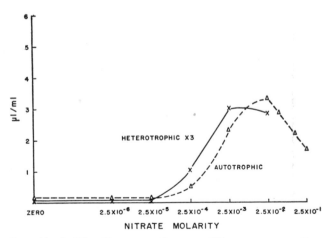

Fig. 1. Growth of *Chlorella pyrenoidosa* at different concentrations of nitrate. Autotrophic: 2 days growth from 10 μl. washed cells. Heterotrophic: 15 days growth from 1 loopful cells.

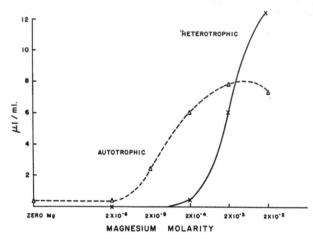

Fig. 2. Growth of *Chlorella pyrenoidosa* at different concentrations of magnesium. Autotrophic: 4 days growth from 12 μl. washed cells. Heterotrophic: 25 days growth from 1 loopful cells.

heterotrophic requirements for iron and zinc would be much less than their requirements for autotrophic growth. Manganese has been shown to fit such a pattern (described in Section IV).

It is evident that *Chlorella pyrenoidosa* requires more manganese, iron, zinc, and nitrate, and less magnesium for autotrophic growth than for heterotrophic growth. Slight differences in the requirements for potassium and phosphorus are questionable variations. These differences in the

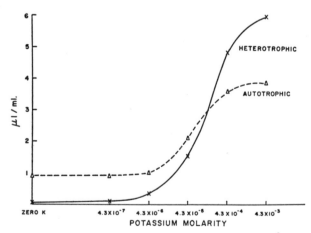

Fig. 3. Growth of *Chlorella pyrenoidosa* at different concentrations of potassium. Autotrophic: 4 days growth from 1 μl. washed cells. Heterotrophic: 20 days growth from 1 loopful cells grown previously with 1.7 p.p.m. potassium in the medium.

mineral requirements for autotrophic and heterotrophic growth are summarized in Table III.

TABLE III

A Comparison of the Mineral Requirements for Autotrophic
and Heterotrophic Growth of *Chlorella pyrenoidosa*

Autotrophic growth has greater requirement for	Heterotrophic growth has greater requirement for
Mn	Mg
Fe	K (slightly more)
Zn	
NO_3	
P (slightly more)	

IV. MANGANESE AND GROWTH RESPONSE
A. Rate of Growth

There are three ways in which *Chlorella* can be grown: autotrophically in the light without sugar but with carbon dioxide as a carbon source, heterotrophically in the dark with sugar, and mixotrophically in light with sugar and carbon dioxide. Figure 9 compares the growth rates of *Chlorella* grown in these three different ways both with and without manganese. Cultures were started with a loop inoculum from a previously autotrophic plus-manganese culture. Heterotrophic growth both with

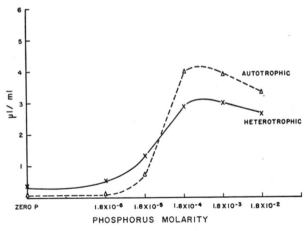

FIG. 4. Growth of *Chlorella pyrenoidosa* at different concentrations of phosphorus. Autotrophic: 3 days growth from 1 μl. washed cells. Heterotrophic: 34 days growth from 1 loopful cells.

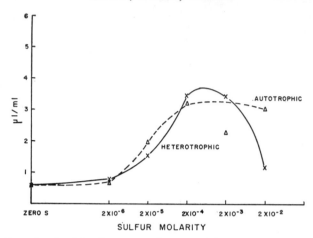

FIG. 5. Growth of *Chlorella pyrenoidosa* at different concentrations of sulfur. Autotrophic: 2 days growth from 10 μl. washed cells. Heterotrophic: 35 days growth from 1 loopful cells.

and without manganese required a short lag period of about 10 days, and minus-manganese mixotrophic cultures required a very long lag period of about 4 weeks. Investigations of the factors determining the excessive lag period of mixotrophic growth are under way. It was found that a heterotrophic inoculum and/or "used" heterotrophic medium will reduce the lag period of the minus-manganese mixotrophic cultures to about 10 days. The character of minus-manganese mixotrophic cells is entirely

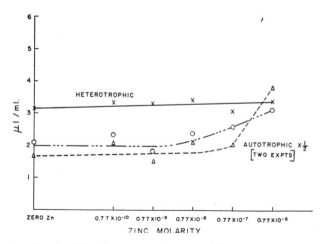

FIG. 6. Growth of *Chlorella pyrenoidosa* at different concentrations of zinc. Autotrophic: (upper) 5 days growth from 0.1 μl. washed cells; (lower) 3 days growth from 1.4 μl. washed cells. Heterotrophic: 35 days growth from 1 loopful cells.

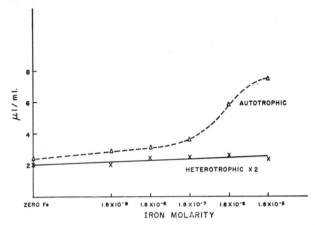

FIG. 7. Growth of *Chlorella pyrenoidosa* at different concentrations of iron. Autotrophic: 4 days growth from 1.4 μl. washed cells. Heterotrophic: 21 days growth from 1 loopful cells.

heterotrophic, since they have shown capacity for neither the Hill reaction nor photosynthesis.

The most rapid growth occurred in cultures containing manganese growing autotrophically and mixotrophically. Heterotrophic plus-manganese cultures required about 18 days to produce the growth obtained in 6 days with plus-manganese autotrophic and plus-manganese mixotrophic cultures. Minus-manganese autotrophic cultures did not produce

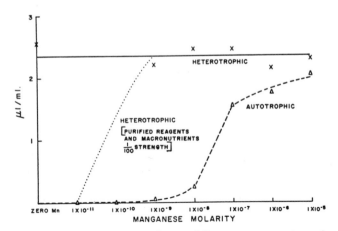

FIG. 8. Growth of *Chlorella pyrenoidosa* at different concentrations of manganese. Autotrophic: 1 day growth from 88 μl. washed cells which had previously been grown in the dark without added manganese. Heterotrophic: 18 days growth from 1 loopful cells.

as exemplified by manganese, it is possible that the concentration requirements of the element may be sufficiently spread to indicate its separate
functions.

II. Culture Methods and Procedure

Chlorella pyrenoidosa (Emerson strain) was obtained from Dr. Jack
Myers of the University of Texas. The alga was cultured in Warburg and
Burk medium (1950) supplemented with 1 p.p.m. iron as $FeSO_4 \cdot 7H_2O$
made up freshly each week and with the usual A_5 trace element combination, except that manganese, zinc, and copper were added as sulfates
instead of chlorides. The best reagent grade chemicals were used to
furnish the macronutrients and Specpure (Johnson, Matthey and Co.,
Ltd.) iron and trace element salts were used ($MnSO_4 \cdot 7H_2O$, $CuSO_4 \cdot$
$5H_2O$, H_3BO_3, $ZnSO_4 \cdot 7H_2O$, $NH_4MoO_{24} \cdot 4H_2O$ to furnish 0.5 p.p.m.
manganese, 0.02 p.p.m. copper, 0.5 p.p.m. boron, 0.05 p.p.m. zinc, and
0.01 p.p.m. molybdenum, respectively). The Warburg and Burk medium
was modified in such a way that the concentration of the element under
investigation could be varied. The nitrate concentration series involved
the omission of KNO_3 to obtain zero nitrate medium and then the additions of KNO_3 to give the nitrate concentrations desired. For the magnesium concentration series, Na_2SO_4 was substituted for $MgSO_4$, and
$MgCl_2$ was added to supply the magnesium. Sodium nitrate and NaH_2PO_4
replaced KNO_3 and KH_2PO_4, and potassium was added as KCl to set up
the potassium concentration series; whereas KH_2PO_4 was omitted to
obtain zero phosphate, and additions of KH_2PO_4 made possible the phosphorus concentration series. Magnesium chloride instead of $MgSO_4$, the
addition of chlorides of iron, manganese, zinc and copper instead of the
sulfates of these metals, and various increments of Na_2SO_4 were used in
the sulfur concentration series. Iron, zinc, and manganese concentrations
were set up simply by varying the supplements of these elements.

Scenedesmus quadricauda was obtained from the Indiana Culture
Collection of Algae (Dr. Richard C. Starr, Department of Botany, University of Indiana, Bloomington, Indiana) and was cultured on a modified Chicago medium, containing 500 mg. per liter. $MgSO_4 \cdot 7H_2O$, 250 mg.
per liter KNO_3, 250 mg. per liter K_2HPO_4, 200 mg. per liter NaCl, 27 mg.
per liter Specpure $CaCl_2$, 1.88 millimoles NaOH prepared from special
reagent grade sodium (C. P. Baker's Analyzed), iron and trace elements
as for *Chlorella. Nostoc muscorum* was obtained from Dr. G. C. Gerloff,
University of Wisconsin, and was cultured on a modified Chu medium,
containing 125 mg. per liter $MgSO_4 \cdot 7H_2O$, 250 mg. per liter KNO_3, 30
mg. per liter K_2HPO_4, 27 mg. per liter Specpure $CaCl_2$, 3.76 millimoles

ganese to a level which no longer supported heterotrophic growth (Fig. 10). There was no growth in the culture to which 5×10^{-7} p.p.m. Mn ($10^{-11}M$) was added, but growth occurred in all cultures containing at least 5×10^{-6} p.p.m. Mn ($10^{-10}M$). The culture with 5×10^{-6} p.p.m. Mn was appreciably slower in getting started than the cultures with higher concentrations of manganese. Pirson and Bergmann (1955) obtained no reduction in growth in minus-manganese heterotrophic cultures compared with cultures containing 0.056 p.p.m. manganese. However, Reisner and Thompson (1956) were able to show reduction in the growth of heterotrophic manganese-deficient *Chlorella* cultures down to 75 per

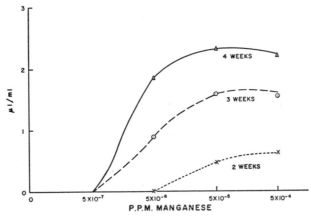

Fig. 10. Heterotrophic growth of *Chlorella pyrenoidosa* at very low concentrations of manganese. Growth from 1 loopful heterotrophic zero manganese culture.

cent of the manganese sufficient cultures. It is now apparent that manganese functions in heterotrophic growth of *Chlorella* as well as in autotrophic growth, and that these functions are distinctly separate.

B. Chlorophyll Content

There are conflicting reports on the chlorophyll content of manganese-deficient plants. Bishop (1928) stated that manganese deficiency interfered with the synthesis of chlorophyll, thereby affecting carbon assimilation. According to Portsmouth (1949), manganese-treated leaves of potato became very much greener and healthier looking than the manganese-deficient controls. However, Pirson *et al.* (1952) as well as others generally agree that manganese deficiency does not directly produce chlorosis. Bergmann (1955) reported a 42 per cent increase in chlorophyll content of manganese-deficient mixotrophic *Chlorella vulgaris* over the normal, and the data of Alberts-Dietert (1941) showed that manganese-deficient mixotrophic cultures of *Chlorella pyrenoidosa* had 80 per cent more chlorophyll than the normal controls; however, the normal autotrophically-grown cultures had 44 per cent more chlorophyll than the manganese-deficient ones. Rao and Lal (1955) studied the effect of manganese deficiency on barley plants, and reported that the manganese-deficient plants had a chlorophyll content more than double that of the controls, and that carotene and xanthophyll were respectively 2.4 and 17 times more concentrated in the manganese-deficient plants than in the control plants.

The relationship of chlorophyll content to manganese concentration of the culture medium was investigated at the Kettering Foundation. The results of this study are given in Table IV. Both *Chlorella pyrenoid-*

TABLE IV

Chlorophyll Contents of Algae Cultured at Different Levels of Manganese

Organism	Type of culture	Chlorophyll content[a] at indicated Mn concentrations					
		Zero (p.p.m.)	5×10^{-5} (p.p.m.)	5×10^{-4} (p.p.m.)	5×10^{-3} (p.p.m.)	5×10^{-2} (p.p.m.)	5×10^{-1} (p.p.m.)
Chlorella	Autotrophic	6.00	5.30	6.20	5.30	5.25	4.80
Chlorella	Mixotrophic	5.00	5.30	4.20	3.45	2.80	2.95
Chlorella	Heterotrophic	6.25	6.20	4.50	4.50	4.65	5.20
Scenedesmus	Autotrophic	3.52[b]	3.90[b]	3.62[b]	4.60	2.67	2.86
Nostoc	Autotrophic	1.22	1.40	1.44	1.75	1.9	1.68

[a] Mg./ml. p.c.
[b] Incomplete extraction.

osa and *Scenedesmus quadricauda* showed the greatest chlorophyll content to be in the most deficient cultures. On the contrary, the chlorophyll content of *Nostroc muscorum* increased with an increase in manganese content of the culture medium. There was a drop in the chlorophyll content of *Chlorella* in the exact range of concentration where manganese produced its greatest effect on the Hill reaction, photosynthesis, and autotrophic growth. The indicated drop in the chlorophyll content of *Chlorella* grown autotrophically amounted to about 15 per cent of the maximum value. The chlorophyll contents of heterotrophically grown and mixotrophically grown *Chlorella* showed even greater differences due to the presence and absence of manganese in the medium than did the autotrophic cultures. The decrease for the heterotrophic cultures amounted to about 30 per cent, and to about 45 per cent for the mixotrophic cultures.

Contrariwise, it was found that continued prolonged illumination of

manganese-deficient autotrophic cultures of *Chlorella* produced a bleaching effect such that the manganese-deficient algae displayed marked
chlorosis. Manganese-deficient *Chlorella* exposed to about 1000 ft.-c. of
light autotrophically for 3 days, one culture with 0.5 p.p.m. manganese
added and another with no manganese added were found to contain 7.4
mg. and 0.9 mg., respectively, of chlorophyll per ml. of packed cells. In a
repeat experiment, values of 11.3 mg. and 2.3 mg. of chlorophyll per ml.
of packed cells were obtained for the respective plus- and minus-man-
ganese-cultured cells.

C. The Chlorophyll Unit in Photosynthesis

The chlorophyll unit in photosynthesis seems to be centered around
the requirement for manganese. Emerson and Arnold (1932–33) calculated from their data that approximately 2500 molecules of chlorophyll
were required for each molecule of carbon dioxide reduced per flash of
light by *Chlorella pyrenoidosa*. Extending the measurements to six species
of plants, representing four phyla, Arnold and Kohn (1934) stated that
the minimum number of chlorophyll molecules present for each molecule
of carbon dioxide reduced appeared to lie between 2000 and 3000, and
that this relationship suggested the existence of a chlorophyll unit.

For the reduction of 1 molecule of carbon dioxide there must be the
photolysis of 4 molecules of water, according to the following scheme:

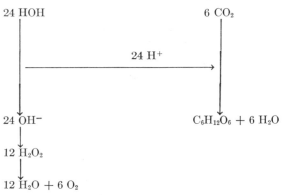

This boils down to the photolysis of 4 molecules of water for the reduction of each molecule of carbon dioxide, and suggests that carbon
dioxide is reduced stepwise by 4 steps. The minimum number of chlorophyll molecules required for each step, based on the findings of
Emerson and Arnold (1932–1933) would, therefore, be approximately 625
(¼ of 2500).

Our data (Eyster, Brown, Tanner and Hood, unpublished) show that
the chlorophyll molarity of *Chlorella* at the critical manganese concentra-

tion exceeded the manganese molarity by a factor of 614. By the use of radioactive manganese, it has been possible to determine the manganese content of *Chlorella* cells. At the critical concentration of manganese, minimum amount for maximum growth, the manganese was found to be 114 times more concentrated in the cells than in the medium. The amount in the cells then would be 114 times the critical concentration (1×10^{-7} M). This would give a value of 0.0114×10^{-9} moles manganese per μl. packed cells, or approximately 136,800 atoms manganese per *Chlorella* cell as minimal for full growth and Hill reaction activity. There are approximately 50×10^6 packed *Chlorella* cells per μl. On the basis of 22 separate chlorophyll determinations on normal cells during the past two years, each milliliter of packed *Chlorella* cells was found to have an average of 7.0 mg. chlorophyll (range 4.0 to 12.8 mg. per ml.). This would mean that there were approximately 7.0×10^{-9} moles chlorophyll per μl. of packed cells, or approximately 84×10^6 molecules of chlorophyll per *Chlorella* cell.

Calculations for the chlorophyll-manganese ratio factor are briefly as follows:

$$\frac{7.0 \times 10^{-9} \text{ moles chlorophyll per } \mu\text{l. p.c.}}{0.0114 \times 10^{-9} \text{ moles Mn per } \mu\text{l. p.c.}} = 614$$

or

$$\frac{84 \times 10^6 \text{ molecules chlorophyll per } Chlorella \text{ cell}}{136,800 \text{ atoms Mn per } Chlorella \text{ cell}} = 614$$

V. CHLORIDE AND GROWTH RESPONSE

A special *Chlorella* medium was formulated on the basis of the critical concentrations of nutrients for autotrophic growth. The special medium had, in addition to the usual amount of iron and trace elements:

25 mg. per liter KH_2PO_4	$1.8 \times 10^{-4} M$
34 mg. per liter K_2SO_4	$1.95 \times 10^{-4} M$
3200 mg. per liter $Mg(NO_3)_2 \cdot 6H_2O$	$1.25 \times 10^{-2} M$

All of the elements in the special medium were approximately at the critical concentration except that magnesium was 10-fold more concentrated.

The special *Chlorella* medium was found to be seriously inadequate (Table V). The growth of *Chlorella pyrenoidosa* in the special medium was only 25 per cent of its growth in the regular Warburg and Burk medium. In an attempt to improve the growth of *Chlorella* in the special medium, separate additions of $MgSO_4$, KH_2PO_4, and NaCl were made to successive aliquots of medium so as to make the nutrient the same strength as in the Warburg and Burk medium. Each of these nutrients improved the growth of *Chlorella* but the greatest improvement occurred

TABLE V

Comparative Growth of *Chlorella pyrenoidosa* in the Special Medium
and in the Special Medium with Various Anion Supplements

Medium	Relative yield (%)
Warburg and Burk (with NaCl)	100
Warburg and Burk (without NaCl)	102
Special	25
Special + 500 mg. $MgSO_4 \cdot 7H_2O$/100 ml.	64
Special + 225 mg. KH_2PO_4/100 ml.	51
Special + 200 mg. NaCl/100 ml.	122
Special + 352 mg. NaBr/100 ml.	100
Special + 144 mg. NaF/100 ml.	21
Special + 513 mg. NaI/100 ml.	4

with the addition of NaCl. Subsequently, it was shown that NaBr was
almost as effective as NaCl, and that NaF and NaI were quite ineffective.
The Warburg and Burk medium has consistently shown no difference in
the yield of *Chlorella pyrenoidosa* with or without the addition of NaCl
to the medium.

A logarithmic gradient of NaCl concentrations superimposed on the
special medium (Table VI) showed (*1*) that the amount of growth of

TABLE VI

Comparative Growth of *Chlorella pyrenoidosa* in the Special Medium upon
Which a Gradient of NaCl Concentrations Had Been Superimposed

Medium	Relative[a] yield (%)
Special (no chloride)	25
Special + 0.02 mg. NaCl/100 ml.	51
Special + 0.2 mg. NaCl/100 ml.	60
Special + 2 mg. NaCl/100 ml.	66
Special + 20 mg. NaCl/100 ml.	62
Special + 200 mg. NaCl/100 ml.	122
Special + 300 mg. NaCl/100 ml.	127
Special + 400 mg. NaCl/100 ml.	127
Special + 600 mg. NaCl/100 ml.	104
Special + 800 mg. NaCl/100 ml.	69

[a] Assuming yield of 100 per cent in regular Warburg and Burk medium.

Chlorella could be doubled with the addition of merely 0.02 mg./100 ml.
(3.4×10^{-6} *M*), (*2*) that the critical concentration was about 200
mg./100 ml. (3.4×10^{-2} *M*), and (*3*) that optimum NaCl additions
produced a medium which was fully 25 per cent better than the Warburg
and Burk medium.

A more careful study of the effects of nutrient supplements to the special medium is presented in Table VII. It should be noted that the chloride effect was prevented in the presence of much phosphate. This fact seems to be correlated with the apparent ineffectiveness of NaCl in the Warburg and Burk medium. There was no ineffectiveness of chloride, however, in the presence of much sulfate. The supplement in which 250 mg. KH_2PO_4 and 348.5 mg. K_2SO_4 were combined produced approximately the same amount of growth as the regular Warburg and Burk medium did. This combined supplement formulated a special medium

TABLE VII

Comparative Growth of *Chlorella pyrenoidosa* in the Special Medium
to Which Various Anion Supplements Had Been Added

Medium	Relative[a] yield (%)
Special	25
Special + 348.5 mg. K_2SO_4/100 ml.	87
Special + 348.5 mg. K_2SO_4 + 200 mg. NaCl/100 ml.	120
Special + 250 mg. KH_2PO_4/100 ml.	84
Special + 250 mg. KH_2PO_4 + 200 mg. NaCl/100 ml.	83
Special + 250 mg. KH_2PO_4 + 348.5 mg. K_2SO_4[b]/100 ml.	96
Special + 250 mg. KH_2PO_4 + 348.5 mg. K_2SO_4 + 200 mg. NaCl/100 ml.	87

[a] Assuming yield of 100 per cent in regular Warburg and Burk medium.

[b] Approximately same amount of phosphate and sulfate as in the regular Warburg and Burk medium.

which had approximately the same amounts of both phosphate and sulfate as those present in the Warburg and Burk medium.

The varied effectiveness of sulfate, phosphate, and chloride indicates that the improvement of the special medium was really an anion effect rather than a specific chloride effect. It is evident from the data that chloride was the most effective anion.

Of especial interest is the comparison between autotrophic growth and heterotrophic growth as regards the requirement for chloride. Figure 11 gives this comparison. Chloride has only a slight effect (17 per cent) on heterotrophic growth. The stimulating effect on autotrophic growth was 4-fold or 400 per cent.

A chloride (anion) effect has been reported for washed chloroplasts (Warburg and Luttgens, 1946; Arnon and Whatley, 1949; Gorham and Clendenning, 1952) and for lyophilized *Chlorella* cells (Schwartz, 1956). Broyer *et al.* (1954), Ozanne *et al.* (1957), and Johnson *et al.* (1957) reported evidence to show that chlorine is a micronutrient element. The first experiments were done with the tomato plant. More recently, severe

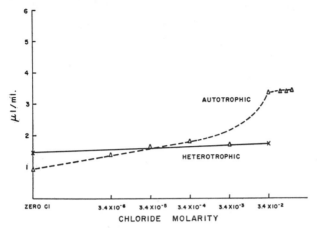

FIG. 11. Growth of *Chlorella pyrenoidosa* at different concentrations of chloride (NaCl). Autotrophic: 3 days growth from 0.65 μl. washed cells. Heterotrophic: 20 days growth from 1 loopful cells.

chlorine-deficiency symptoms were produced with and reported for lettuce, cabbage, carrot, sugar beet, barley, and alfalfa, and it was also shown that the absence of chloride decreased the yields of buckwheat, corn, and beans. Bromide could be substituted for chloride. In general, the findings of the influence of other anions on the oxygen evolution of washed chloroplasts match the effects of bromide, fluoride, and iodide on the autotrophic growth of *Chlorella pyrenoidosa*. That chloride is far more effective for autotrophic growth than for heterotrophic growth seems not to have been observed and reported before.

VI. RECOMMENDED AUTOTROPHIC MEDIUM

The following autotrophic growth medium is recommended for *Chlorella pyrenoidosa* (mg. per liter): KH_2PO_4, 25; K_2SO_4, 34; $Mg(NO_3)_2 \cdot 6H_2O$, 3200; NaCl, 2000; and Fe, 1 p.p.m.; plus the usual A_5 supplement of manganese, molybdenum, copper, zinc, and boron. Since omissions of molybdenum, copper, and boron have been found not to depress growth these three trace elements could very well be omitted from the growth medium. Autotrophic growth of *Chlorella pyrenoidosa* is about 25 per cent greater in this medium than in the Warburg and Burk medium.

REFERENCES

Alberts-Dietert, F. 1941. *Planta* **32**, 88–177.

Arnold, W., and Kohn, H. I. 1934. *J. Gen. Physiol.* **18**, 109–112.

Arnon, D. I. 1949. *Plant Physiol.* **24**, 1–15.

Arnon, D. I., and Whatley, F. R. 1949. *Science* **110**, 554–556.

Bergmann, L. 1955. *Flora (Jena)* **142**, 493–539.

Bishop, W. B. S. 1928. *Australian J. Exptl. Biol. Med. Sci.* **5**, 125–141.

Broyer, T. C., Carlton, A. B., Johnson, C. M., and Stout, P. R. 1954. *Plant Physiol.* **29**, 526–532.

Emerson, R., and Arnold, W. 1932–1933. *J. Gen. Physiol.* **16**, 191–205.

Gorham, P. R., and Clendenning, K. A. 1952. *Arch. Biochem. Biophys.* **37**, 199–223.

Hewitt, E. J. 1951. *Ann. Rev. Plant Physiol.* **2**, 25–52.

Hopkins, E. F. 1930. *Science* **72**, 609–610.

Johnson, C. M., Stout, P. R., Broyer, T. C., and Carlton, A. B. 1957. *Plant and Soil* **8**, 337–353.

Lehninger, A. L. 1950. *Physiol. Revs.* **30**, 393–429.

MacKinney, G. 1941. *J. Biol. Chem.* **140**, 315–322.

Macy, P. 1936. *Plant Physiol.* **11**, 749–764.

Mahler, H. R. 1956. *Advances in Enzymol.* **17**, 233–291.

Ozanne, P. G., Woolley, J. T., and Broyer, T. C. 1957. *Australian J. Biol. Sci.* **10**, 66–79.

Pirson, A., and Bergmann, L. 1955. *Nature* **176**, 209–210.

Pirson, A., Tichy, C., and Wilhelmi, G. 1952. *Planta* **40**, 199–253.

Portsmouth, G. B. 1949. *Ann. Botany* **13**, 113–133.

Ramig, R. E., and Vandecaveye, S. C. 1950. *Plant Physiol.* **25**, 617–629.

Rao, M. S. S., and Lal, K. N. 1955. *Science and Culture (Calcutta)* **21**, 319–320.

Reisner, G. S., and Thompson, J. F. 1956. *Nature* **178**, 1473–1474.

Schwartz, M. 1956. *Biochim. et Biophys. Acta* **22**, 463–470.

Ulrich, A. 1945. *Soil Sci. Soc. Am. Proc.* **10**, 150–161.

Warburg, O., and Burk, D. 1950. *Arch. Biochem.* **25**, 410–443.

Warburg, O., and Luttgens, W. 1946. *Biokhimiya* **11**, 303-322.

Waring, W. S., and Werkman, C. H. 1942. *Arch. Biochem.* **1**, 303–310.

CHAPTER 12

Selenium: Its Occurrence in Rocks and Soils, Absorption by Plants, Toxic Action in Animals, and Possible Essential Role in Animal Nutrition

A. L. MOXON
Ohio Agricultural Experiment Station
Wooster, Ohio

	Page
I. Introduction	175
II. Geological Distribution of Selenium	177
III. Selenium in Soils	178
A. Forms of Selenium in Soils	179
B. Treatment of Soils to Inhibit Absorption of Selenium by Plants	180
IV. Selenium in Plants	180
A. Forms of Selenium in Plants	182
V. Selenium Poisoning in Livestock	183
VI. Selenium Poisoning in Laboratory Animals	183
VII. Selenium Poisoning in Poultry	184
VIII. Toxicity of Selenium in Animals	185
IX. Some Dietary Factors which Influence Selenium Toxicity	185
X. Selenium and Public Health	187
XI. Selenium as an Essential Element in Animal Nutrition	187
References	188

I. INTRODUCTION

Selenium was discovered in 1817 by Berzelius and Gahn in sediments from a sulfuric acid plant at Gripsholm, Sweden. Selenium ranks about fifteenth in order of abundance of the elements, which makes it about as rare as silver. The word selenium is derived from the Greek word selēnē, meaning the moon. Selenium has several industrial uses and currently is in great demand for the production of rectifiers for use in electronic equipment.

Interest in selenium as a trace element has resulted mainly from its toxic effects upon animals although within the past year its role as an

175

essential element at very low concentrations for the rat and chick (Schwarz and Foltz, 1957; Schwarz et al., 1957; Stokstad, 1957) has been announced.

Japha (1842) found that selenium was toxic to animals, but it was not associated with poisoning of livestock until 1931 (Moxon, 1937). A livestock malady called "alkali disease," which we now know was caused by selenium, was described in 1856 in a report by Madison (1860), an Army surgeon stationed at Fort Randall, territory of Nebraska. He described a disease among the Army horses which had grazed in a specific area near the Fort. The symptoms which he described are similar to those suffered by horses which have grazed in the same general area in more recent times and have been definitely linked to the selenium content of the vegetation grown on soils derived from seleniferous geological formations (Williams et al., 1941). The symptoms of selenium poisoning in horses are stiffness, lameness, cracking of the hoofs, and loss of the long hair from the mane and tail (Moxon, 1937).

The territory around Fort Randall was opened for settlement about 1891, and the homesteaders observed symptoms in their livestock similar to those described by Madison in 1856. They called it "alkali disease" because they associated the trouble with alkali seeps and waters of high salt content (alkali waters). Experiments were completed in 1912 at the South Dakota Agricultural Experiment Station which showed that the suspected water did not cause the malady (Larsen and Bailey, 1912), but the name "alkali disease" is still associated with the condition which is now known to be chronic selenium poisoning.

In 1929, Franke started investigations on the alkali disease at the South Dakota Agricultural Experiment Station which led to cooperation with several Bureaus of the U.S. Department of Agriculture and the discovery by Robinson (1933) of selenium in cereals which Franke had found to be toxic to laboratory animals.

Plants which have absorbed selenium from the soil have been found at various locations in most of the states in the Great Plains and Rocky Mountain areas (Trelease and Beath, 1949) as well as in certain Provinces in Canada (Williams et al., 1941; Lakin and Byers, 1948; Thorvaldson and Johnson, 1940). Selenium has also been found in soils and plants from Mexico (Byers, 1937) and in wheat or other plant materials from Columbia, Argentina, Peru, Hawaii, Australia, New Zealand, South Africa, Spain, Bulgaria, France, and Germany (Robinson, 1936). Selenium toxicity in livestock has been observed in County Limerick, Ireland (Walsh et al., 1951; O'Moore, 1952). During the present year, selenium has been reported to occur in soils and plants in the Huleh Valley and several other locations in Israel. The selenium content of the plants was high enough to cause alkali disease in cattle (Ravikovitch and Margolin, 1957).

II. Geological Distribution of Selenium

In a preliminary field survey of the alkali disease by Franke *et al.* (1934), the cases observed all occurred on "gumbo" soils derived from Pierre shales. Beath *et al.* (1934), at the Wyoming Agricultural Experiment Station, were the first to work on geological distribution of selenium as related to livestock poisoning. They had associated poisonous plants with Cretaceous shales before they found selenium in the plants.

In the Great Plains area, the selenium which is present in soils has been derived from the soil parent materials, largely sedimentary rocks of Cretaceous age. These formations were deposited in a shallow sea which covered most of the area during the Mesozoic era. These sedimentary rocks are, thus, not the primary source of selenium, but the element must have gotten into the erosion cycle from some other source, possibly from volcanic gasses and other volcanic materials. Selenium occurs in present-day volcanic material (Byers *et al.*, 1936). Selenium is easily precipitated from solution by combination with iron hydroxide (Strock, 1935; Byers *et al.*, 1938; Olson and Jensen, 1940), which would explain its removal from sea water and its presence in sea-floor deposits. Selenium which has been dissolved from soils and rocks and carried by river water to the sea is precipitated and appears in sea-bottom deposits (Moxon *et al.*, 1939). Only traces of selenium appear in most sea-bottom deposits, but samples taken from the Gulf of California contained from 3 to 5 p.p.m. (Lakin and Byers, 1941). A composite sample from 12 locations in the Gulf of Mexico contained 0.77 p.p.m. of selenium (Moxon *et al.*, 1939). Drainage waters from the seleniferous areas of the United States enter both the Gulf of California and the Gulf of Mexico.

The selenium content of sedimentary rock formations is not uniform (Moxon *et al.*, 1939), which would indicate that selenium was supplied from the primary source at a variable rate as compared to other sedimentary materials.

In South Dakota the various geological formations, especially the Cretaceous formations, have been mapped, sampled, and analyzed for selenium (Moxon *et al.*, 1938a, 1939). Stratigraphically, the parent materials from which most of the seleniferous soils in South Dakota were produced occur in the upper portion of the Pierre formation in the Mobridge member, at the base of the Pierre, in the Sharron Springs member and in the Smoky Hill (upper) member of the Niobrara formation which lies just below the base of the Pierre formation.

Seleniferous soils which produce toxic vegetation have been derived from the Mobridge member of the Pierre formation in northern Nebraska and in southern South Dakota. This member of the Pierre formation, because of its stratigraphic position, has been the parent material for soils over relatively large areas. Fortunately, the selenium content of soils derived from the Mobridge member is high only in areas adjacent to the Missouri River in south central South Dakota and north central Nebraska. To the north and west of this area the selenium content of the Mobridge member and soils derived therefrom, decreases to unimportant amounts. The soils which have been developed from the Mobridge member are better suited for crop production than the soils derived from any other member of the Pierre formation.

The Sharron Springs member at the base of the Pierre formation contains considerable quantities of selenium where it outcrops in South Dakota. These areas of outcrop are limited to small areas along the Missouri River and around the foothills of the Black Hills. It does not weather readily, and very little productive soil has been derived from it in South Dakota.

The upper member (Smoky Hill) of the Niobrara formation is the parent material of some of the most seleniferous soils in western South Dakota (Moxon et al., 1938a, 1939), Wyoming (Byers, 1935, 1936; Knight and Beath, 1937), Kansas (Byers, 1936), and Colorado (Byers, 1935, 1936).

Selenium is present in some formations which are older than the Cretaceous formations, but the amount is insufficient to produce highly seleniferous soils. Formations of Permian and Triassic age in Wyoming and Idaho have been reported to contain selenium (Beath et al., 1937a).

Glacial drift, which is younger than Cretaceous formations, has been reported to contain selenium in Canada and North Dakota (Williams et al., 1941) and in South Dakota (Searight and Moxon, 1945). The selenium in glacial drift probably originated in materials of Cretaceous age which were worked over by glacial action.

III. Selenium in Soils

It has been estimated that from 60 to 80 per cent of the selenium in parent geological formations is lost in soil-forming processes (Moxon et al., 1939). Soils which contain 2 to 4 p.p.m. of selenium have been formed from formations which contained about 10 p.p.m. The balance of the selenium was lost into the erosion cycle through leaching during the soil-forming processes. Much of the selenium which entered the erosion cycle is probably now in sea-bottom deposits.

The selenium content of surface soils has been studied in reconnaissance-type surveys carried out by Byers and co-workers (Byers, 1935, 1936; Byers *et al.*, 1938; Lakin and Byers, 1941). Intensive field studies on sampling of soil and subsoil has pointed out the limited value of surface samples in predicting the capability of a soil to produce toxic vegetation. The water-soluble selenium values in soil profiles and the uptake of selenium by *Agropyron smithii* (western wheatgrass) in samples taken from a ranch in central South Dakota are shown in Table I. (Olson *et al.*, 1942c.)

TABLE I

Selenium Content of Soil and of *Agropyron smithii* within a Small Area in South Dakota

| Location | Depth (feet) | Total Se (p.p.m.) | Water-soluble Se | | Se content of *Agropyron smithii* (p.p.m.) |
			Actual (p.p.m.)	% of total	
6	1	2.7	0.12	4.4	18
	2	5.5	2.76	50.2	
	3	11.5	0.58	5.0	
7	1	4.3	0.43	10.0	79
	2	15.8	5.00	31.6	
	3	29.0	10.85	37.4	
8	1	3.0	1.43	47.7	8
	2	4.5	0.48	10.7	
	3	11.5	2.66	23.1	
14	1	4.4	0.91	20.7	35
	2	28.4	17.60	62.0	
	3	38.4	18.99	49.5	
21	1	4.4	0.08	1.8	2
	2	4.8	0.10	2.1	
	3	6.4	0.12	1.9	
32	1	5.9	0.11	1.9	2
	2	4.6	0.05	1.1	
	3	6.0	0.11	1.8	

A. Forms of Selenium in Soils

Williams and Byers (1936) have studied the forms of selenium in soils and have reported that it occurs in five forms, as follows: (*1*) elemental; (*2*) pyritic or selenide; (*3*) selenite; (*4*) selenate; and (*5*) organic. Olson *et al.* (1942a,b) have reported on field studies in which they found that the selenium content of the surface soil was of little influence on the selenium content of grass plants. The water-soluble selenates of the second and third feet of the soil profile constituted the important source of selenium for grass plants. Surveys have revealed areas of highly seleniferous soils in Hawaii and Puerto Rico which do not produce toxic vegetation, probably because the selenium occurs largely as basic iron selenite (Lakin *et al.*, 1938; Williams *et al.*, 1940). Greenhouse trials have shown that basic iron selenite is not readily available to plants (Moxon *et al.*, 1939).

B. *Treatment of Soils to Inhibit Absorption of Selenium by Plants*

The addition of sulfur to cultures and soils was shown by Hurd-Karrar (1933, 1934, 1935) to inhibit the absorption of selenium added as selenate in wheat plants grown in a greenhouse.

Martin (1936) found that sulfur had little effect in reducing the toxicity of selenium as selenite to wheat and buckwheat plants grown in either culture or soil in greenhouse experiments.

As a result of the work of Hurd-Karrar (1933, 1934, 1935), the addition of sulfur to seleniferous soils was advocated as a measure to prevent the production of toxic vegetation. The addition of sulfur to naturally seleniferous soils under field conditions, however, failed to inhibit the absorption of selenium by wheat and corn plants (Franke and Painter, 1937). This lack of effectiveness in naturally seleniferous soils should, however, be expected since these soils usually contain high concentrations of sulphates.

IV. Selenium in Plants

Cameron (1880) demonstrated that selenium added to soils would be absorbed by plants. Taboury (1932) of France reported that selenium occurred in certain species of *Sium*. Beath *et al.* (1934, 1935) found *Sium cicutaefolium* growing in areas where blind staggers of livestock was common, and this was the start of a series of experiments and observations which demonstrated the relationship between plants of high-selenium content and blind staggers, an acute form of selenium poisoning in livestock.

Beath *et al.* (1934) reported that certain species of plants contained much more selenium than other species grown in the same soils. They observed, further, that these plants grew only where the soil contained selenium and, thus, were a valuable tool as "indicators" of seleniferous soils and seleniferous geological formations. "Indicator" plants have been a great aid in the mapping of seleniferous soil areas. The indicator plants are all classified in the genera: *Stanleya, Oonopsis, Xylorrhiza,* and

Astragalus (certain species). In range grazing areas, these highly seleniferous plants are a livestock hazard. In farming areas, they are normally not as abundant as in range areas and thus are not as much of a livestock hazard. In farming areas, the crop plants and grasses are sources of the selenium which causes the alkali disease. The selenium content of indicator plants often reaches several thousand parts per million while the selenium content of cereals and grasses is normally less than 100 p.p.m. and most often is of the order of 5 to 10 p.p.m.

Robinson (1936) has analyzed wheat samples from various parts of the world, outside of the United States, for selenium content. The selenium content ranged from 0.1 to 1.9 p.p.m. The sample with 1.9 p.p.m. came from Saskatchewan, Canada. The next highest sample came from South Africa and contained 1.5 p.p.m. of selenium. Thorvaldson and Johnson (1940) analyzed 230 composite samples representing 2230 individual samples of wheat grown in Saskatchewan for selenium content. The maximum selenium content found in composite samples was 1.55 p.p.m. They did analyze some individual samples and found a maximum of 4.0 p.p.m. selenium. Eighty-six samples of wheat grown in 1939 and taken at random from 14 counties in south central South Dakota were analyzed for selenium (Moxon and Rhian, 1943). Seventy-two of these samples contained less than 1.0 p.p.m. of selenium. The highest content was 5.0 p.p.m. in the only sample that contained over 4.0 p.p.m.

Wheat grown in a field in which the soil was derived from Niobrara formation was found to contain 63.0 p.p.m. of selenium. This is the highest concentration found in field-grown wheat. A sample of this wheat was milled on an experimental mill and the fractions analyzed for selenium (Moxon *et al.*, 1943). The bran contained 88.44 p.p.m., the shorts 77.18 p.p.m., and the patent flour 53.26 p.p.m. of selenium. Three other samples of wheat of lower selenium content were milled at the same time and showed similar percentage distribution of selenium in the different fractions.

Range grasses collected over a 3-year period from fenced plots on a seleniferous ranch in central South Dakota were analyzed for selenium content (Olson *et al.*, 1942a). The grasses contained as much as 20 p.p.m. of selenium, and observations of cattle on the ranch indicated that grasses with 10.0 to 20.0 p.p.m. of selenium will produce typical symptoms of chronic selenium poisoning (alkali disease) in cattle.

Plants grown in soils to which selenium has been added are toxic to certain insects. Hurd-Karrar and Poos (1936) found that aphids were killed by selenium in wheat plants at a concentration which did not cause injury to the plants. Experiments carried out in Trinidad by Phillis and

Mason (1938a,b) have shown that cotton plants can be made toxic to the cotton stainer and the pink bollworm by the application of sodium selenate to the soil.

Neiswander and Morris (1940) found that the application of selenium to soil will control red spiders on ornamental plants. They observed, also, a reduction in mites and other insects on these ornamental plants which had absorbed selenium from the soil. The application of selenium to soils for the control of insects is not recommended, however, because the concentrations needed will produce vegetation toxic to man and animals.

A. Forms of Selenium in Plants

Selenium occurs in plants in inorganic and organic forms (Trelease and Beath, 1949). Much of the inorganic selenium is present as the selenate. They list eight species of *Astragalus* and three of *Stanleya* in which the selenium was present only in organic form. A number of plants which they list, however, had much of the selenium present as selenate, e.g., a sample of saltbush (*Atriplex confertifolia*) contained 1,734 p.p.m. of selenium, 90 per cent of which was present as selenate. Two species of woody aster (*Xylorrhiza*) contained 3,486 p.p.m. and 1,431 p.p.m. of selenium, about three-fourths of which was present as the selenate. Beath and Eppson (1947) have observed that these plants are responsible for serious livestock losses.

Selenium in cereals (corn, wheat, and barley) is associated with the protein (Franke, 1934a), where it probably replaces some of the sulfur that normally is present in protein. Westfall and Smith (1939) have reported that the selenium was removed from grain protein with bromine in hydrobromine acid or with hydrogen peroxide. Seleniferous proteins and their acid hydrolysates are toxic to laboratory animals, but the selenium was removed from the hydrolysates and they were then nontoxic (Painter and Franke, 1936). Amino acids of seleniferous wheat protein hydrolysates have been separated by paper chromatography, and the papers have been divided into strips and analyzed for selenium. Much of the selenium appeared in the same areas as methionine and cystine (Smith, 1949; Smith and Moxon, 1949). Some was present in another area and was identified as selenate selenium (Johnson, 1952). The selenium analog of cystine has been prepared by Fredga (1936, 1937). The toxicity of selenium in the selenium analog of cystine is comparable to the toxicity of selenium in naturally seleniferous grains and in sodium selenite (Moxon et al., 1938b), while the selenium in other organic selenium compounds, such as selenopropionic acid has been shown to be less toxic. Selenium in the selenium analog of methionine has also proven to be very toxic (Klug *et al.*, 1949). These toxicity comparisons are additional evidence that selenium may occur in cereal proteins as the selenium analog of a sulfur amino acid.

V. SELENIUM POISONING IN LIVESTOCK

Selenium poisoning of livestock has been divided into two general classes—the acute type, blind staggers, and the chronic type, alkali disease. There are also all degrees of poisoning between these two extreme types. The symptoms are a function of intake level and length of time the intake of selenium is continued. Under farm and ranch conditions, the blind staggers, or acute type of poisoning, is associated with the ingestion of highly seleniferous plants which contain 1000 p.p.m. or more of selenium, and the chronic type is associated with the ingestion of grains and grasses which contain 5 to 20 p.p.m. of selenium (Moxon, 1937; Draize and Beath, 1935).

The symptoms of the final stage of blind staggers are blindness, abdominal pain, salivation, grating of the teeth, and some degree of paralysis. Respiration is disturbed, and death usually results from respiration failure.

In general, the symptoms of alkali disease or chronic selenium poisoning are dullness and lack of vitality, loss of long hair from mane and tail of horses, soreness and sloughing of hoofs, stiffness and lameness, emaciation, roughening of the coat, atrophy of the heart, atrophy and cirrhosis of the liver, and anemia.

VI. SELENIUM POISONING IN LABORATORY ANIMALS

The symptoms of selenium poisoning in the rat have been described by Franke (1934a) and Franke and Potter (1934) and include: (*1*) marked restriction of food intake; (*2*) decreased growth rate; (*3*) severe progressive anemia; (*4*) definite pathological changes, especially in the liver. Rats fed diets containing 15 to 25 p.p.m. of selenium will restrict their food intake to as little as 25 per cent of that consumed by rats fed a similar diet which does not contain selenium. This reduction in food intake takes place within a day or two after selenium is added to the diet. When rats are given a choice of diets, they invariably avoid those containing selenium (Franke and Potter, 1936a). Rats fed diets containing less than 15 p.p.m. of selenium may gain some weight and appear to be in fair condition but reproduction may be impaired (Franke and Potter, 1936b). Anemia of progressive severity usually develops, and the rats may die with hemoglobin levels as low as 2.0 g. per 100 cc. of blood

(Franke and Potter, 1934). The livers of rats become atrophied, necrotic, cirrhotic, and hemorrhagic to varying degrees. The left lateral and central lobes are most susceptible to atrophy. Ascites and pleural edema are common, and in some cases internal hemorrhage is the immediate cause of death (Moxon and Rhian, 1943). In general, laboratory dogs have shown the same symptoms as rats when fed on selenium-containing feeds (Rhian and Moxon, 1943).

Selenium in the ration has been reported to depress blood levels of vitamin A and vitamin C in sheep (Rosenfeld and Beath, 1946). Bieri *et al.* (1957) have determined with rats that sodium selenite in the diet impaired utilization of carotene when given either orally or intravenously. Storage of preformed vitamin A was reduced, but storage of carotene was not influenced by the selenium. Selenium-poisoned rats show lowered liver vitamin C values (Svirbely, 1938; Lardy and Moxon, 1942). Selenium may react with vitamin C directly, or it may bind sulfhydryl groups which normally act as stabilizers of vitamin C.

Symptoms of selenium poisoning in livestock and laboratory animals have been reviewed by Moxon (1937), Moxon and Rhian (1943), Trelease and Beath (1949), and Underwood (1956).

VII. Selenium Poisoning in Poultry

Hatchability of chicken and turkey eggs is interfered with by concentrations of selenium in feeds which are low enough so that they may not cause noticeable symptoms in other farm animals (Moxon, 1937). It was a popular belief among farmers of the area where selenium occurs in the soil that the poor hatchability was caused by low fertility. Actually, the embryos were developing but were malformed and could not crack the shell at hatching time (Franke and Tully, 1935). Those chicks which did not hatch had a peculiar condition of the down which made them appear as though they had been greased. Deformities in the embryos included upper beaks short or missing, eyes missing, wings and feet deformed in addition to the abnormal down (Franke *et al.*, 1936).

It has been demonstrated that concentrations of selenium (as sodium selenite) as low as 0.1 p.p.m. when injected into the air cell of normal fertile eggs will cause the typical deformed embryos (Franke *et al.*, 1936). Poley and Moxon (1938) found that after feeding selenium in the ration (15 p.p.m.) for 7 days, the hatchability of the eggs produced decreased to zero but returned to normal 7 days after selenium was removed from the ration. It was later found that 10 p.p.m. of selenium in the ration would reduce the hatchability to zero and 5 p.p.m. reduced hatchability slightly. Starting rations for chicks should contain less than 5.0 p.p.m. selenium for a normal growth rate (Poley *et al.,* 1941).

VIII. Toxicity of Selenium in Animals

The minimum oral intake of selenium to produce symptoms of chronic selenium poisoning in any species would be difficult to establish. Variables which influence toxicity include: individual variations, species differences, the form of the selenium, and dietary factors including proteins.

Miller and Williams (1940a,b) administered selenite orally to farm animals. They give the minimum lethal dose for horses and mules as 3.3 mg. per kg. body weight; for cattle, 11.0 mg., and for swine, 15.0 mg.

Minimum lethal levels of selenium, administered by injection, have been established for some species. Minimum lethal dose values for selenium as sodium selenite, by injection, in mg. per kg. body weight, for the rat is 5.7; for the rabbit, 0.9–1.5; and for the dog, 1.5–2.0, as determined by Moxon and Rhian (1943) and Anderson and Moxon (1942). Lethal doses of selenium in dogs (1.5–2.0 mg. per kg. body weight, given subcutaneously) caused an increase in hematocrit and hemoglobin values of the blood. Anderson and Moxon (1942) reported that in many cases the hemoglobin levels increased by 60 per cent in 1 to 2 hours. Blood pressure was not increased at any time after the administration of selenium but showed a rapid terminal drop accompanied by the accumulation of fluid in the thoracic and abdominal cavities.

The mechanism of selenium toxicity is not clear. Several investigators have shown that selenium compounds will inhibit succinic oxidase activity of animal tissues *in vitro* (Collett, 1924; Potter and Elvehjem, 1937; Wright, 1938; see Klug *et al.,* 1950, for others). Other workers have shown that it is the succinic dehydrogenase portion of the enzyme system which is inhibited by selenium (Labes and Krebs, 1935; Stotz and Hastings, 1937). Klug and associates (1950) found that selenium lowers the liver succinic dehydrogenase levels of rats fed a specific synthetic diet.

IX. Some Dietary Factors Which Influence Selenium Toxicity

In early studies on the alkali disease, attempts were made to find dietary factors which would reduce or prevent the toxicity. Feeding trials with rats showed that changes in calcium and phosphorus levels, increases in the vitamin A and vitamin D levels of the diets, and the addition of yeast to the diets to supply added B-complex vitamins had no beneficial effects. The addition of orange juice, dry yeast, and cod liver oil to a toxic diet gave some increase in growth of rats but failed to change the characteristics of pathology due to the selenium. The addition of cystine at levels up to 0.6 per cent of the diet (Schneider, 1936) gave no beneficial results with rats, and sulfur at 0.5 per cent of the ration was slightly detrimental to rats and chicks (Moxon, 1937). Early work with high and low protein levels in rat diets indicated that the high level gave some protection against selenium toxicity (Moxon, 1937). This protein effect on selenium toxicity was confirmed by another laboratory (Smith, 1939). Further studies with commercial protein feeds showed that linseed meal gave good protection against the symptoms of selenium poisoning in both rats and dogs (Moxon and Rhian, 1943). Attempts have been made to fractionate flaxseed to isolate the protein or other material which is effective against selenium (Halverson et al., 1951).

In 1938, it was found that arsenic, at a level of 5.0 p.p.m. in the drinking water, would prevent the toxic action of selenium (10 p.p.m. in feed) in the rat (Moxon, 1938). Further work showed that arsenite and arsenate were equally effective while the sulfides of arsenic (AsS_2 and AsS_3) were not effective. Sodium arsenite was equally effective against selenium in three forms—selenite, seleniferous wheat, and the selenium analog of cystine (Du Bois et al., 1940).

It had been suggested that arsenic counteracts the toxicity of selenium by combining with the selenium in the gastrointestinal tract, thus decreasing the absorption of selenium (Anonymous, 1940). A study of the metabolism of selenium indicated, however, that arsenic did not interfere with selenium absorption because the amounts deposited in tissues were similar when selenium was fed with and without arsenic (Petersen et al., 1950).

Arsenic is effective in counteracting selenium toxicity regardless of the route of administration (orally or subcutaneously) of either element (Moxon et al., 1945). In rats, arsenic prevented the symptoms of selenium toxicity when the selenium had been fed for 20 days before the initiation of the arsenic treatment. When the initiation of arsenic treatment was delayed for 30 days, however, it did not prevent the toxic action of selenium, possibly because the selenium had already caused extensive liver damage (Du Bois et al., 1940). The work of Klug et al. (1950) which showed that selenium lowered rat liver succinic dehydrogenase levels also revealed that the inclusion of arsenic along with selenium in the diet would maintain the enzyme at normal values.

Arsenic as sodium arsenite is effective against selenium toxicity in the pig (Moxon, 1941) and in the dog (Rhian and Moxon, 1943), and to some extent in cattle (Moxon et al., 1944). Organic arsenicals (arsenilic acid and 3-nitro-4-hydroxyphenylarsonic acid) have proven to be as effective as sodium arsenite for the prevention of selenium toxicity in the pig (Wahlstrom *et al.*, 1955) when fed at the same level as used for growth stimulation in swine (Carpenter, 1951). The organic arsenicals are also effective against selenium toxicity in the rat (Hendrick *et al.*, 1953).

X. SELENIUM AND PUBLIC HEALTH

A survey of families living in seleniferous areas has been conducted (Smith *et al.*, 1936). The survey gave proof that selenium was being ingested by the finding of selenium in the urine in the range of 10 to 200 micrograms per 100 ml. Urine samples from people living outside the seleniferous area normally contains no selenium. Vegetables grown in seleniferous soils take up only low concentrations of selenium. Milk is also low in selenium. Meat is a more likely source of selenium in the human diet than either milk or vegetables, although meat from healthy animals would probably be safe. Selenized animals would have fairly high concentrations of selenium in their tissues but would not be slaughtered for food under normal conditions.

A human case of selenium poisoning in which the patient appeared to be sensitized to selenium and suffered from skin lesions has been reported (Lemley, 1940). Human cases of selenium poisoning, however, are more likely to occur from the use of selenium in industry than from the consumption of foods in the areas of seleniferous soils in the United States. Some of the hazards involved in the use of selenium in certain industries have been described (Dudley, 1938).

XI. SELENIUM AS AN ESSENTIAL ELEMENT IN ANIMAL NUTRITION

Research by Beath and associates (Beath *et al.*, 1934) and by Trelease and Trelease (1938) has shown that selenium stimulates the growth of *Astragalus racemosus* and other indicator plants. Since these plants will grow only on soils which contain selenium, it has been referred to as an essential element for certain plant species. Some degree of growth stimulation has been reported for the addition of selenium to the soils or culture solutions in which nonindicator plants were grown, especially wheat plants (Levine, 1925; Hurd-Karrar, 1937; Beath *et al.*, 1937b; Perkins and King, 1938; and Stanford and Olson, 1939). The stimulation of growth in these plants has been very small when compared with the growth response in indicator species of *Astragalus*.

Selenium in the form of naturally seleniferous wheat, when fed to chicks at a level of 2.0 p.p.m., gave a slight growth response in studies reported in 1941 (Poley *et al.*, 1941). During the past few months, Schwarz *et al.* (1957), Patterson *et al.* (1957), and Stokstad (1957) have reported that selenium, in very low concentrations, is effective in the prevention of liver necrosis in rats and exudative diathesis in chicks when the rats and chicks were maintained on a certain special diet which contained torula yeast. In the case of chicks, selenium at a level of 0.1 p.p.m. gave a growth response and prevented the development of the exudative diathesis. Vitamin E as α-tocopheryl succinate gave the same response as selenium but 20.0 p.p.m. of the α-tocopheryl succinate was required to give a response equal to 0.1 p.p.m. of selenium. These results indicate that selenium and vitamin E are interchangeable for the prevention of exudative diathesis in the chick, but there is no evidence that selenium will replace vitamin E in other functions, such as the prevention of encephalomalacia. The requirement for selenium in the rat and the chick is so low, even on special purified type diets, it is quite probable that most feedstuffs normally used will contain sufficient amounts of selenium to meet the requirements for the rat and the chick.

REFERENCES

Anderson, H. D., and Moxon, A. L. 1942. *J. Pharmacol. Exptl. Therap.* **76**, 343–354.
Anonymous. 1940. *J. Am. Med. Assoc.* **114**, 1083.
Beath, O. A., Draize, J. H., Eppson, H. F., Gilbert, C. S., and McCreary, O. C. 1934. *J. Am. Pharm. Assoc., Sci. Ed.* **23**, 94–97.
Beath, O. A., Eppson, H. F., and Gilbert, C. S. 1935. *Wyoming Agr. Expt. Sta. Bull.* **206**, 55 pp.
Beath, O. A., and Eppson, H. F. 1947. *Wyoming Agr. Exp. Sta. Bull.* **278**, 1–15.
Beath, O. A., Gilbert, C. S., and Eppson, H. F. 1937a. *Am. J. Botany* **24**, 96 pp.
Beath, O. A., Eppson, H. F., and Gilbert, C. S. 1937b. *J. Am. Pharm. Assoc., Sci. Ed.* **26**, 394–405.
Bieri, J. G., Pollard, C. J., and Cardenas, R. R., Jr. 1957. *Proc. Soc. Exptl. Biol. Med.* **94**, 318–320.
Byers, H. G. 1935. *U.S. Dept. Agr. Tech. Bull.* **482**, 47 pp.
Byers, H. G. 1936. *U.S. Dept. Agr. Tech. Bull.* **530**, 78 pp.
Byers, H. G. 1937. *Ind. Eng. Chem.* **29**, 1200–1202.
Byers, H. G., Williams, K. T., and Lakin, H. W. 1936. *Ind. Eng. Chem.* **28**, 821.
Byers, H. G., Miller, J. T., Williams, K. T., and Lakin, H. W. 1938. *U.S. Dept. Atr. Tech. Bull.* **601**, 74 pp.
Carpenter, L. E. 1951. *Arch. Biochem. Biophys.* **32**, 181–186.
Cameron, C. A. 1880. *Proc. Roy. Soc. (Dublin)* **2**, 231–233.
Collett, M. E. 1924. *J. Biol. Chem.* **58**, 793–797.
Draize, J. H., and Beath, O. A. 1935. *J. Am. Vet. Med. Assoc.* **86**, 753–763.
DuBois, K. P., Moxon, A. L., and Olson, O. E. 1940. *J. Nutrition* **19**, 477–482.
Dudley, H. C. 1938. *Public Health Repts. (U.S.)* **53**, 281–292.
Franke, K. W. 1934a. *J. Nutrition* **8**, 597–608.

Franke, K. W. 1934b. *J. Nutrition* **8**, 609–613.

Franke, K. W., and Painter, E. P. 1937. *Ind. Eng. Chem.* **29**, 591–595.

Franke, K. W., and Potter, V. R. 1934. *J. Nutrition* **8**, 615–624.

Franke, K. W., and Potter, V. R. 1936a. *Science* **83**, 330–332.

Franke, K. W., and Potter, V. R. 1936b. *J. Nutrition* **12**, 205–214.

Franke, K. W., and Tully, W. C. 1935. *Poultry Sci.* **14**, 273–279.

Franke, K. W., Rice, T. D., Johnson, A. G., and Schoening, H. W. 1934. *U.S. Dept. Agr. Circ.* **320**, 9 pp.

Franke, K. W., Moxon, A. L., Poley, W. E., and Tully, W. C. 1936. *Anat. Record* **65**, 15–22.

Fredga, A. 1936. *Svensk Kem. Tidskr.* **48**, 160.

Fredga, A. 1937. *Svensk. Kem. Tidskr.* **49**, 124–130.

Halverson, A. W., Petersen, D. F., and Klug, H. L. 1951. *Proc. South Dakota Acad. Sci.* **30**, 127–132.

Hendrick, C., Klug, H. L., and Olson, O. E. 1953. *J. Nutrition* **51**, 131–137.

Hurd-Karrar, A. M. 1933. *Science* **78**, 560.

Hurd-Karrar, A. M. 1934. *J. Agr. Research* **49**, 343–357.

Hurd-Karrar, A. M. 1935. *J. Agr. Research* **50**, 413–427.

Hurd-Karrar, A. M. 1937. *Am. J. Botany* **24**, 720–728.

Hurd-Karrar, A. M., and Poos, F. W. 1936. *Science* **84**, 252.

Japha, A. 1842. Ph.D. Dissertation, Halle, Germany.

Johnson, R. R. 1952. M.S. Thesis, South Dakota State College.

Klug, H. L., Petersen, D. F., and Moxon, A. L. 1949. *Proc. South Dakota Acad. Sci.* **28**, 117–120.

Klug, H. L., Moxon, A. L., Petersen, D. F., and Potter, V. R. 1950. *Arch. Biochem.* **28**, 253–259.

Knight, S. H., and Beath, O. A. 1937. *Wyoming Agr. Expt. Sta. Bull.* **221**.

Labes, R., and Krebs, H. 1935. *Fermentforschung* **14**, 430–442.

Lakin, H. W., and Byers, H. G. 1941. *U.S. Dept. Agr. Tech. Bull.* **783**, 26 pp.

Lakin, H. W., and Byers, H. G. 1948. *U.S. Dept. Agr. Tech. Bull.* **950**, 36 pp.

Lakin, H. W., Williams, K. T., and Byers, H. G. 1938. *Ind. Eng. Chem.* **30**, 599–600.

Lardy, H. A., and Moxon, A. L. 1942. *Proc. South Dakota Acad. Sci.* **22**, 39–42.

Larsen, C., and Bailey, D. E. 1912. *South Dakota Agr. Expt. Sta. Bull.* **132**, 220–254.

Lemley, R. E. 1940. *J.-Lancet* **60**, 528–531.

Levine, V. E. 1925. *Am. J. Botany* **12**, 82–90.

Madison, T. C. 1860. *Congr.* (*U.S.*) *36th* (*1st*) *Session. Senate Ex. Doc.* **52**, 37–41.

Martin, A. L. 1936. *Am. J. Botany* **23**, 471–483.

Miller, W. T., and Williams, K. T. 1940a. *J. Agr. Research* **60**, 163–173.

Miller, W. T., and Williams, K. T. 1940b. *J. Agr. Research* **61**, 353–368.

Moxon, A. L. 1937. *South Dakota Agr. Expt. Sta. Bull.* **311**, 1–91.

Moxon, A. L. 1938. *Science* **88**, 81.

Moxon, A. L. 1940. *J. Am. Pharm. Assoc., Sci. Ed.* **29**, 249.

Moxon, A. L. 1941. *Proc. South Dakota Acad. Sci.* **21**, 34–36.

Moxon, A. L., and Rhian, M. 1943. *Physiol. Revs.* **23**, 305–337.

Moxon, A. L., Olson, O. E., Searight, W. V., and Sandals, K. M. 1938a. *Am. J. Botany* **25**, 794–809.

Moxon, A. L., Anderson, H. D., and Painter, E. P. 1938b. *J. Pharmacol. Exptl. Therap.* **63**, 357–368.

Moxon, A. L., Olson, O. E., and Searight, W. V. 1939. *South Dakota Agr. Expt. Sta. Tech. Bull.* **2** (Revised 1950).

Moxon, A. L., Olson, O. E., Whitehead, E. J., Hilmoe, R. J., and White, S. N. 1943. *Cereal Chem.* **20**, 376–380.

Moxon, A. L., Rhian, M., Anderson, H. D., and Olson, O. E. 1944. *J. Animal Sci.* **3**, 299–309.

Moxon, A. L., Paynter, C. R., and Halverson, A. W. 1945. *J. Pharmacol. Exptl. Therap.* **84**, 115–119.

Neiswander, C. R., and Morris, V. H. 1940. *J. Econ. Entomol.* **33**, 517–525.

Olson, O. E., and Jensen, C. W. 1940. *Proc. South Dakota Acad. Sci.* **20**, 115–121.

Olson, O. E., Jornlin, D. F., and Moxon, A. L. 1942a. *Agron. J.* **34**, 607–615.

Olson, O. E., Jornlin, D. F., and Moxon, A. L. 1942b. *Soil Sci.* **53**, 365–368.

Olson, O. E., Whitehead, E. I., and Moxon, A. L. 1942c. *Soil Sci.* **54**. 47–53.

O'Moore, L. B. 1952. *Irish Vet. J.* **6**, 392–404.

Painter, E. P., and Franke, K. W. 1935. *J. Biol. Chem.* **111**, 643–651.

Painter, E. P., and Franke, K. W. 1936. *Cereal Chem.* **13**, 172–179.

Patterson, E. L., Milstrey, R., and Stokstad, E. L. R. 1957. **95**, 617–620.

Perkins, A. T., and King, H. H. 1938. *Jour. Am. Soc. Agron.* **30**, 664–667.

Petersen, D. F., Klug, H. L., Harschfield, R. D., and Moxon, A. L. 1950. *Proc. South Dakota Acad. Sci.* **29**, 123–127.

Phillis, E., and Mason, T. G. 1938a. *Empire Cotton Growing Rev.* **15**, 290–294.

Phillis, E., and Mason, T. G. 1938b. *Empire Cotton Growing Corp., 3rd Conf. Cotton Growing Problems, Rept. and Summary of Proc., 1938*, pp. 84–87.

Poley, W. E., and Moxon, A. L. 1938. *Poultry Sci.* **17**, 72–76.

Poley, W. E., Wilson, W. O., Moxon, A. L., and Taylor, J. B. 1941. *Poultry Sci.* **20**, 171–179.

Potter, V. R., and Elvehjem, C. A. 1937. *J. Biol. Chem.* **117**, 341–349.

Ravikovitch, S., and Margolin, M. 1957. *Ktavim* **7**, 41–52.

Rhian, M., and Moxon, A. L. 1943. *J. Pharmacol.* **78**, 249–264.

Robinson, W. O. 1933. *J. Assoc. Offic. Agr. Chemists* **16**, 423–424.

Robinson, W. O. 1936. *Ind. Eng. Chem.* **28**, 736–738.

Rosenfeld, I., and Beath, O. A. 1946. *Am. J. Vet. Research* **7**, 57–61.

Schneider, H. A. 1936. *Science* **83**, 32–34.

Schwarz, K., and Foltz, C. M. 1957. *J. Am. Chem. Soc.* **79**, 3292–3293.

Schwarz, K., Bieri, J. G., Briggs, G. M., and Scott, M. L. 1957. *Proc. Soc. Exptl. Biol. Med.* **95**, 621–625.

Searight, W. V., and Moxon, A. L. *S. Dakota State Coll., Agr. Expt. Sta. Tech. Bull.* **5**, 33 pp.

Searight, W. V., Moxon, A. L., Whitehead, E. I., and Viets, F. G., Jr. 1947. *Proc. South Dakota Acad. Sci.* **26**, 87–98.

Smith, A. 1949. M.S. Thesis, South Dakota State College.

Smith, A., and Moxon, A. L. 1949. *Proc. South Dakota Acad. Sci.* **28**, 46–49.

Smith, M. I. 1939. *Public Health Repts.* (*U.S.*) **54**, 1441–1453.

Smith, M. I., Franke, K. W., and Westfall, B. B. 1936. *Public Health Repts.* (*U.S.*) **51**, 1496–1505.

Stanford, G. W., and Olson, O. E. 1939. *Proc. South Dakota Acad. Sci.* **19**, 25–31.

Stokstad, E. L. R. 1957. *Feedstuffs* **29** (35), 30–31.

Stotz, E., and Hastings, A. B. 1937. *J. Biol. Chem.* **118**, 479–498.

Strock, L. W. 1935. *Am. J. Pharm.* **107**, 144–157.

Svirbely, J. L. 1938. *Biochem. J.* **32**, 467–473.

Taboury, M. 1932. *Compt. rend.* **195**, 171.

Thorvaldson, T., and Johnson, L. R. 1940. *Can. J. Research* **18B,** 138–150.

Trelease, S. F., and Beath, O. A. 1949. "Selenium Its Geological Occurrence and Its Biological Effects in Relation to Botany, Chemistry, Agriculture, Nutrition and Medicine." Authors, New York.

Trelease, S. F., and Trelease, H. M. 1938. *Am. J. Botany* **25,** 372–380.

Underwood, E. J. 1956. "Trace Elements in Human and Animal Nutrition." Academic Press, New York.

Wahlstrom, R. C., Kamstra, L. D., and Olson, O. E. 1955. *J. Animal Sci.* **14,** 105–110.

Walsh, T., Fleming, G. A., O'Connor, R., and Sweeney, A. 1951. *Nature* **168,** 881.

Westfall, B. B., and Smith, M. I. 1939. *Cereal Chem.* **28,** 912–914.

Williams, K. T., and Byers, H. G. 1936. *Ind. Eng. Chem.* **28,** 912–914.

Williams, K. T., Lakin, H. W., and Byers, H. G. 1940. *U.S. Dept. Agr. Tech. Bull.* **702,** 59 pp.

Williams, K. T., Lakin, H. W., and Byers, H. G. 1941. *U.S. Dept. Agr. Tech. Bull.* **758,** 69 pp.

Wright, C. I. 1938. *U.S. Public Health Bull.* **53,** 1825–1836.

CHAPTER 13

Metabolic Function and Practical Use of Cobalt in Nutrition

GEORGE K. DAVIS

Florida Agricultural Experiment Station
Gainesville, Florida

		Page
I.	Introduction	193
II.	Cobalt Deficiency in Sheep	194
	A. Cobalt Deficiency Anemia, Loss of Appetite, and Parasitism	194
III.	Cobalt Deficiency in Cattle	196
	A. Deficiency Observations in Florida	197
IV.	Cobalt Therapy	198
	A. Methods of Supplying Cobalt	198
	B. Limitations of Various Methods	199
V.	Cobalt Requirements	200
	A. Pasture and Supplement Sources	200
VI.	Cobalt Metabolism	201
	A. Vitamin B_{12} Requirements of Ruminants	201
	B. Cobalt in Monogastric Species	202
	C. Cobalt and Microorganism Function	203
	D. Vitamin B_{12} Absorbtion by Ruminants	203
VII.	Phalaris Staggers	204
VIII.	Cobalt Supplementation of Swine	204
IX.	Mechanism of Cobalt Function	205
	A. Cobalt Polycythemia	206
	B. Cobalt Toxicity	206
	C. Cobalt in Animal Tissues and Radioactive Isotope Studies	207
X.	Summary	208
	References	209

I. INTRODUCTION

To the layman and scientist alike, the trace elements present a certain mystery and fascination that is nowhere better illustrated than with cobalt. Required by ruminants in amounts so small as to have baffled the analyst, a deficiency is so devastating as to have prevented the development of a healthy livestock industry over vast areas. Included in the diet in quantities

193

so miniscule as to stretch the imagination, the response in animal health in another day would have been given the aura of magic. The present time sees cobalt as a part of vitamin B_{12}, and in microgram quantities, curing an age-old disease of man, pernicious anemia. Truly there is a wonderful fascination to the study of this trace element, cobalt.

The presence of cobalt in animal tissues was shown in a series of papers published by Bertrand and Macheboeuf (1925, 1926), but it was known that cobalt occurred in plant tissue, by the middle of the 19th century. It was the demonstration that cobalt was the element in limonites which prevented the development of a wasting disease in Australia in 1934, however, that began the long series of experiments and reports on the role of small amounts of cobalt in ruminant nutrition (Lines, 1935; Marston, 1935; Underwood and Filmer, 1935).

The condition now attributed to cobalt deficiency has been recognized for centuries and has gone by common names such as "pining," "daising," "vinquish," "salt sick," "bush sickness," "coastal disease," "enzootic marasmus," "neck ail," and "nakuritus." Since the publication of the original work in Australia, cobalt deficiency has been identified in many parts of the world. In the United States, cobalt deficiency was first identified in Florida in cattle (Neal and Ahmann, 1937), but has since been shown to exist in South Carolina, Georgia, North Carolina, New York, New Hampshire, Wisconsin, Vermont, and many other states. It is probable that cobalt deficiency, of more or less acute nature, may be found over much of the United States. A similar situation could be reported from many other countries of the world including Canada, middle Europe, northern Europe, and many parts of Asia.

The early history of cobalt and its discovery as a vital element in nutrition has been admirably traced by E. J. Underwood in his book, "Trace Elements in Human and Animal Nutrition" and need not be reviewed here (Underwood, 1956).

II. Cobalt Deficiency in Sheep

In discussing the metabolic function and practical use of cobalt in nutrition, perhaps the best approach will be to describe, first, the acute cobalt deficiency syndrome as it has occurred in many parts of the world. The syndrome of cobalt deficiency in sheep is essentially that of starvation. There is a gradual wasting of the animals. With this, there develops the usual straggly, rough wool and a severe anemia with almost complete appetite failure. As the condition becomes more advanced, the animal is dull, listless, and because of the anemia all the exposed skin surfaces around the eyes and mouth take on a blanched or pale anemic look. The oxygen carrying capacity of the blood is markedly reduced, and the blood volume may be severely reduced (McNaught, 1937; Marston *et al.*, 1938). Early in the deficiency, the blood picture is one indicative of an aplastic condition of the bone marrow.

A. *Cobalt Deficiency Anemia, Loss of Appetite, and Parasitism*

The actual description of the anemia which develops in the latter stages has differed in reports from different parts of the world. Workers in Australia have reported a normocytic and hypochromic anemia in lambs, whereas in New York, a normocytic and normochromic anemia was observed. Other reports from Australia for sheep indicate a macrocytic anemia with marked poikilocytosis and polychromasia. If no remedy is supplied, the animal will succumb in a state of starvation. Autopsy is peculiarly unrevealing in that, except for an edema associated with starvation, the fatty liver, and a hemosiderosed spleen, there are no gross changes peculiar to the condition. In sheep at least, there appear to be no nervous reactions such as might be expected in some other trace element deficiencies (Filmer, 1933; Smith *et al.*, 1950; Marston, 1952).

Perhaps it should be pointed out that there is good reason to believe that there is little relationship between the development of the anemia and the acute symptoms of cobalt deficiency. In less acute conditions, the range of reaction may be from a slight loss in weight with reduced growth rate or a slight listlessness all the way to a sudden death with no apparent reason. On borderline deficient pastures, ewes may carry their lambs to term, but these lambs are dropped in a weakened condition and may live only a few days, depending on the degree of deficiency. In numerous reports, it has been noted that more than half of the lambs dropped from cobalt-deficient ewes are very weak, and the mortality may exceed 90 per cent. The high mortality of lambs is also accompanied by poor wool quality. The quantity may be very little different from that obtained from ewes with normal cobalt nutrition (Bowstead *et al.*, 1942).

A confusing factor has been the very frequent, not to say usual, observation of a very heavy internal parasite infection upon postmortem examination of animals suffering from cobalt deficiency (Pope *et al.*, 1947). By the same token, the administration of anthelmintics has been completely ineffective in those cases where cobalt deficiency had subsequently been shown to exist. Repeatedly, investigators in many parts of the world have reported that the most pronounced feature of the cobalt deficiency syndrome has been the lack of appetite, and some have even traced the differences in weight gain observed in various levels of cobalt deficiency to this differing appetite for feed. The workers in New Hampshire and in New York showed that compared with cobalt deficient sheep with marked cobalt deficiency symptoms, animals receiving a cobalt supplement gained approximately 7 times as much in weight with 5 times as much concentrate, 6 times as much hay, and drank twice as much water as the deficient animals (Keener *et al.*, 1950). In the New Hampshire and New York work, there was a marked reduction in wool production in those sheep which were deficient in cobalt, in this respect, differing from earlier work reported from Canada.

III. COBALT DEFICIENCY IN CATTLE

The original work with cobalt and sheep was paralleled almost immediately by studies with cobalt in cattle with a description of the cobalt deficiency syndrome in this species. While not as spectacular as the effects in sheep, the syndrome is none the less similar and in general may be said to resemble inanition. The first symptom of cobalt deficiency is the failure of appetite, and following this the loss in condition and development of anemia. Young cattle are particularly susceptible to cobalt deficiency, and may become unthrifty and anemic after comparatively short exposure to cobalt-deficient areas. One of the signs of cobalt deficiency is the dropping of weak and puny calves that may survive a very short time after birth. The actual degree of cobalt deficiency determines the severity with which the deficiency state appears in grazing cattle, and for this reason cobalt deficiency has often been overlooked (McIntosh, 1945; Baltzer *et al.*, 1941; Huffman, 1947; Becker *et al.*, 1953). In a subacute stage, the appetite is decreased, condition is lost, milk production is lowered, and calves in general show thinness and poor development. The same type of symptoms seen on pasture will develop under stall-fed conditions where the ration is largely one of cobalt-deficient hay.

General symptoms of the deficiency are an expression of a defect in metabolism which precedes, and is not the result of, the anemia which develops. The symptoms may be very marked before anemia appears, and on treatment the symptoms may disappear long before the blood condition improves (Baltzer *et al.*, 1941).

Often the first suspicion of a cobalt deficiency in cattle has been the response of animals fed a cobalt supplement. As the severity of the cobalt deficiency has increased, it has generally been marked by increasing unthriftiness, a lack of appetite, and a depraved appetite. Frequently in dairy cattle, the development of a ketosis of the so-called "digestive" type has been much more severe and has responded to cobalt treatment (Henderson, 1947). This has led at least one investigator to propose that the cobalt probably plays a role, perhaps through the synthesis of vitamin B_{12}, in the normal functioning of the adrenal gland with the consequent production of cortisone (White, 1955). Until more information has been obtained under controlled conditions, ketosis probably should be included only as a possible symptom of cobalt deficiency.

A. Deficiency Observations in Florida

The problem of cobalt deficiency, or "salt sick," in Florida is apparently as old as the grazing of cattle in this state, since early travelers reported that cattle which the Indians had acquired from the Spanish were showing difficulties, which in light of our present knowledge would appear to have been those of a cobalt deficiency. The second Experiment Station bulletin published in 1888 was directed toward this problem (Maxwell, 1888). The widespread existence of cobalt deficiency has been recognized in much of Florida and in adjoining portions of the coastal plain in Georgia and South Carolina.

The symptoms reported by workers in Florida are essentially the same as those reported by workers in other parts of the world. These include a lack of appetite, a roughening of the hair coat, development of anemia, poor reproduction, wasting away as in starvation, an abnormal appetite, and eventual death if supplements of cobalt are not made available. Young stock are particularly affected and develop cobalt deficiency much more rapidly than older stock. Losses from cobalt deficiency may be close to 100 per cent in areas where cobalt is not supplied and where cattle must depend almost entirely on roughage from pasture. The lack of any specific clear-cut symptoms of a nutritional deficiency condition and the wide range of severity have made identification of cobalt deficiency conditions a difficult one, and in fact, the condition is often overlooked. The results of cobalt feeding when a severe cobalt deficiency exists can be little short of spectacular (Becker et al., 1953).

Cattle in Florida suffering from severe cobalt deficiency have been observed that were so weak that a man had no difficulty whatsoever in restraining a mature cow simply by taking hold of her horns. These animals usually do not suffer from stiffness as might be expected in phosphorus deficiency or as has been observed in copper deficiency. Since many of them come from the open range, they are often quite wild, however, under conditions of cobalt deficiency, they might well be described as, "the spirit is willing but the flesh is weak." When feed has been placed before them, they have had no interest in it, and after mouthing a few bites have left the remainder.

When cobalt therapy has been instituted, the response from this treatment has been very rapid. Daily administration of 1 milligram of cobalt as cobalt chloride in water solution, given orally as a drench, may take no longer than 48 to 72 hours to show an almost complete restoration of appetite. With recovery of appetite and continued administration of cobalt, recovery of condition becomes a matter of time and capacity to consume feed. The recovery in condition and gain in weight is not paralleled by an increase in hemoglobin and the remission of the anemia, but the latter condition appears to follow the former. In Florida experiments, hemoglobin levels as low as 5 g. per 100 ml. of blood in animals administered supplemental cobalt may take as long as 6 months to be restored to values of 10 to 12 g. per 100 ml. of blood.

IV. Cobalt Therapy

The rather unique development of cobalt deficiency in ruminant animals has led to extensive investigations of the role of cobalt in nutrition. It was early discovered that cobalt did not reach maximum effectiveness unless it was administered orally to the ruminant animal. Further, it was evident that repeated administration or consumption of cobalt was necessary if the full benefit of cobalt supplements was to be realized (Marston, 1952; Lee, 1950; Filmer, 1941).

Investigations with radioactive isotopes quickly established that the animal body has a very limited capacity for cobalt storage and further established that intravenously injected cobalt is rapidly eliminated from the body and only very small amounts of injected material reach the rumen of the animal (Comar and Davis, 1947).

From a practical standpoint, the necessity of administering cobalt at comparatively short intervals has posed many problems. A number of investigators have shown that drenching with cobalt in adequate quantities less frequently than once a week is ineffective in the control of a cobalt deficiency condition. In acute situations, drenching on a 3-day or biweekly interval has been necessary to obtain rapid recovery from the deficiency condition (Becker et al., 1953; Marston, 1952).

A. Methods of Supplying Cobalt

The difficulty of treating animals at frequent intervals has led to the adoption of many practices designed to insure regular and adequate intakes of cobalt. Where pastures supply the entire feed supply of sheep and cattle, some method of fertilization with cobalt is frequently used. While application of as little as 5 ounces of cobalt sulfate per acre has been sufficient to raise the level of cobalt in forage to satisfactory levels, the more common practice has been to apply 1 or as much as 2 pounds of a cobalt salt, such as cobalt carbonate or cobalt sulfate or an equivalent amount of cobalt-containing ore. This has been true, particularly where soil conditions and rainfall are such as to retain the cobalt application (Askew, 1946; Askew and Dixon, 1937; Andrews, 1953; Rossiter *et al.*, 1948). Under conditions such as those that exist in Florida with acid sands and large areas of range with native pastures supporting a low population of cattle (Becker *et al.*, 1946), fertilization has not been economically practical. This has led to the development of mineral mixtures which contain cobalt and are kept available to the cattle constantly (Becker *et al.*, 1953). Where animals are given supplementary feed, either in the form of pellets distributed on the range or in the form of salt-controlled protein supplements, the introduction of cobalt has been a very satisfactory means of insuring adequate cobalt intakes on a regular basis.

B. *Limitations of Various Methods*

It may not be out of place to point out that all of these methods have some drawbacks. It may be pointed out that under Florida conditions, the application of as much as 2 pounds of cobalt sulfate per acre of improved pasture cannot be relied upon to meet the cobalt needs of cattle grazing this area for longer than three years. This amount of cobalt applied as fertilizer will meet the needs of perhaps 10 animals over the period of 3 years. The same amount of cobalt will take care of the needs of several hundreds of animals when given as part of a mineral mixture or of supplemental feeds. Economics has tended to favor use of the mineral supplements.

The use of mineral supplements also has drawbacks. Though most animals will consume a mineral supplement regularly, some animals, for one reason or another, fail to make use of the mineral box, and these may develop more or less acute cobalt deficiency conditions. That this condition is not more severe than it is may well be due to the fact that the animals consuming cobalt in the mineral mixture retain so little of it and serve as fertilizing agents for the pastures. An example of a more severe condition which may develop with this type of practice occurred not far from the city of Gainesville, Florida.

On one of the large ranches with substantial holdings of cattle, it had been the practice for years to market calves at approximately 7 months of age. For various reasons, large numbers of these young animals were kept for a longer period of time and grazed in a separate pasture area during 1954–55. The mineral mixture, containing adequate amounts of cobalt, was supplied to the mature cattle and calves when they ranged together, and mineral supplements were made available to the calves after they had been weaned and placed in a pasture by themselves. The calves failed to use the mineral supplement and within several months after weaning, large numbers of the calves began to show signs of starvation, and there were heavy losses.

Since autopsy revealed numerous internal parasites, use of anthelmintics was instituted. When there was no response after 2 months of treatment, the possibility of a deficiency was suspected. Two hundred of the affected animals were isolated and given cobalt drenches twice weekly with a rapid response indicating the nature of the problem. In this instance, the cattleman found it was advantageous to mix cobalt sulfate with molasses and to make the cobalt available to the cattle in this form. In subsequent years, he has been able to avoid losses by providing some form of feed supplement containing cobalt until the animals learned to consume the mineral supplement regularly.

V. Cobalt Requirements

The cobalt requirement of sheep and of cattle is quite low, and it has been the general observation in Florida that pastures which contain 0.07 p.p.m. and above on the dry basis are healthy pastures, and cobalt deficiency does not appear in animals grazing them. On the other hand, pastures which contain less than 0.05 p.p.m. on the dry matter basis have consistently shown the development of a cobalt deficiency in cattle unless supplements are provided. In the range between 0.05 and 0.07 p.p.m., there has been occasional development of cobalt deficiency, and this has led the workers in Florida to the conclusion that this is the borderline level so far as cattle requirements are concerned (Becker *et al.*, 1953).

A. Pasture and Supplement Sources

Analytical values for pastures have shown ranges from 0.01 p.p.m. to as high as 1 p.p.m. on the dry matter basis. In the case of sheep, workers in Scotland, Australia, and New Zealand have indicated that a total ingestion of between 0.07 and 0.08 mg. of cobalt per day will meet the requirements of sheep, or put in another way, 0.08 p.p.m. in the dry matter will suffice to meet the needs for sheep (Askew, 1939; McNaught, 1938; Stewart, 1949; Underwood and Harvey, 1938; Beeson *et al.*, 1947). From a practical standpoint, work with cattle in Florida has demonstrated that 1 mg. of cobalt sulfate a day for an adult cow quite adequately meets requirements for cobalt.

It was early observed that to be effective, cobalt had to be supplied to ruminant animals regularly and at short intervals in as much as storage did not occur as with copper, for example. It was soon known that cobalt, to be fully effective, had to be administered orally rather than by injection. While it was true that large amounts of cobalt injected intravenously or intramuscularly would give some response, this was very slow in comparison with the response secured by oral administration of cobalt (Becker *et al.*, 1949; Marston and Lee, 1949; Phillipson and Mitchell, 1952; Ray *et al.*, 1948). This led to the very logical assumption that cobalt was functioning within the digestive tract and probably within the rumen. Radioactive isotope studies showed that comparatively small amounts of cobalt are absorbed from the digestive tract and also indicated that injected cobalt was rapidly eliminated through the urine and that very probably any effect which was secured from the injection of large amounts of cobalt was due to the excretion in the saliva which then permitted the cobalt to reach the rumen (Comar *et al.*, 1946a,b).

VI. Cobalt Metabolism

It was at this stage in studies of cobalt metabolism that several developments made it apparent that cobalt functioned in the rumen in the synthesis of a factor needed by the ruminant. Presumably this was a compound in which cobalt was a necessary part or for which cobalt was required in its formation. Work with liver, liver extracts, and liver ash demonstrated that liver and liver extracts were beneficial in the treatment of the deficiency disease. Liver ash in equivalent amounts was ineffective in the treatment of the deficiency condition (Filmer, 1933; Filmer and Underwood, 1937; Becker and Smith, 1951a,b). Liver preparations administered orally were not nearly so effective as those which were injected, and the early experiments with injection of vitamin B_{12} suggested the possibility that some other factor was being formed that was curative for the deficiency condition. Subsequent work indicated that the effect of the antipernicious anemia factor of liver and vitamin B_{12} were highly correlated in the treatment of sheep, and this led to the discovery that vitamin B_{12} was indeed effective when injected into sheep suffering from cobalt deficiency when administered at levels considerably higher than those which had been postulated and used earlier on the basis of the antipernicious anemia response in man to the vitamin B_{12} (Becker and Smith, 1951a,b).

A. Vitamin B_{12} Requirement of Ruminants

It has become apparent with continued studies with vitamin B_{12} that lambs, at least, appear to have a requirement that is very close to 100 micrograms per week and that with levels of this order there is an immediate and rapid recovery from the symptoms of cobalt deficiency (Koch and Smith, 1951; Smith *et al.*, 1951; Andrews and Anderson, 1954;

Marston and Lee, 1952; Marston and Smith, 1952). Response to injected vitamin B_{12} at these levels, perhaps even somewhat more rapid than recovery from oral administration of cobalt, suggest that there is perhaps a brief lag between the administration of cobalt and the formation of vitamin B_{12} and its availability in the rumen (Anderson and Andrews, 1952). It has been demonstrated that the continuous administration of vitamin B_{12} appears to be necessary for satisfactory response in sheep. Injection of massive doses of vitamin B_{12}, while giving temporary response, does not appear to be as satisfactory as feeding cobalt or as giving smaller doses of vitamin B_{12} over a continuous period with individual doses not more than a week apart (Walker and Hunter, 1952).

At the present time, it seems quite obvious that the principal, if not the sole mechanism, by which cobalt acts in the ruminant is through the formation of vitamin B_{12} and the absorption of this vitamin by the ruminant animal (Hoekstra et al., 1952a,b). The evidence thus far available certainly would indicate that a cobalt deficiency in ruminants is in reality a vitamin B_{12} deficiency in these animals and that the function of cobalt is to provide the necessary medium in the rumen for the microorganisms of that organ to produce vitamin B_{12} which is then available in sufficient quantities to meet the needs of the ruminant animal.

B. Cobalt in Monogastric Species

Cobalt has been administered therapeutically to monogastric species, and at least some reports have claimed that a cobalt deficiency has been demonstrated. Further evidence for the fact that cobalt functions in the animal as a part of vitamin B_{12} can be obtained from the observations that high levels of cobalt per se in the tissues of a ruminant animal do not protect it from the development of cobalt deficiency. Injection of cobalt, even in amounts considerably in excess of those required when given orally, do not cause a remission of the deficiency symptoms. Vitamin B_{12}, when injected or given orally (Kercher and Smith, 1955), will cause a remission of the cobalt deficiency symptoms. Orally administered cobalt with the resultant rapid increase in vitamin B_{12} in the rumen ingesta likewise will cause a rapid remisson of the defecency symptoms (Hoekstra et al., 1952a). The evidence for the relationship between vitamin B_{12} formation and cobalt ingestion within the rumen is quite conclusive. With a low cobalt intake below the normal requirement, a reduced vitamin B_{12} synthesis is readily observed. The rapid recovery and return to vitamin B_{12} formation is likewise readily demonstrated with the inclusion of adequate amounts of cobalt in the diet. This change appears to be separate from any change which might develop because of the quantity of feed available to the animal. Further evidence for the effectiveness of cobalt is apparent in the urinary excretion and the tissue accumulation of vitamin B_{12} with and without adequate cobalt in the diet (Davis *et al.*, 1956).

While increases in the cobalt level of the tissues, particularly the liver, occur with oral cobalt supplementation, it is a rapid rise in vitamin B_{12} that occurs rather than a rise of elemental cobalt, which is not part of the vitamin B_{12} molecule.

C. Cobalt and Microorganism Function

The possibility that cobalt may function as a stimulant to microorganism function in the rumen other than as a precursor for vitamin B_{12} cannot be ignored, but as yet the evidence that cobalt functions directly or as a part of still other compounds in such a way as to favor organisms concerned with cellulose digestion still lacks satisfactory proof to be considered as established (Salsbury *et al.*, 1956). Other compounds containing cobalt, which have vitamin B_{12} activity for some microorganisms are formed in the rumen, and perhaps to some extent are absorbed by the animal from the intestinal tract. Some of these compounds may be necessary for proper microorganism function, but they apparently do not have vitamin B_{12} activity in so far as the animal tissue is concerned (Pfiffner *et al.*, 1952).

Assuming that the principal, if not the only, function of cobalt in the ruminant is as vitamin B_{12}, the very much higher requirement of ruminants for vitamin B_{12} as compared to monogastric species remains unexplained. It may be assumed that proper rumen function determines to a large extent the appetite of the ruminant, and certainly there is a very close relationship between vitamin B_{12} and the appetite of these species. However, the exact mechanism of this relationship remains in question for want of further experimental evidence. Admittedly, the digestive process in ruminants is quite different from that of monogastric species, and it may be that it is this difference in intermediary metabolism that accounts for the requirement of vitamin B_{12}.

D. Vitamin B_{12} Absorbtion by Ruminants

Assay techniques show very considerable differences in the amounts of vitamin B_{12} that are formed in the rumen, and therefore, available to the animal, but it is quite apparent that the quantities which are formed are very large in comparison to the quantities which are required by the animal for adequate health and nutrition and extremely high in comparison to the amounts required by the monogastric species (Hale *et al.*, 1950; Porter, 1953).

Chick assay values for the total amount of vitamin B_{12} in rumen contents are probably the most conservative (Hale *et al.*, 1950). At a given time, amounts of vitamin B_{12} ranging from 800 to 1000 micrograms for sheep and from 8000 to 10,000 micrograms for cattle may be present. Since microbiological assays of vitamin B_{12} often greatly exceed these levels, it becomes quite apparent that the actual amount of vitamin B_{12} available to the animal is extremely large in terms of the actual requirement for this vitamin. The actual amount which is absorbed and utilized by the animal is by comparison very low, and on the basis of studies with radioactive vitamin B_{12} it appears that as low as 5 per cent of the vitamin B_{12} is actually absorbed from the intestinal tract by the animal (Pearson *et al.*, 1953; Davis *et al.*, 1956).

VII. Phalaris Staggers

Underwood (1956) has reviewed a condition that appears to be peculiar to Australia which is known by the name of "phalaris staggers." This occurs in animals grazed on *Phalaris tuberosa* and occurs in both cattle and sheep. It is clinically characterized by muscular tremors and incoordination and by rapid breathing and pounding of the heart (McDonald, 1942, 1946). Evidence has accumulated to show that either top dressing with cobalt or the supplemental feeding of cobalt will prevent the occurrence of this condition. A satisfactory explanation for the development of this condition and the relationship to cobalt or vitamin B_{12} still remains to be developed (Marston, 1952). It has been postulated that the cobalt either prevents the development of a neurotoxic agent or that the vitamin B_{12} serves as a detoxifying agent for the material once absorbed into the system (Lee and Kuchel, 1953). Since the latter possibility is suggestive of the relationship between vitamin B_{12} and the neurological disturbances observed in pernicious anemia in man, Underwood (1956), at least, seems to favor this possible explanation. So far as is known, the neurological changes have not been observed in other parts of the world where cobalt deficiency occurs.

VIII. Cobalt Supplementation of Swine

Thus far in the discussion of cobalt, special emphasis has been placed upon the role of cobalt in ruminant nutrition. It has been mentioned that a cobalt deficiency has not been demonstrated in other than ruminant species. This is not to say that cobalt has not been reported as giving response in monogastric animals. Special attention might well be given to the role of cobalt in swine nutrition. Workers at Iowa (Speer *et al.*,

1952) concluded that trace minerals including cobalt fed to sows during the period of gestation and to sows and litters during lactation may have a subsequent influence upon the growth response of the pigs from weaning to market. These results indicate the possibility of natural feed-stuffs being deficient in one or more of the trace elements, cobalt, iron, copper, manganese, or zinc.

A similar report came from Cornell where a highly significant increase in rate of gain in 4 trials was secured when the 4 trace elements, cobalt, iron, copper, and manganese were added to the basal ration (Noland et al., 1951). Feed efficiency was also improved. A response was not obtained when individual elements were added. These reports admittedly do not provide evidence for a specific role of cobalt in the nutrition of swine, but they do point to the possibility that mineral balance may play a role in maximum productive performance.

Most specific evidence of a role of cobalt in swine nutrition has come from North Dakota where the results reported show that addition of cobalt to swine rations stimulated weight gains more than the addition of 8 per cent of meat scraps and almost as much as the use of an animal protein factor supplement (Klosterman et al., 1950; Dinusson et al., 1951). The work from this same station has shown that the addition of small amounts of cobalt, an equivalent of 885 micrograms per pound of feed as cobalt chloride or as carbonate, increased the rate of gain of grow-ing, fattening pigs by from 0.1 to 0.2 pound per day. On the basis of these reports, it would seem that addition of cobalt to swine rations, especially in deficient areas, might result in increased swine production and feed efficiency. However, much more experimental evidence would be neces-sary before a deficiency might be said to exist.

IX. Mechanism of Cobalt Function

The mechanism of action of cobalt in ruminant nutrition might well be said to be the mechanism of formation of vitamin B_{12} and logically could lead to a discussion of the mechanism of action of vitamin B_{12} in animal nutrition. This is plainly beyond the scope of this paper. Vitamin B_{12}, and its modifications which possess vitamin B_{12} activity, properly belong in a discussion of vitamins. Vitamin B_{12} appears to be required by most animal species; it occurs in food products of animal origin but is apparently synthesized only by microorganisms; it is apparently identical with the extrinsic factor in the treatment of pernicious anemia; it certainly is concerned with protein metabolism and with the synthesis of methyl groups in the animal body and very probably in the utilization of single carbon fragments. For those who are interested in this particular phase of vitamin metabolism, reference should be made to the recent publication of "The Vitamins" which was edited by Sebrell and Harris (1954).

A. Cobalt Polycythemia

The role of cobalt in the prevention of a deficiency has been discussed at length, but the role of cobalt in animal metabolism was first pointed out because of the production of polycythemia when it was included in diets in amounts considerably in excess of what are now known to be requirements (Waltner and Waltner, 1929). Whether administered orally or by injection, cobalt in amounts which exceed by several hundred times the amount normally consumed in food will cause the development in rats, in pigs, in chickens, in man, and in a number of other species, a marked increase in number of blood cells, hemoglobin level, and in the packed red cell volume (Grant and Root, 1952; Keener et al., 1949). The manner in which cobalt produces polycythemia which, incidentally, develops only when the diet is adequate for red blood cell formation is still quite uncertain. The hemoglobin which is formed under the influence of excess cobalt appears to be no different from the hemoglobin of normal animals nor is there any indication that the increased cobalt increases the requirement for iron or copper (Berk et al., 1949). It is known that cobalt functions other than through the excessive formation of vitamin B_{12} (Levey and Orten, 1951), and it is also known that methionine or the sulfur-containing amino acids will reduce the toxicity of high levels of orally administered cobalt (Dunn et al., 1952; Griffith et al., 1942). Apparently, this effect of the amino acids is through the formation of coordination complexes which thus remove cobalt from the active sphere of its influence. The failure of cobalt to produce polycythemia in mature ruminants may perhaps raise some question with regards to the proposal that cobalt because of coordination complexes with amino acids suppresses cell respiration (Griffith et al., 1942). It is only fair to say that the mechanism of the production of cobalt polycythemia is in need of considerable research before satisfactory explanations can be proposed.

B. Cobalt Toxicity

Cobalt salts are not particularly toxic to animals, and there is a very wide margin, particularly in the ruminants, between the levels which may be administered to prevent deficiency conditions and those which will cause toxicity in cattle and sheep. If one assumes that 1 mg. per day of cobalt is a satisfactory therapeutic level for the treatment of cobalt deficiency, then it is equally fair to say that levels of 100 times this amount administered to either cattle or to sheep are quite well tolerated

(Becker and Smith, 1951a,b; Ely et al., 1948). Levels of 200 to 500 mg. of cobalt per 100-weight daily cause a severe depression of appetite and body weight losses with an anemia occurring at the higher levels (Becker and Smith, 1951a,b; Keener et al., 1949). Cobalt toxicity does not appear to be a likely hazard with the common therapeutic treatments.

Cobalt toxicity may occur under practical conditions as has been demonstrated in Florida. Due to a lack of understanding, preparation of mineral mixtures for commercial sale had included in them levels of cobalt at the rate of 2 pounds of cobalt carbonate per 100 pounds of mineral mixture, instead of the 1 ounce of cobalt carbonate usually recommended. The mixture was provided for dairy cattle and, within 2 weeks time, milk flow was depressed by more than 75 per cent, the animals became obviously off feed, and a dull, listless attitude was apparent. Removal of the mineral mixture containing the high level of cobalt resulted in rapid recovery in approximately 5 days.

C. Cobalt in Animal Tissues and Radioactive Isotope Studies

The distribution of cobalt in plant sources (Hurwitz and Beeson, 1944) has been mentioned in connection with the supplying of adequate cobalt to ruminants, and it may be mentioned here that the workers at North Carolina and the Regional Laboratory in Ithaca have found that certain plants are good indicators of the cobalt status of areas where cobalt deficiency may be expected to occur. Radioactive cobalt has provided a very good tool for observing the distribution of cobalt which is administered either orally or injected parenterally, and these have shown that cobalt reaches its highest concentrations in the liver and kidneys, and to a somewhat lesser degree, in the pancreas (Braude et al., 1949; Comar, 1948; Rothery et al., 1953). Other tissues have quite low values. It is probable that a high proportion of the cobalt found in the liver of ruminants, for example, is present in the form of vitamin B_{12}. Normally, livers of healthy animals will contain between .08 and 0.3 p.p.m. on the dry matter basis. The range of kidney values will be approximately the same as that found for liver, but may actually exceed the value found in liver on a p.p.m. dry matter basis due to the excretory function of the kidney, and reflecting the level of cobalt intake.

Cobalt is peculiar in that it does not increase in large degree in the developing fetus in the same way that iron and copper normally accumulate. As has been mentioned before, the level of cobalt in animal tissues does not reach high levels under normal conditions because there appears to be a very poor absorption of cobalt from the intestinal tract, and a very poor retention of this element, storage being very small in comparison with the levels present in the diet of the ruminant animals which exhibit a cobalt requirement. It is very likely that the milk of cattle may contain approximately 0.6 of a microgram per liter with a range of, perhaps, from 0.02 to as high as 1.2 micrograms per liter (Archibald, 1947). This reflects to some degree the low level of cobalt that may be expected in blood serum with values ranging from approximately 0.04 to 0.06 p.p.m. to levels 0.1 this amount for cobalt deficient animals (Anthony *et al.*, 1951).

X. SUMMARY

From a practical point of view, cobalt deficiency is a problem of the ruminant species. Cattle and sheep which are maintained on rations that contain less than 0.05 p.p.m. of cobalt in the dry matter will begin to show signs of cobalt deficiency within a period of from 2 to 3 weeks, and this may continue for periods up to well over a year depending upon the level of cobalt actually present in the feed. This wide range in the severity of symptoms which develop may well serve to confuse the diagnosis of a cobalt deficiency condition in cattle and in sheep. Since neither of these species exhibits any appreciable storage of cobalt, it is necessary to supply cobalt to them at regular and quite short intervals, if they are exposed to cobalt deficiency conditions.

Under practical farm conditions, this has meant the inclusion of cobalt in the diet in some manner, either as top dressing of the soil, which results in an increased cobalt content of the forage and feed or through supplementation by means of including cobalt in feed or in mineral mixtures. Some positive assurance must be obtained that cattle and sheep are actually obtaining the cobalt, since the signs of cobalt deficiency are not always obvious. In the United States, the common practice has been to provide a mineral supplement, free-choice, to the animals and to include cobalt in supplemental feeds which are given to these animals.

Cobalt ranks with iodine in the amount that is required. A total daily intake of 1 mg. supplies a surplus for ruminant requirements but differs from other minerals in that the animals do not store this element in the tissues.

During the conference at Wooster, Ohio, Dr. E. J. Underwood brought to the attention of the author that unpublished data from work in Australia suggest that the kangaroo should be included in the list of species requiring cobalt.

Dr. Underwood also mentioned that development of a cobalt "bullet" in Australia (a pellet of a cobalt salt and clay resembling in some respects a ceramic preparation), which can be given to sheep, may well solve the problem of continuous administration of cobalt. The "bullet" remains in the reticulum and releases approximately 0.1 mg. of cobalt daily to the rumen-reticulum contents. Effective life of the "bullets" may approach the normal life span of the sheep.

REFERENCES

Anderson, J. P., and Andrews, E. D. 1952. *Nature* **170**, 807.

Andrews, E. D. 1953. *New Zealand J. Sci. Technol.* **35A**, 301–310.

Andrews, E. D., and Anderson, J. P. 1954. *New Zealand J. Sci. Technol.* **35A**, 483–488.

Anthony, W. B., Rupel, I. W., and Couch, J. R. 1951. *J. Dairy Sci.* **34**, 295–298.

Archibald, J. G. 1947. *J. Dairy Sci.* **30**, 293–297.

Askew, H. O. 1939. *New Zealand J. Sci. Technol.* **20A**, 315–318.

Askew, H. O., 1946. *New Zealand J. Sci. Technol.* **28A**, 37–43.

Askew, H. O., and Dixon, J. K. 1937. *New Zealand J. Sci. Technol,* **18A**, 688–693.

Baltzer, A. C., Killham, B. J., Duncan, C. W., and Huffman, C. F. 1941. *Michigan Agr. Expt. Sta. Quart. Bull.* **24**, 69–70.

Becker, D. E., and Smith, S. E. 1951a. *J. Nutrition* **43**, 87–100.

Becker, D. E., and Smith, S. E., 1951b. *J. Animal Sci.* **10**, 266–271.

Becker, D. E., Smith, S. E., and Loosli, J. K. 1949. *Science* **110**, 71–72.

Becker, R. B., Erwin, T. C., and Henderson, J. R. 1946. *Soil Sci.* **62**, 383–392.

Becker, R. B., Arnold, P. T. Dix., Kirk, W. G., Davis, G. K., and Kidder, R. W. 1953. *Florida Agr. Expt. Sta. Bull.* **513**.

Beeson, K. C., Gray, L. F., and Adams, M. B. 1947. *J. Am. Soc. Agron.* **39**, 356–362.

Berk, L., Burchenal, J. H., and Castle, W. B. 1949. *New Engl. J. Med.* **240**, 754–761.

Bertrand, G., and Macheboeuf, M. 1925. *Compt. rend.* **180**, 1380–1383, 1993–1997; *Ibid.* **182**, 1504–1507; **183**, 5–8.

Bowstead, J. E., Sackville, J. P., and Sinclair, R. D. 1942. *Sci. Agr.* **22**, 314–325.

Braude, R., Free, A. A., Paye, J. E., and Smith, E. L. 1949. *Brit. J. Nutrition* **3**, 289–292.

Comar, C. L. 1948. *Nucleonics* **3**, 32–45.

Comar, C. L., and Davis, G. K. 1947. *J. Biol. Chem.* **170**, 379–389.

Comar, C. L., Davis, G. K., and Taylor, R. F. 1946a. *Arch. Biochem.* **9**, 149–158.

Comar, C. L., Davis, G. K., Taylor, R. F., Huffman, C. F., and Ely, R. E. 1946b. *J. Nutrition* **32**, 61–68.

Davis, G. K., Jack, F. H., and McCall, J. T. 1956. *J. Animal Sci.* **15**, 1232.

Dinusson, W. E., Klosterman, E. W., Lasley, E. L., Holm, G. C., and Buchanan, M. L. 1951. *North Dakota Agr. Expt. Sta. Bimonthly* **13**, 146–149.

Dunn, K. M., Ely, R. E., and Huffman, C. F. 1952. *J. Animal Sci.* **11**, 326–331.

Ely, R. E., Dunn, K. M., and Huffman, C. F. 1948. *J. Animal Sci.* **7**, 239–246.

Filmer, J. F. 1933. *Australian Vet. J.* **9**, 163–179.

Filmer, J. F. 1941. *New Zealand J. Agr.* **63**, 287–90.

Filmer, J. F., and Underwood, E. J. 1937. *Australian Vet. J.* **13**, 57–64.

Grant, W. C., and Root, W. S. 1952. *Physiol. Revs.* **32**, 449–498.

Griffith, W. H., Pavcek, C. L., and Mulford, D. J. 1942. *J. Nutrition* **23**, 603–612.

Hale, W. J., Pope, A. L., Phillips, P. H., and Bohstedt, G. 1950. *J. Animal Sci.* **9**, 414–19.

Henderson, J. A. 1947. *Cornell Vet.* **37**, 292–304.

Hoekstra, W. G., Pope, A. L., and Phillips, P. H. 1952a. *J. Nutrition* **48**, 421–430.

Hoekstra, W. G., Pope, A. L., and Phillips, P. H. 1952b. *J. Nutrition* **48**, 431–441.

Huffman, C. F. 1947. *Michigan State College Vet.* **7**, 63–67.

Hurwitz, C., and Beeson, K. C. 1944. *Food Research* **9**, 348–357.

Keener, H. A., Percival, G. P., Morrow, K. S., and Ellis, G. H. 1949. *J. Dairy Sci.* **32**, 527–533.

Keener, H. A., Percival, G. P., Ellis, G. H., and Beeson, K. C. 1950. *J. Animal Sci.* **9**, 404–413.

Kercher, C. J., and Smith, S. E. 1955. *J. Animal Sci.* **14**, 458–464.

Klosterman, E. W., Dinusson, W. E., Lasley, E. L., and Buchanan, M. L. 1950. *Science* **112**, 168–169.

Koch, B. A., and Smith, S. E. 1951. *J. Animal Sci.* **10**, 1017.

Lee, H. J. 1950. *Australian Vet. J.* **26**, 152–159.

Lee, H. J., and Kuchel, R. E., 1953. *Australian J. Agr. Research* **4**, 88–99.

Levey, S., and Orten, J. M. 1951. *J. Nutrition* **45**, 487–492.

Lines, E. W. 1935. *J. Council Sci. Ind. Research* **8**, 117–19.

McDonald, I. W. 1942. *Australian Vet. J.* **18**, 165–172.

McDonald, I. W. 1946. *Australian Vet. J.* **22**, 91–94.

McIntosh, R. A. 1945. *Can. J. Comp. Med. Vet. Sci.* **9**, 179–182.

McNaught, K. J. 1937. *New Zealand J. Sci. Technol.* **18A**, 655–661.

McNaught, K. J. 1938. *New Zealand J. Sci. Technol.* **20A**, 14–30A.

Marston, H. R. 1935. *J. Council Sci. Ind. Research* **8**, 111–116.

Marston, H. R. 1952. *Physiol. Revs.* **32**, 66–121.

Marston, H. R., and Lee, H. J. 1949. *Nature* **164**, 529–30.

Marston, H. R., and Lee, H. J. 1952. *Nature* **170**, 791.

Marston, H. R., and Smith, R. M. 1952. *Nature* **170**, 792–793.

Marston, H. R., Thomas, R. G., Murnane, D., Lines, E. W., McDonald, I. W., and Bull, L. B. 1938. *Australia, Commonwealth, Council Sci. Ind. Research Bull.* **113**, 91 pp.

Maxwell, G. T. 1888. *Florida, Univ. Agr. Exp. Sts. (Gainesville) Bull.* **2**, 10–12.

Neal, W. M., and Ahmann, C. F. 1937. *J. Dairy Sci.* **20**, 741–153.

Noland, P. R., Willman, J. P., and Morrison, F. B. 1951. *J. Animal Sci.* **10**, 875–884.

Pearson, P. B., Struglia, L., and Lindahl, I. L. 1953. *J. Animal Sci.* **12**, 213–218.

Pfiffner, J. J., Dion, H. W., and Calkins, D. G. 1952. *Federation Proc.* **11**, 269.

Phillipson, G. T., and Mitchell, R. L. 1952. *Brit. J. Nutrition* **6**, 176–189.

Pope, A. L., Phillips, P. H., and Bohstedt, G. 1947. *J. Animal Sci.* **6**, 334–342.

Porter, J. W. G. 1953. *Proc. Nutrition Soc. (Engl. and Scot.)* **12**, 106–114.

Ray, S. N., Weir, W. C., Pope, A. L., Bohstedt, G., and Phillips, P. H. 1948. *J. Animal Sci.* **7**, 3–15.

Rossiter, R. C., Curnow, D. H., and Underwood, E. J. 1948. *J. Australian Inst. Agr. Sci.* **14**, 9–14.

Rothery, P., Bell, J. M., and Spinks, J. W. T. 1953. *J. Nutrition* **49**, 173–181.

Salsbury, R. L., Smith, C. K., and Huffman, C. F. 1956. *J. Animal Sci.* **15**, 863–868.

Sebrell, W. H., Jr., and Harris, R. S., eds. 1954. "The Vitamins," Volume **1**, Chapter 3. Academic Press, New York.

Smith, S. E., Becker, D. E., Loosli, J. K., and Beeson, K. C. 1950. *J. Animal Sci.* **9**, 221–230.

Smith, S. E., Koch, B. A., and Turk, K. L. 1951. *J. Nutrition* **44**, 455–464.

Speer, V. C., Catron, D. V., Homeyer, P. G., and Culbertson, C. C. 1952. *J. Animal Sci.* **11**, 112–117.

Stewart, J. 1949. *Brit. Commonwealth, Sci. Officers Conf., Australia.*

Underwood, E. J. 1956. "Trace Elements in Human and Animal Nutrition," Academic Press, New York.
Underwood, E. J., and Filmer, J. F. 1935. *Australian Vet. J.* **11**, 84–92.
Underwood, E. J., and Harvey, R. J. 1938. *Australian Vet. J.* **14**, 183–189.
Walker, W., and Hunter, R. B. 1952. *Brit. Med. J.* **II**, 593–5.
Waltner, K., and Waltner, K. 1929. *Klin. Wochschr.* **8**, 313.
White, E. A. 1955. *Vet. Med.* **50**, 199–202, 205.

CHAPTER 14

Cobalt and the Synthesis of Vitamin B_{12} and Vitamin B_{12}-like Substances by Rumen Microorganisms*

RONALD R. JOHNSON AND ORVILLE G. BENTLEY

Ohio Agricultural Experiment Station Wooster, Ohio

		Page
I.	Introduction	213
II.	The Relationship of Cobalt to Vitamin B_{12} Synthesis in Ruminants	214
	A. The Effect of Cobalt on Vitamin B_{12} Synthesis *in Vivo* and Animal Performance	214
	B. Vitamin B_{12} Synthesis by Rumen Microorganisms *in Vitro*	216
III.	The Synthesis of Vitamin B_{12}-like Substances by Rumen Microorganisms	217
	A. *In Vitro* Synthesis of Vitamin B_{12}-like Substances	217
	1. Historical	217
	2. Electrophoretic Separations and Detection Techniques	218
	3. Vitamin B_{12} and Co^{60} Distribution	219
	4. Identification with Known Vitamin B_{12} Active Substances	219
	B. *In Vivo* Synthesis of Vitamin B_{12}-like Substances	221
	1. Sheep Experiments	221
	2. Rat Experiments	221
IV.	Conclusions	223
	References	223

I. INTRODUCTION

The cobalt requirement for the synthesis of vitamin B_{12} and related vitamin B_{12}-like substances by microflora explains an important physiological function of cobalt. The cobalt-vitamin B_{12} relationship has a vital role in the nutrition of the ruminants, cattle and sheep, where microbial synthesis is the major source of all B vitamins, including vitamin B_{12}. The cobalt requirement of sheep appears to be more critical than for cattle; however, cobalt deficiencies in cattle have been reported by Filmer and Underwood (1937), Neal and Ahmann (1937), Baltzer *et al.* (1941), and McIntosh (1945). The objective of this paper is to review the results

* The studies reported herein were supported in part by the Atomic Energy Commission, contract No. AT(11–1)–272.

213

of research with cobalt and a trace element mixture at the Ohio Station which emerged from a practical feeding problem encountered in growing-fattening steers full-fed on a high corn ration with poor quality timothy hay. The *in vitro* and *in vivo* synthesis of vitamin B_{12} and B_{12}-like substances as affected by cobalt were important phases of this study. More extensive papers on cobalt presented at this Symposium cover the review of the literature; therefore, reference will be made only to reports pertinent to the results presented herein. Excellent reviews by Marston (1952), Underwood (1956), and Beeson (1950) covering all phases of the research on cobalt are suggested to the reader.

II. THE RELATIONSHIP OF COBALT TO VITAMIN B_{12} SYNTHESIS IN RUMINANTS

A. The Effect of Cobalt on Vitamin B_{12} Synthesis in Vivo and Animal Performance

Improved performance of steers fed the ashed residue of molasses or alfalfa hay or trace minerals as a supplement to a ground ear corn, soybean oil meal, and poor quality timothy hay ration was observed by Klosterman *et al.* (1953, 1956). Subsequent experiments by Bentley *et al.* (1954) showed that cobalt alone gave a significant response in growth and feed efficiency in growing-fattening steers when added to a ration composed of ground ear corn, urea, U.S.P. grade calcium and phosphorus salts, corn sugar, iodized salt, poor quality timothy hay, and vitamin A. The hay contained from 0.06 to 0.07 p.p.m. cobalt, but under this feeding regimen animals consumed an average of only 1.6 to 1.8 pounds of hay per day per head and 8 to 10 pounds of ground ear corn. The total cobalt content of the ration as consumed was 0.03 to 0.04 p.p.m. due to the high proportion of corn, which is low in cobalt, in the ration. The cobalt deficiency was borderline as blood hemoglobin levels were not depressed; however, an increased feed intake was observed, probably as a result of improved appetite from feeding cobalt or alfalfa ash to the steers. In terms of total digestible nutrient (TDN) intake over maintenance requirements, the cobalt or alfalfa ash-fed steers consumed 47 per cent more TDN which was available for growth, etc., than did the animals on the basal ration.

The addition of cobalt to the ration had a marked effect on vitamin B_{12} synthesis, as indicated by vitamin B_{12} analyses of various tissues. Data reported by Bentley *et al.* (1954) are summarized in Table I.

Vitamin B_{12} excreted via the feces is not necessarily an indication of the vitamin B_{12} available to the animal. Teeri *et al.* (1955) found that the

TABLE I

Cobalt Feeding and Vitamin B$_{12}$ Synthesis in Steers

Sample	Vitamin B$_{12}$ content[a]	
	Basal rations[b]	Basal plus cobalt
Liver, wet wt. µg./g.	0.116	0.68
Kidney, wet wt., µg./g.	0.053	0.21
Blood plasma, µg./100 ml.	0.007	0.018
Dried feces, µg./g.	0.243	1.2

[a] *Lactobacillus leichmannii* assay.
[b] Mature timothy hay, corn, urea, minerals.

amount of vitamin B$_{12}$ excreted was 40 to 55 times more than the amount ingested. Similar results were obtained with sheep by Pearson *et al.* (1953), where fecal excretion was 120 to 210 times the intake. Kercher and Smith (1955) confirmed earlier observations that injected cobalt did not alleviate cobalt deficiency symptoms in sheep, yet as much or more vitamin B$_{12}$ was found in the contents of the large intestine of cobalt-injected sheep as in those receiving it orally. Presumably, the cobalt was carried by the bile into the intestine where it became available to the microflora for use in vitamin synthesis. Thus it would appear that vitamin B$_{12}$ absorption from the lower intestinal tract appears to be rather limited in ruminants. Liver data should be indicative of the vitamin B$_{12}$ status of the animal, however.

A direct estimation of the effect of cobalt on the rumen microbial synthesis of vitamin B$_{12}$ in animals fed poor quality hay (mature timothy) was obtained by feeding cobaltized salt to a steer fitted with permanent ruminal fistula. Analyses of the rumen juice both before and after feeding the cobalt clearly indicates that cobalt increased its vitamin B$_{12}$ content (see Table II). The analyses were carried out by Dr. M. Moinuddin in our laboratory.

TABLE II

Cobalt Stimulation of Vitamin B$_{12}$ Synthesis *in Vivo* in
Steers with Ruminal Fistula

Ration	B$_{12}$ in rumen juice[a] (µg./l.)
Alfalfa hay	37.8 (25–64)
Mature timothy hay	14.9 (8–21)
Mature timothy hay + cobalt	126.0 (94–169)

[a] Samples collected over a 2-year period. Numbers in parentheses represent the range.

The results of these experiments with growing-fattening steers are comparable to the results as presented by Smith *et al.* (1951), Hoekstra *et al.* (1952), and Marston (1952) on the cobalt-vitamin B_{12} relationship using sheep.

B. *Vitamin B_{12} Synthesis by Rumen Microorganisms in Vitro*

Evidence for increase vitamin B_{12} synthesis *in vivo* in steers has been presented in Section II,A. An *in vitro* rumen fermentation using the methods described by Bentley *et al.* (1954, 1955) made it possible to study the effect of adding cobalt to the medium on (*1*) the amount of vitamin B_{12} synthesized and (*2*) its effect on nonprotein nitrogen utilization and cellulose digestion by the mixed rumen culture. Vitamin B_{12} analyses given in Table III indicate that cobalt additions increased vita-

TABLE III

Vitamin B_{12} Synthesis *in Vitro* (48-Hour Fermentation)

Medium	B_{12} (μg./l.)
Basal	19.2
Basal + 0.001 p.p.m. Co	26.8
Basal + 0.01 p.p.m. Co	41.4
Basal + 0.001 p.p.m. Co + 10 μg. B_{12}/l.	38.8
Basal + 0.01 p.p.m. Co + 10 μg. B_{12}/l.	50.0

min B_{12} synthesis markedly. The question arose as to whether or not cobalt per se or the vitamin B_{12} formed exerted a beneficial effect on the flora as grown *in vitro*. Gall *et al.* (1949) reported that the flora from severely cobalt-deficient sheep was altered by reduced numbers and effectiveness. In Table IV it can be seen that adding cobalt at a level of 0.01

TABLE IV

The Effect of Cobalt on Growth and Activity of Rumen Organisms *in Vitro*

Medium	Increase in TCA-N (mg. N/100 ml.)	Cellulose digestion (%)
Basal	12.7	48.5
Basal + 0.01 p.p.m. Co	10.1	34.9
Basal + 0.1 p.p.m. Co	11.6	42.8
Basal + 1.0 p.p.m. Co	7.4	22.5

p.p.m. did not increase the rate of cellulose digestion or nonprotein nitrogen utilization. In fact, with the purified medium used, the organisms appeared to be particularly sensitive to cobalt additions, and at levels of 1.0 p.p.m. it was found to be inhibitory in this and other experiments carried out in our laboratory. Salsbury *et al.* (1956) found that when whole rumen juice was used for an inoculum instead of cells separated by centrifugation, as workers in our laboratory had done, inhibition from cobalt did not occur until levels of 12 p.p.m. were reached. McNaught *et al.* (1950) reported 10 p.p.m. cobalt adversely affected protein synthesis by rumen organisms. However, in our experience, and in that of Salsbury *et al.* (1956), neither cobalt nor vitamin B$_{12}$ appears to exert a beneficial effect on the rate of cellulose digestion or growth of the microorganisms as determined by the increase in trichloroacetic acid-insoluble protein during an *in vitro* fermentation.

The cobalt requirement of rumen microorganisms appears to be extremely low. Dr. B. A. Dehority attempted to demonstrate a cobalt requirement for mixed rumen organizations grown *in vitro* while working in our laboratory. He was not successful even though he went to rather elaborate steps to remove cobalt present in the medium as a contaminant and to wash the inoculum. It has been reported that organisms in the rumen concentrate cobalt within the cells (Tosic and Mitchell, 1948). Organisms taken from an animal on poor quality timothy (low cobalt) and used to inoculate *in vitro* fermentation flasks did not respond to cobalt additions by increased cellulose digestion even though an increase in the amount of vitamin B$_{12}$ synthesized occurred.

III. The Synthesis of Vitamin B$_{12}$-like Substances by Rumen Microorganisms

A. *In Vitro Synthesis of Vitamin B$_{12}$-like Substances*

1. Historical. Previous reports by Ford *et al.* (1951), Ford and Porter (1952), Wijmenga (1951), Pfiffner *et al.* (1951), and Lewis *et al.* (1952) had indicated that ruminal and intestinal microorganisms could produce different substances having vitamin B$_{12}$ activity for test microorganisms but varying activity for rats and chicks. Holdsworth *et al.* (1953) developed a procedure for separation of these vitamin B$_{12}$-like substances by electrophoresis on filter paper. Not only could more distinct separations be obtained by this method but accurate comparisons of one substance to another could be made. These vitamin B$_{12}$-like substances had different electrophoretic mobilities, and many had different microbiological activities as well (Coates *et al.*, 1951; Ford *et al.*, 1951; Ford and Porter, 1952; Coates *et al.*, 1952). Moinuddin and Bentley (1955) in this laboratory found that the vitamin B$_{12}$ activities (as determined by *L. leichmannii*) in steer feces and rumen liquor were fully active and 70 per cent active, respectively, in rats, but both materials were less active in chicks. It became of interest then to investigate the complexity of the vitamin B_{12} activity synthesized by the rumen microorganisms in our laboratory. Parts of this work were reported previously by Johnson et al. (1956).

2. *Electrophoretic Separations and Detection Techniques.* Rumen microorganisms were grown *in vitro* in the presence of Co^{60} according to the procedure described by Bentley et al. (1954). At the end of the fermentation, the flask contents were dried and extracted with water. It was found that for distinct separations, it was necessary to clarify the water extract by adsorbing on charcoal and eluting with hot 70 per cent acetone. After concentration of this eluate, aliquots were spotted on strips of filter paper. The strips were wetted with 2 N acetic acid and

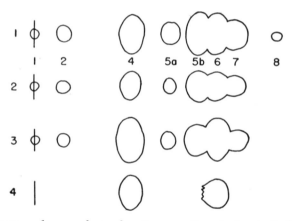

Fig. 1. Diagram of paper electrophoretic separation of vitamin B_{12}-like substances synthesized by rumen microorganisms. (*1*) Ten aliquots of sample applied on original spot (long vertical lines); (*2*) five aliquots; (*3*) five aliquots + vitamins B_{12} and B_{12b}; (*4*) vitamins B_{12} and B_{12b}.

placed in an electrophoresis apparatus using 2 N acetic acid as the electrolyte, as described by Holdsworth et al. (1953). After applying a current for 12 hours, the strips were dried and the distribution of vitamin B_{12} activity was determined bioautographically by laying the strips on agar beds heavily seeded with *Escherichia coli* ATCC 11105. Cobalt-60 activity was detected by laying similar strips on Type K X-ray film. A diagrammatic sketch of the type of separation obtained is shown in Fig. 1. Seven or eight substances with different electrophoretic mobilities were found to contain vitamin B_{12} activity. In addition, all substances contained Co^{60}. These substances were labeled substances 1, 2, 3, 4, 5*a*, 5*b*, 6, 7, and 8. (Substance 3 is not shown in Fig. 1 but appeared occasionally between substances 2 and 4.)

3. *Vitamin B$_{12}$ Activity and Co^{60} Distribution.* Sections of strips containing each substance were cut out and assayed quantitatively for vitamin B$_{12}$ activity (*L. leichmannii*) and Co^{60} activity. An example of this distribution is given in Table V. Obviously, several substances con-

TABLE V

Vitamin B$_{12}$ Activity and Co^{60} Distribution in *in Vitro* Rumen Contents[a]

Substance	Total B$_{12}$ (%)	Total Co^{60} (%)
1	1.8	2.6
2	3.6	6.2
3	9.9	19.2
4	26.3	25.7
5	38.7	24.0
6	27.6	24.8
7	2.1	13.3

[a] Substances 1, 2, and 3 were determined on water extract samples, while substances 4–7 were determined on charcoal eluates of these water extracts. Hence, the per cent activities do not add up to exactly 100 per cent.

tributed major portions to the total activity, both in terms of vitamin B$_{12}$ and Co^{60} activity. Substance 5 was later found to be two substances, 5*a* and 5*b*. Although substances 4, 5 (5*a* + 5*b*), and 6 were most prominent, substances 3 and 7 contained significant quantities of Co^{60} activity.

4. *Identification with Known Vitamin B$_{12}$ Active Substances.* When samples of crystalline vitamin B$_{12}$ were separated by this technique, two spots were obtained which corresponded with substances 4 and 6 in the rumen samples (cf. Fig. 1). Further experiments indicated these were vitamin B$_{12}$ (cyanocobalamin) and vitamin B$_{12b}$ (hydroxycobalamin), respectively. Samples of pseudovitamin B$_{12}$ and pseudovitamin B$_{12d}$ as isolated by Pfiffner *et al.* (1951) were kindly supplied to us by Dr. Pfiffner. Dr. B. A. Dehority, in our laboratory, tested samples of these along with vitamins B$_{12}$ and B$_{12b}$ by electrophoresis on paper to compare their mobilities with the substances found in rumen liquor. In this case, the finished electrophoretic strips were cut into 1-cm. sections, and each section was assayed quantitatively for vitamin B$_{12}$. These separations are illustrated in Fig. 2. Vitamins B$_{12}$ and B$_{12b}$ again separated into two peaks of activity corresponding to substances 4 and 6, respectively. Pseudovitamin B$_{12}$ demonstrated its greatest activity at a mobility corresponding to substances 5*a* while pseudovitamin B$_{12d}$ compared with substance 5*b*. In the curves for pseudovitamins B$_{12}$ and B$_{12d}$, small peaks appeared

beyond the position of substance 6 (-21 and -25 cm.). These may be identical with substances 7 and 8. It is also possible that these may represent hydroxy forms of the pseudovitamins B_{12}.

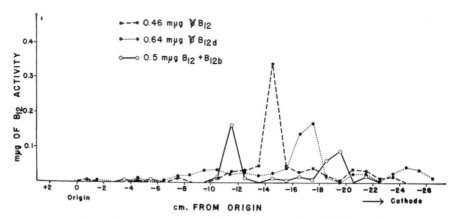

Fig. 2. Electrophoretic separation of vitamins B_{12} and B_{12b} and pseudovitamins B_{12} and B_{12d}.

Since the isolation of the vitamin B_{12}-like substances, many of them have been characterized structurally and shown to differ from true vitamin B_{12}, as characterized structurally by Hodgkin et al. (1955) and Bonnett et al. (1955) only in the purine type base in the nucleotide portion of the molecule. Dion et al. (1952) demonstrated that adenine was the base in pseudovitamin B_{12}. Independently, Dion et al. (1954) and Brown et al. (1955) demonstrated the presence of 2-methyladenine in pseudovitamin B_{12d} and Factor A, respectively, and stated that this substance also appeared to be identical with vitamin B_{12m} (Wijmenga, 1951). Factor B, described by Ford and Porter (1952), was shown to be the denucleotided portion of any of the above factors by Gant et al.

TABLE VI

The Purine Bases in the Nucleotide Portion of Various Vitamin B_{12}-like Substances

B_{12}-like substance	Purine base
Vitamins B_{12} and B_{12b}	5,6-Dimethyl benzimidazole
Pseudo B_{12}	Adenine
Factor A, pseudo B_{12d}, vitamin B_{12m}	2-Methyladenine
Factor B	No nucleotide portion
Factor G	Hypoxanthine
Factor H	2-Methyl hypoxanthine
Factor C, D, E, F, and I	Unknown

(1954). Recently, many more vitamin B$_{12}$-like substances, including Factors D-I, have been isolated from calf and pig feces by Brown and Smith (1954) and Brown *et al.* (1955). Although they are not all characterized, it appears they differ mainly in the purine base of the nucleotide. The various purines present in the different vitamin B$_{12}$-like substances are listed in Table VI.

B. In Vivo Synthesis of Vitamin B$_{12}$-like Substances

1. *Sheep Experiments.* The analyses reported above (III,A) were made on *in vitro* rumen fermentation contents. It was desirable to determine whether this distribution of vitamin B$_{12}$ activity occurred *in vivo* as well. Inorganic cobalt was injected into the rumen of a wether lamb on each of 4 successive days, after which the lamb was slaughtered. Samples of rumen contents, feces, and liver were taken and analyzed for vitamin B$_{12}$ activity distribution by the electrophoretic procedure described in III,A,2. This distribution is given in Table VII.

TABLE VII

Distribution of Vitamin B$_{12}$ Activity in Rumen Liquor and Other Sheep Tissues[a]

| Substance | Rumen liquor | | Sheep feces | Sheep liver |
	in vitro	*in vivo*		
1	0.9	2.6	—	2.5
2	1.3	—	5.2	—
4	12.8	29.0	23.3	44.2
5a	27.7	9.6	8.0	5.2
5b	19.7	26.8	21.2	15.9
6	26.3	20.1	29.3	30.3
7	8.8	10.6	12.9	—
8	—	1.3	—	1.9

[a] Activity given as per cent of the total activity in the electrophoretic strip of a given sample as determined by *L. leichmannii* assay.

Qualitatively, sheep rumen liquor and feces contained the same vitamin B$_{12}$-like substances as did *in vitro* rumen liquor, although there appeared to be less substance 5a. Sheep liver contained substances 4, 5a, 5b, and 6, although most of the activity was in substances 4 and 6 (vitamins B$_{12}$ and B$_{12b}$).

2. *Rat Experiments.* The ability of rat intestinal microorganisms to produce vitamin B$_{12}$ had previously been shown by Hartman *et al.* (1949) and Davis and Chow (1951), but the nature of the activity had not been determined. Analyses were performed on rat feces, urine, and kidney

to determine the nature of the vitamin B_{12} activity synthesized by intestinal microorganisms in that species. This distribution is shown in Table VIII. Apparently many of the same vitamin B_{12}-like substances synthe-

TABLE VIII

Distribution of Vitamin B_{12} Activity in Rat Kidney, Urine, and Feces[a]

Substance	Feces	Urine[b]	Kidney[b]
1	2.1	1.7	4.2
3	3.2	1.7	4.2
4	8.7	37.9	11.3
5a	15.6	13.1	11.2
5b	27.9	9.5	21.1
6	25.9	35.4	48.6
7	16.5	2.4	3.4

[a] Activity given as per cent of total *L. leichmannii* activity on an electrophoretic strip from a given sample.

[b] Substances 1 and 3 were not distinct in urine and kidney and that section of the strip was assayed as one region.

sized by rumen microorganisms were also synthesized by rat intestinal microorganisms. Their proportions are even quite similar in the rat feces as compared to rumen contents. It is of interest to note the presence of significant amounts of activity in substances 5a and 5b in rat urine and kidney. This would indicate that some absorption of these substances was taking place in addition to absorption of vitamins B_{12} and B_{12b}, which are the true B_{12} vitamins.

The ability of rat intestinal flora to synthesize vitamin B_{12} was further tested by giving young rats a diet as completely deficient as possible in vitamin B_{12} and in cobalt (Johnson, 1954). A similar group of rats was given the purified basal diet plus 2.5 p.p.m. of cobalt. Vitamin B_{12} analyses were performed on the feces on the 6th, 14th, and 19th day of the experiment and on the liver and kidney after slaughter. These data are shown in Table IX.

The presence of cobalt in the ration obviously stimulated vitamin B_{12} synthesis by the intestinal microorganisms as is seen in the vitamin B_{12} values for the feces. Also, it appeared there was some aborption of this synthesized vitamin B_{12} since the liver and kidney values were higher in the cobalt supplemented rats. Since the animals did not have access to their own feces, this absorption must have taken place from the site of synthesis, i.e., the large intestine.

Klosterman *et al.* (1950) and Robison (1950) demonstrated that swine

TABLE IX

Vitamin B$_{12}$ (*L. leichmannii*) Content of Rat Tissues from Rats Supplemented with Cobalt

	Rat feces[a]			Rat[b]	Rat[b]
	6th day	14th day	19th day	Kidney	Liver
Basal diet	2.9	3.7	2.6	133	41
Basal + 2.5 p.p.m. Co	5.2	5.4	4.4	194	60

[a] Given as μg./g. dried feces.

[b] Given as mμg./g. fresh tissue.

on vitamin B$_{12}$-deficient rations exhibited a growth response to cobalt supplementation, presumably through intestinal synthesis of vitamin B$_{12}$. Similar results with rats and chicks were reported by Burns and Salmon (1954). Kercher and Smith (1956) have recently demonstrated that cobalt injected intravenously into cobalt-deficient sheep enters the intestine via the bile and stimulates vitamin B$_{12}$ synthesis by the microorganisms in the cecum and large intestine. However, they state that this vitamin B$_{12}$ appears to be of little value to the host animal, presumably because of poor absorption from the large intestine.

IV. CONCLUSIONS

Although the *L. leichmannii* assay was used throughout these studies, it is recognized that the *Ochromonas malhemensis* assay would have given a more accurate estimation of the vitamin B$_{12}$ in the various tissues (Ford, 1953), since that organism is specific for true vitamin B$_{12}$. However, for the purposes of this study the former assay technique responded to the vitamin B$_{12}$-like substances as well as vitamin B$_{12}$.

It is obvious from the work of other workers as well as that reported here that the microorganisms living in the rumen and intestinal tracts of animals are capable of producing a host of substances possessing vitamin B$_{12}$ activity for certain test organisms. The primary difference in the structure of these substances lies in the nitrogen base of the nucleotide portion of the molecule. Although many microorganisms are now known to be capable of synthesizing vitamin B$_{12}$-like substances, the significance of such substances remains obscure.

REFERENCES

Baltzer, A. C., Killham, B. J., Duncan, C. W., and Huffman, C. F. 1941. *Michigan Agr. Expt. Sta. Quart. Bull.* 24, 68–70.

Beeson, K. C. 1950. *U.S. Dept. Agr., Wash. Agr. Inform. Bull.* 7.

Bentley, O. G., Johnson, R. R., Vanecko, S., and Hunt, C. H. 1954. *J. Animal Sci.* **13**, 581–593.

Bentley, O. G., Johnson, R. R., Hershberger, T. V., Cline, J. H., and Moxon, A. L. 1955. *J. Nutrition* **57**, 389–400.

Bonnett, R., Cannon, J. R., Johnson, A. W., Sutherland, I., Todd, A. R., and Smith, E. L. 1955. *Nature* **176**, 328–330.

Brown, F. B., and Smith, E. L. 1954. *Biochem. J.* **56**, xxxiv.

Brown, F. B., Cain, J. C., Gant, D. E., Parker, L. F. J., and Smith, E. L. 1955. *Biochem. J.* **59**, 82–86.

Burns, M. J., and Salmon, W. D. 1954. *Federation Proc.* **13**, 452.

Coates, M. E., Ford, J. E., Harrison, G. F., Kon, S. K., Porter, J. W. G., Cuthbertson, W. F. J., and Pegler, H. F. 1951. *Biochem. J.* **49**, lxvii.

Coates, M. E., Ford, J. E., Harrison, G. F., Kon, S. K., and Porter, J. W. G. 1952. *Biochem. J.* **51**, vi.

Davis, R. L., and Chow, B. F. 1951. *Proc. Soc. Exptl. Biol. Med.* **77**, 218–221.

Dion, H. W., Calkins, D. G., and Pfiffner, J. J. 1952. *J. Am. Chem. Soc.* **74**, 1108.

Dion, H. W., Calkins, D. G., and Pfiffner, J. J. 1954. *J. Am. Chem. Soc.* **76**, 948.

Filmer, J. F., and Underwood, E. J. 1937. *Australian Vet. J.* **13**, 57–64.

Ford, J. E. 1953. *Brit. J. Nutrition* **7**, 299–306.

Ford, J. E., and Porter, J. W. G. 1952. *Biochem. J.* **51**, v.

Ford, J. E., Kon, S. K., and Porter, J. W. G. 1951. *Biochem. J.* **50**, ix.

Gall, L. S., Smith, S. E., Becker, D. E., Stark, C. N., and Loosli, J. K. 1949. *Science* **109**, 468–469.

Gant, D. E., Smith, E. L., and Parker, L. F. J. 1954. *Biochem. J.* **56**, xxxiv.

Hartman, A. M., Dryden, L. P., and Cary, C. A. 1949. *Federation Proc.* **8**, 205.

Hodgkin, D. C., Pickworth, J., Robertson, J. H., Trueblood, K. N., Prosen, R. J., and White, J. G. 1955. *Nature* **176**, 325–328.

Hoekstra, W. G., Pope, A. L., and Phillips, P. H. 1952. *J. Nutrition* **48**, 421–430.

Holdsworth, E. S., Ford, J. E., Kon, S. K., and Porter, J. W. G. 1953. *Nature* **171**, 148–151.

Johnson, R. R. 1954. "The Role of Cobalt in the Ruminant Animal," Ph.D. Dissertation. The Ohio State University.

Johnson, R. R., Bentley, O. G., and Moxon, A. L. 1956. *J. Biol. Chem.* **218**, 379–390.

Kercher, C. J., and Smith, S. E. 1956. *J. Animal Sci.* **15**, 550–558.

Klosterman, E. W., Dinusson, W. E., Lasley, E. L., and Buchanan, M. L. 1950. *Science* **112**, 168–169.

Klosterman, E. W., Kunkle, L. E., Bentley, O. G., and Burroughs, W. 1953. *Ohio Agr. Expt. Sta. Research Bull.* **732**.

Klosterman, E. W., Bentley, O. G., Moxon, A. L., and Kunkle, L. E. 1956. *J. Animal Sci.* **15**, 456–463.

Lewis, U. J., Tappan, D. V., and Elvehjem, C. A. 1952. *J. Biol. Chem.* **194**, 539–548.

McIntosh, R. A. 1945. *Can. J. Comp. Med. Vet. Sci.* **9**, 179–182.

McNaught, M. L., Owen, E. C., and Smith, J. A. B. 1950. *Biochem. J.* **46**, 35–43.

Marston, H. R. 1952. *Physiol. Revs.* **32**, 66–116.

Moinuddin, M., and Bentley, O. G. 1955. *J. Nutrition* **56**, 335–348.

Neal, W. M., and Ahmann, C. F. 1937. *J. Dairy Sci.* **20**, 741–753.

Pearson, P. B., Struglia, L., and Lindahl, I. L. 1953. *J. Animal Sci.* **12**, 213–218.

Pfiffner, J. J., Calkins, D. G., Peterson, R. C., Bird, O. D., McGlohon, V., and Stipek, R. W. 1951. *Meeting Am. Chem. Soc. Abstr. 120th*, p. 22c.

Robison, W. L. 1950. *J. Animal Sci.* **9**, 665.

Salsbury, R. L., Smith, C. K., and Huffman, C. F. 1956. *J. Animal Sci.* **15**, 863–868.

Smith, S. E., Koch, B. A., and Turk, K. L. 1951. *J. Nutrition* **44**, 455–464.

Teeri, A. E., Enos, H. F., Jr., Pomerantz, E., and Colovos, N. F. 1955. *J. Animal Sci.* **14**, 268–271.

Tosic, J., and Mitchell, R. L. 1948. *Nature* **162**, 502–504.

Underwood, E. J. 1956. "Trace Elements in Human and Animal Nutrition." Academic Press, New York.

Wijmenga, H. G. 1951. "Onderzoekingen over Vitamin B₁₂ en Verwante Factoren." Thesis, University of Utrecht, Holland.

CHAPTER 15

The Role of Boron in the Plant Cell *

JOHN SKOK

Argonne National Laboratory
Lemont, Illinois

	Page
I. Introduction	227
II. Boron in Agriculture	228
III. The Plant Boron Requirement	229
A. Deficiency Symptoms	229
B. Utilization of Boron	230
C. Distribution of Boron in the Plant Cell	231
IV. Role of Boron in Cellular Functions	233
A. In Relation to Enzymes	233
B. In Relation to the Complexing Property of the Borate Ion	233
1. Substitution of Complexing Substances for Boron	234
2. Sugar Translocation	234
C. In Relation to Cellular Development	237
1. Cellular Maturation and Differentiation	237
2. Cell Wall Formation	239
3. Pectic Substances	240
4. Interrelationships	241
V. Summary	241
References	242

I. INTRODUCTION

The essentiality of boron as a micronutrient for higher plants is well established. The major unsolved problems confronting us deal with the nature of its exact function or functions in growth. Well over forty years ago Agulhon (1910) published evidence that pointed to its essential nature. He stated that Bertrand suggested the investigations after the latter postulated at the 1903 Chemical Congress in Berlin that boron might have a possible physiological role. In this early paper Agulhon reported that although he found no favorable growth effects of boron on yeast or

* Contribution from the Division of Biological and Medical Research, Argonne National Laboratory under the auspices of the U.S. Atomic Energy Commission.

Aspergillus niger, he obtained definite increases in growth with various higher plants; he suggested that boron could be advantageously added to fertilizers. He noted further that its abundance in lignified tissues and bark suggests that boron is involved in the formation of vascular tissues or of compounds which impregnate these tisues. These, or similar thoughts have been expressed in various later writings by other investigators.

Shortly after Agulhon's experiments were published, Haselhoff (1913) reported that low concentrations of boron appeared favorable for the growth of several plants, and Brenchley (1914) showed that it increased growth of peas. Then Mazé (1915) found that it was required by maize and added it to his list of essential elements. Even more convincing evidence for its requirement was provided when Warington (1923) and Sommer and Lipman (1926) showed conclusively that normal growth of the broad bean and several other plants was dependent upon this element.

Following this early work a great abundance of additional experimental work has provided detailed accounts of boron deficiency symptoms for a large number of species and has established the requirement for boron by higher plants beyond any doubt. Gauch and Dugger (1954) have written an extremely useful and comprehensive review of the boron literature and have discussed the various roles that have been assigned to this element.

II. Boron in Agriculture

No extensive review will be attempted on this very important subject. The agricultural importance of boron is well known, and the boron responses and field requirements for most major crops have been documented (Chilean Nitrate Educational Bureau, Inc., 1948, 1951, 1953). The first known instance in which a crop "disease" in the field was recognized as a boron deficiency that could be successfully corrected by the addition of boron occurred when Brandenburg (1931) discovered that "heart rot" of sugar beets, a disease that had become prevalent in certain German fields, was caused by a deficiency of boron in the soil. This was confirmed by several other workers and resulted in the control of "heart rot" in fields of various parts of the world including areas in Michigan and Ohio. A similar situation involving "cracked stem" of celery existed in Florida. This nonparasitic disease, also of undetermined cause, was prevalent for many years until Purvis and Ruprecht (1937) found that it too was caused by boron deficiency and could be controlled by the addition of borax to the soils of affected fields. Since these two discoveries were made, boron deficiencies have been found among many other crops and, in general, their practical control is usually easily accomplished. Crop members of the Cruciferae in many areas require boron application either for the prevention of visible deficiency symptoms or for assurance of maximum yields.

Boron is usually administered by the addition of boron compounds (generally borax) to the soil, often mixed with other fertilizers, although it may also be applied as a foliar spray (Boynton, 1954).

Certain agricultural and soil problems also arise when boron is present in excess amounts (Eaton, 1944) as this element then becomes very toxic. The range between the concentrations of the external boron supply that support maximum growth and those of incipient toxicity is often very narrow.

Berger's review (1949) should be consulted for an excellent discussion covering factors affecting boron availability in the soil, interrelations of boron to other elements, and boron responses and requirements of various crops. Allen (1954) has discussed the effects of host environment, including mineral nutrients, on the development of fungus plant diseases. Apparently a number of elements have marked effects on infection and on the establishment of the parasite, although very little information of this type has thus far become available for boron.

III. The Plant Boron Requirement

As has already been stated, boron is an essential micronutrient element for the growth of higher plants. All three of the criteria for essentiality proposed by Arnon and Stout (1939) are satisfied, since (1) no higher plant is known that can complete all its growth requirements without boron, (2) no other element can replace the requirement for boron (the substitution of germanium for boron described under Section IV,B,1 does not satisfy (1) above), and (3) boron is directly involved in the nutrition of the plant. Boron appears to be essential for some algae (Eyster, 1952; McIlrath and Skok, 1957) but apparently is not required by fungi or animals. At least *Aspergillus niger,* the fungus most thoroughly investigated, seems to have no boron requirement (Steinberg, 1945). Unfortunately, very little is known concerning its requirement among the other plant groups, although it would be reasonable to expect further investigations to demonstrate a requirement for the ferns and mosses.

A. *Deficiency Symptoms*

The careful study of boron deficiency symptoms is helpful, as they may be a guide in looking for the sequential steps that lead up to them and in obtaining an insight on the real function of boron. These symptoms, however, are end results of various events or of the failure of occurrence of various events, and therefore it is not surprising that even the most detailed scrutiny of the symptoms themselves has been insufficient for the solution of the nutritional role of boron. Nevertheless they must continue to be studied, and they must be taken into full consideration in the construction of a working hypothesis of the function of boron.

Boron deficiency symptoms vary in a number of specific ways among the different plant species, but a remarkable uniformity persists in that the growing regions are always involved. Retardation of growth and eventual death of the terminal buds and root tips takes place.

The absence of boron often alters the growth of various tissues at different rates, which may result in various types of distortion, cracking, splitting, or checking (Purvis and Ruprecht, 1937; Chandler, 1941; Skok, 1941).

Certain manifestations of boron deficiency are often noticeable very early, long before visual symptoms are apparent. Alexander (1942) noted among other effects that the boron-deficient squash plant lost its capacity for geotropic response as early as the second day of treatment. Skok (1957b) likewise found that the response of sunflower plants to X-irradiation was altered by deprivation of boron for as little as 2 days (this will be referred to more fully in Section IV,C,1). Examination under a dissecting scope of 10-day-old sunflower seedlings grown for 3 days with or without boron revealed that the deficient plants had made one less node than the control plants, and the nodes were comparatively compacted. There was, however, no necrosis or visible tissue damage at this time; these early morphological changes preceded the characteristic visible deficiency symptoms that developed subsequently.

Because of the involvement of the growing regions, insufficient amounts of boron result in abnormalities in flowering, fruiting, or any subsequent developmental growth. In the complete or nearly complete absence of boron, death of the plant occurs very early, preventing even the formation of these latter structures. For this reason it is somewhat pointless to stress the effect of boron on flowering and fruiting, or in any way to convey the thought that boron has a special function in reproduction or reproductive growth that is different from its function in growth in general.

B. Utilization of Boron

It has been known for some time that an external source of boron is required throughout the growth period of a plant and that there is little or no reutilization of boron. Sunflower plants grown in nutrient solution containing a total of 50 μg. boron per plant developed deficiency symptoms at about the 18th or 19th day (Skok, 1957b). It is interesting to note that although the symptoms progressed until the terminal regions had become characteristically necrotic, the first and second pairs of leaves, which had matured before the available boron was depleted, remained healthy and free of all symptoms. The leaves at the fourth and fifth nodes which developed during a time when the available boron was suboptimal also showed severe symptoms. Boron clearly is required for the formation of tissues but apparently is not required for the maintenance of tissues already matured. It appears to be required for the formation of certain structures and is then unavailable for further reutilization.

The utilization of boron in the formation of tissues is reflected in well-known observations that actively growing plants require larger amounts of boron than slowly growing plants. Likewise, deficiency symptoms appear more readily in the former than in the latter. Such climatic factors as day length (Gauch and Dugger, 1954) most likely alter the boron requirement of plants by their effects on total growth or growth rate. This appears to be the case in radish (Skok, 1941).

It is often noted that crop plants in the field appear to grow normally at first but at a later stage exhibit boron deficiency symptoms. The reason for this is that most soils are not entirely devoid of boron, and the plants are thus permitted to make a certain amount of growth. As the rate of tissue formation increases, the low level of boron in the soil becomes insufficient for maximum growth and boron deficiency symptoms appear. If the symptoms are recognized early, applications of boron by the use of foliar sprays (Boynton, 1954) have often proven successful in preventing losses.

C. Distribution of Boron in the Plant Cell

Comparatively little work has been done on the distribution of boron within the cell. Since specific functions of boron might be associated with certain cellular constituents, information on its distribution within the plant cell would be of value. Skok and McIlrath (1957) have separated intracellular fractions of sunflower and mung bean tissues by differential centrifugation. Boron determinations on these cellular fractions indicated that none of them were entirely free of boron, although the mitochondria and microsomes contained less than the nuclei, plastids, or the supernatant portion. Certain changes took place in the supernatant fraction that were related to the appearance of deficiency symptoms. When the plants were growing normally, the nondialyzable portion of the supernatant fraction contained about 25 per cent of the total supernatant boron. As the plants utilized the available boron in the substrate (limited to 50 μg. boron per sunflower plant) the dialyzable boron fraction of the supernatant dropped and finally reached zero when the plants exhibited pronounced boron deficiency symptoms at the terminal buds. The nondialyzable boron fraction of the supernatant, however, remained constant throughout this time. These findings again illustrate that boron is not reutilizable. The relatively small amount of boron in the plant which is available for required plant functions is the unbound or dialyzable portion of the supernatant fraction. When this is depleted the plant exhibits the usual deficiency symptoms. The bound portion is not available for movement to other sites.

It would be of interest to know the specific function of the boron in the nondialyzable portion of the supernatant fraction. It appears that the dialyzable portion of the supernatant fraction represents free boron not yet utilized. Although it is of great importance to the economy of the plant, it may not serve any special physiological requirement in itself but perhaps represents an available pool for use in specific functions. It would seem that boron analyses of crop plants for prognostic purposes could be of additional value if the boron level of the dialyzable portion of the supernatant fraction were included. Undepleted boron levels in this fraction would indicate adequate boron nutrition. It is well known that even boron-deficient plants contain appreciable amounts of total boron.

Considerable attention has been given to the physiological importance of the soluble boron fraction in plants (Shive, 1941; Marsh and Shive, 1941; Marsh, 1942; Reeve and Shive, 1944), but this fraction has generally not been further separated. Shive (1941) has pointed out that monocots contain a higher percentage of their boron in the soluble fraction than do dicots. This is perhaps the reason why monocots usually take longer to show pronounced deficiency symptoms. Important boron-calcium relationships have been shown to exist (see reviews by Gauch and Dugger, 1954; Berger, 1949; and Stiles, 1946) and these relationships appear to involve primarily the soluble boron fraction (Marsh and Shive, 1941; Marsh, 1942; Reeve and Shive, 1944).

It is of interest to recall that while boron deficiency induces necrosis of the young growing regions and has little effect on fully matured tissues, the older tissues (lower leaves) of a plant are the first to exhibit toxic effects when excess amounts of boron are supplied (Eaton, 1940). This may be related to the fact that the actively growing younger tissues utilize boron and remove it from the available pool while the older tissues no longer utilize boron and permit it to accumulate. It then becomes of interest to ask whether the boron in the soluble fraction (or perhaps in the dialyzable portion of the supernatant fraction) is involved in producing boron toxicity symptoms, and if so, in just what manner this is brought about.

IV. Role of Boron in Cellular Functions

Gauch and Dugger (1954) have reviewed most of the experimental work available at the time of their publication that had been offered to substantiate various hypotheses on the suggested roles of boron. Much of this work will not be covered except where required under the following discussions.

A. In Relation to Enzymes

Boron has often been spoken of as a "catalytic" element, chiefly, perhaps, because it is required in minute amounts. Up to the present time it has not been rigorously demonstrated that boron is indispensable for the action of an enzyme or that it is a constituent of an enzyme, as has been done for the other micronutrient as well as for several macronutrient elements (McElroy and Nason, 1954). There is, however, a considerable amount of work, based both on *in vivo* and *in vitro* studies, which shows that either addition of boron or lack of boron alters a number of enzymatic reactions (Alexander, 1942; Dugger *et al.*, 1957; Gauch and Dugger, 1954; Hewitt, 1951; Torssell, 1956, 1957b,d). Changes of this type, however, are difficult to interpret since the complexing property of the borate ion could alter such reactions in a number of ways.

Even if boron functions primarily in the formation of a structural unit in the cell (see Sections III,B and IV,C), biochemical transformations would be involved which would undoubtedly be mediated by enzymes. It is quite possible that although the utilization of boron, in whatever manner this may occur, is controlled by an enzyme or enzymes, the boron itself may not be part of this enzyme but part of the substrate. This would account for the observed changes in enzymatic rates brought about by changes in available boron. It is interesting to note that many metals in enzyme systems function in electron transfer systems by shifts in valence states to carry out oxidation-reduction reactions. As boron exists in only a single valence state of three, it cannot function in this manner. There are, of course, other possible modes of action.

B. In Relation to the Complexing Property of the Borate Ion

Consideration has been given to the possibility that a relationship exists between the physiological action of boron in the plant and the capacity of the borate ion to complex with various polyhydroxy and related compounds, including several of the common sugars. Isbell *et al.* (1948) have discussed this complexing reaction and reviewed much of the early literature pertaining to it. Torssell (1957a,c,d) among others, is giving further attention to this subject and has extended it to various boron compounds. Zittle (1951) has reviewed and discussed the complexing reaction of borate with various substances of biological interest, and Gauch and Dugger (1954) have discussed the possible relationships of sugar-borate complexes to the translocation of sugar. Schmucker (1934), Winfield (1945a), and Hoagland (1948) were among the first to call attention to the possible relationship between the complexing property of borate and the function of boron in the plant, and Gauch and Dugger (1953, 1954) were the first to suggest that sugar translocation might be involved.

1. Substitution of Complexing Substances for Boron. Numerous attempts have been made to substitute other elements for boron, in order to determine whether boron is really indispensable and whether it alone can prevent the symptoms associated with its absence. In no case has any other element successfully replaced boron in promotion of normal growth for any appreciable length of time.

In this connection elements that form complexes similar to the borate complexes should be of particular interest. A demonstration that boron deficiency symptoms are partially alleviated by any of these elements would constitute evidence for the hypothesis that the function of boron is, at least in part, related to the complexing property of the borate ion. Skok (1957a) has shown that germanium temporarily alleviates boron deficiency symptoms in the absence of boron. (Tchakirian (1943) has shown that mannitol and several sugars, as well as other polyhydric alcohols, form complexes with germanic acid.) Sunflower plants grown in boron-free nutrient solutions exhibited visible deficiency symptoms by the fourth day; in the next two days or so the tips became necrotic. Plants that received no boron but that received germanium (free of any detectable boron contaminant) remained free of such symptoms for about 9 days and produced significantly greater amounts of dry weight over the plants receiving neither boron nor germanium. Germanium has been shown repeatedly to alleviate boron deficiency symptoms temporarily, but it should be emphasized that germanium cannot replace boron except for a few days. These results provide further but entirely indirect evidence that some physiological function or functions of boron are related to the complexing property of the borate ion. They do not illustrate the manner in which the complexing reaction functions.

2. Sugar Translocation. A considerable amount of work has indicated that the carbohydrate content of plant tissues is often affected by the state of boron nutrition. Leaves of boron-deficient plants are generally high in sugar and other carbohydrates, suggesting that these materials for some reason have not moved out of the leaves. The accumulation of carbohydrates in the leaves may result partly from a breakdown of the phloem, although this cannot be the entire explanation in all instances. As Gauch and Dugger (1954) have noted, these effects are often noticeable early and may precede any detectable involvement of phloem.

Gauch and Dugger (1953, 1954) have proposed that a major function of boron is in the translocation of sugar, in that a sugar-borate complex may facilitate the passage of sugar through membranes. They postulate that the sugar-borate complexes may move from cell to cell or that boron is a constituent of the membranes forming a temporary union with sugar at these sites to effect its passage. They consider the latter mechanism to be the more likely. They further consider boron deficiency symptoms such as necrosis of apical buds and root terminals to be in reality manifestations of sugar deficiency, in that lack of boron prevents the movement of sugar to the growth sites where carbohydrates are required.

Gauch and Dugger (1953) and Sisler et al. (1956), who measured translocation by use of applied C^{14}-labeled sucrose and by exposure to $C^{14}O_2$, found that boron enhanced the movement of tagged materials. Skok (1957a), however, was unable to obtain consistent or significant increases in translocation by the addition of boron to the applied C^{14}-sucrose.

If boron is essential for sugar translocation and boron deficiency symptoms result from a shortage of carbohydrate materials, it would appear that application of such materials to the deficient sites should at least in part alleviate the symptoms. Experiments to test this have been done by Sisler et al. (1956), McIlrath and Palser (1956), and Skok (1957a); in addition to sugars (dextrose and sucrose) Skok (1957a) also used citric acid, as organic acids are generally more penetrating than sugar. No alleviation of boron deficiency symptoms or increase in growth was obtained in any of these cases. These results are not consistent with the hypothesis that boron functions primarily in the translocation of sugar.

If boron is required for the passage of sugar through membranes, it might be argued that sugar applied to boron-deficient plants could not be expected to enter the cells. In Skok's experiments (1957a), however, the materials were applied at the start of the experiment before the plants showed any indications of boron deficiency, and applications were continued daily for a period of 3 weeks. Furthermore, all the workers who used C^{14}-labeled sugar to study translocation in relation to boron found at least some activity in the upper regions of the boron-deficient plants.

It appears quite probable that some relationship between boron and sugar translocation does exist. This relationship, however, appears to be indirect and related to cellular activity and growth rather than directly to the formation of a boron-sugar complex. Materials, including sugar, move from leaves to such metabolically active regions as growing tips because of a gradient. The active regions utilize sugars faster, both because of a high respiration rate and a high growth rate accompanied by rapid utilization of carbohydrates in syntheses, thus depleting sugar in these regions. In the meristem and terminal region of a boron-deficient plant, metabolism is at a lower rate and translocation of sugar from leaves to this region is reduced. Addition of boron could be expected to raise the metabolic rate toward the normal and to increase movement of sugar into the area.

The high variability generally observed in translocation following application of boron is most likely related to variability in the amount of boron already present in the plant; this would determine whether additions of boron to the plant would have any effect in increasing the activity of the terminal region and growth in general. This indirect relationship of boron to sugar translocation was demonstrated by Skok (1957b), in an experiment designed to determine the rate of translocation of C^{14}-sugar applied to the lower leaves of sunflower plants in relation to the metabolic activity of the apical meristems and terminal bud regions. The sugar was applied to three types of experimental plants: (1) intact boron-sufficient plants, (2) intact plants first supplied with boron and then transferred to solutions lacking boron for 3 days, and (3) healthy and vigorous boron-sufficient plants (as those in 1) but whose terminal buds were excised 24 hours prior to the sugar application. The last treatment was included to determine whether sugar translocation in boron-sufficient plants is retarded by the removal of the active terminal bud region. The plants were harvested 27 hours after the sugar was applied, and radioactivity of the upper portions of the plants was determined. The results indicated that the translocation of sugar into the top portions of the boron-sufficient plants with excised terminal buds was significantly reduced; it was only 57 per cent of that translocated to the top portions of intact boron-sufficient plants. The reduction was even greater than that observed in the partially boron-deficient plants.

Sisler et al. (1956) found that sugar translocation was increased in boron-deficient plants only if boron was added before the deficiency symptoms became severe; after visible symptoms developed, applied boron did not increase translocation. However it is quite likely that the application of boron to plants of the latter type would eventually result in increased translocation. It takes considerably longer to reinduce growth and activity in the bud after visible symptoms have appeared. The observations of Sisler et al. would seem to substantiate the indirect effect of boron on translocation. If the translocation effect of boron is related primarily to the ability of a sugar-borate complex to move more efficiently, the application of boron should be effective at any time, provided the plant is still alive.

Still another indirect effect of boron on sugar translocation is suggested by the work of Dugger *et al.* (1957), who found that the enzymatic conversion of glucose-1-phosphate to starch is reduced by the presence of borate. This effect might be reflected in apparent translocation, in that the first mentioned response could alter the total available amounts of translocatable sugar.

C. In Relation to Cellular Development

Among the most consistent effects of boron deficiency are various abnormalities involving tissue formation on the cellular level. This, quite logically, must lead one to consider seriously the possibility that boron is related to some specific function in cellular maturation and differentiation. The observable histological effects brought about by insufficient amounts of boron have been well documented; the subject has been adequately reviewed by Palser and McIlrath (1956), Gauch and Dugger (1954), and Stiles (1946), as well as by others. In general, the lack of boron may at first result in increased cambial activity often followed by collapse of the meristematic cells, but in almost all cases normal vascular tissue development is prevented. Boron-deficient plants often show poor differentiation as well as disintegration and necrosis both in phloem and xylem tissues. Lignification of the xylem elements rarely takes place in a normal fashion.

1. Cellular Maturation and Differentiation. Frequent reference has been made to boron requirements in cell division. The inference is generally made that boron is required for growth and needed for cell division, since necrosis in apical and root meristems is a typical deficiency symptom. As dividing and differentiating cells are generally in close proximity to each other in actively growing tissues, it is often difficult to recognize clearly which cellular stage is first involved in the early cellular damage resulting from boron deficiency. However, Reed (1947) has shown that in the apical portions of boron-deficient sunflower and celery plants, the subapical cells were first affected while the cells of the primary meristem were normal. The terminal cells became necrotic only after those below had failed. These observations then would indicate that cell division can proceed in the absence of boron although the completion of the growth cycle (cellular maturation and differentiation) is prevented; the failure of the underlying tissues results in death of the entire meristem and bud. Meristematic cells, in fact, often become increasingly active at first when boron is lacking, which would not be expected if boron were specifically required for cell division. McIlrath and Skok (1957) found that lack of boron in *Chlorella* had considerably less effect on cell division than on subsequent cellular growth as reflected in accumulation of dry matter.

There is no doubt that boron is required for some phase of cellular activity; the absence of boron for even short intervals results in retardation of cellular activity and arrested growth in plants. Skok (1957b) postulated that since radiosensitivity is related to cellular and metabolic activity, some relationship might be expected to exist between radiosensitivity and boron nutrition; he suggested that the use of ionizing radiations might be expected to prove useful for the study of the physiological role of boron. Experiments designed to test for the presence of such a relationship indicated that it does exist. They further indicated that boron functions primarily in the maturation and differentation of the plant cell rather than in cell division.

Sunflower plants were grown in nutrient solutions with or without boron for intervals of from 2 to 5 days, after which they were X-irradiated and grown on boron-containing media. Typical radiation symptoms developed in the subsequently formed leaves in both groups of plants irradiated with 1000 r. However, while these symptoms persisted in all leaves produced by the plants grown with boron available at all times, the plants from which boron was withheld for 3 days prior to irradiation developed similar radiation symptoms only in the leaves up to the sixth to seventh node. The following leaves were normal and free of all symptoms. These results indicate an intimate relationship between boron nutrition and radiosensitivity. A reduced rate in some phase of cellular activity, brought about by the temporary withholding of boron, resulted in greater radioresistance; this phase of cellular activity, then, must be specifically dependent upon boron.

An attempt was made to identify this normally radiosensitive growth phase (which can be rendered relatively radioresistant by withholding boron) by irradiating a series of germinating sunflower seedlings at different growth stages. The plants of this series exhibited a marked and measurable change in radiosensitivity during the early stages of germination and seedling development. During the very early part of germination, the cells swell and stretch on taking up water, and then cell division becomes a predominant phase of cellular activity; this phase showed relative radioresistance. Cell division is followed by cellular maturation and differentiation (although cell division continues), and this later phase was characterized by marked radiosensitivity. The relatively high radiosensitivity of this cellular stage, and the fact that it can be prevented by withholding boron during the later seedling stage then suggests a boron requirement for some process or processes concerned with cellular maturation or differentiation rather than with cell division.

Current experiments by the same author, not yet entirely completed, suggest that withholding boron for 3 days prior to X-irradiation with 1000 r also reduces irradiation-induced genetic effects in the following generation.

2. *Cell Wall Formation.* Various investigators have suggested that boron functions somehow in the formation of wall constituents. Schmucker (1934) suggested that the complexing property of boric acid has a direct relationship to the structural formation of membranes. In discussing the role of boron in the various parts of the cell, Smith (1944) assigned special importance to the wall. Torssell (1956) believes that boron is involved in the regulation of cell wall formation, in that complexes between boric acid and carbohydrates control the deposition of oriented cellulose micelles. He attributes the stiffness of boron-deficient tissues and cell walls to improper deposition of the cellulose micelles, which results in the prevention of further stretching. Spurr (1957), who found definite effects of boron on the morphogenesis of plant cell walls, believes that boron is related to some phase of carbohydrate nutrition involving wall formation. He believes that the Gauch-Dugger hypothesis, that boron facilitates sugar translocation, is directly related to the formation of cell walls.

Numerous investigators have reported that lignification of xylem elements in boron-deficient plants is invariably poor, and that boron is generally abundant in bark, wood, and other lignified tissues. A further interesting suggestion that boron may be involved in lignin formation and lignification of the cell wall may be gleaned from the following publications. Reed (1947) has reported that tissues of boron-deficient plants are high in phenolic compounds. Siegel (1953, 1954) has shown that various phenolic compounds act as lignin precursors but that they are converted to lignin in plant tissues only if hydrogen peroxide is added. In this connection it is interesting to note that Alexander (1942) has shown that boron-deficient plants are exceptionally high in catalase activity. This might deplete the hydrogen peroxide level sufficiently to reduce or prevent lignin formation, with resultant accumulation of the phenolic compounds as noted by Reed (1947). All these observations give renewed interest to the claim of Shkol'nik and Steklova (cited in Gauch and Dugger, 1954) that addition of hydrogen peroxide to the substrate improved the growth of boron-deficient plants. Further investigations certainly are required to strengthen this suggestive relationship between boron and lignin formation. Presley and McIlrath (1956) found no increases in growth nor any alleviation of boron deficiency symptoms by the addition of hydrogen peroxide to the substrate of boron-deficient tomato and turnip plants; however, similar additions appeared to produce slight increases in growth of boron-deficient cotton plants. Shkol'nik and Steklova carried out their experiments with flax. Different species, with different quantitative boron requirements, may possibly vary in their responses to hydrogen peroxide.

3. *Pectic Substances.* A number of investigators have considered boron to be related to the formation of pectic substances (Gauch and Dugger, 1954), but little specific information is available. Johnson and Dore (1929) have pointed out that the texture of boron-deficient plants suggests that the pectic materials are absent or less abundant, and Marsh and Shive (1941) believe that boron is in some way related to pectin formation. Baker *et al.* (1956), on the other hand, found leaves of boron-deficient plants to have a higher concentration of pentosans and pectic substances than leaves of normal plants. With respect to the breakdown of cells in the terminal region of a boron-deficient plant, reference is often made to the failure of the formation of pectic materials. Lorenz (1942) in microchemical studies found that boron-deficient tissues of the beet root had a lower protopectin-pectin ratio than normal tissues. He suggested that boron deficiency appears to act in preventing the formation of such compounds as protopectin rather than in the destruction of compounds already formed.

Winfield (1945b) pointed out the interesting fact that *Aspergillus niger* and *Penicillium glaucum,* organisms which are said to require neither boron nor calcium, are also incapable of synthesizing true pectic compounds.

Hoagland (1948) has suggested that boron may have a role in pectin formation, in that it may function in the formation of galactose derivatives from glucose. Skok has carried out some experiments (unpublished) to determine whether boron is related to the formation of substances required for pectin formation and that may be lacking in boron-deficient plants. One per cent solutions of α-D-galacturonic acid (adjusted to pH 6.5 and converted to the sodium salt by the addition of sodium hydroxide), D-(+) galactose and L-(+) arabinose were applied singly and in various combinations to sunflower plants.

The plants were placed in nutrient solutions with or without boron, and the materials were applied to the terminal bud region twice daily starting at the beginning of the experiment and lasting over a period of 12 days. Control plants consisted of untreated plants and plants receiving sucrose and dextrose. None of the applications produced any alleviation of boron deficiency symptoms of any sort; the symptoms appeared at the same time and progressed at the same rate, and death of the tips occurred in all boron-deficient plants regardless of the treatment applied. These experiments do not of course prove that boron is unrelated in any way to the formation of pectic materials; however, they indicate that boron-deficient plants do not lack essential constituents of this type. It is quite likely that the applied materials had entered the cell and were available if needed; carbon from infiltrated C^{14}-labeled galactose was shown to be incorporated in cell wall constituents of *Avena* coleoptile sections (Ordin and Bonner, 1957).

4. Interrelationships. On the basis of information available at the present time, it appears quite likely that boron functions in some manner in the maturation and differentiation of the plant cell. It apparently is built into some structural unit where it is then unavailable for movement to and reutilization at another site. Further research is required to identify the structures and compounds in which it is involved and to determine the manner in which it functions in their formation. It has been stated (Skok, 1957b) that the boron requirement for cellular maturation and differentiation may be specific in the sense that cellular differentiation is boron-dependent only in certain cell types. Such specificity may be the basis for the essentiality or nonessentiality of boron among the various plant groups and other living forms. The requirements for cell maturation in higher plants must be quite different from the requirements in fungal or animal cells. If boron is required for some other more basic physiological function in the cell, it is reasonable to expect its requirement to be more widespread among living organisms, and if it is of importance in facilitating diffusion of sugars through membranes, it would be expected to have equal importance in animal and plant cells.

V. Summary

Boron is an essential micronutrient for the growth of higher plants. It appears to be required by algae, but not by fungi or animals. Little is known concerning its essentiality among the other plant groups.

There is little or no reutilization of boron, and a continuous external supply is required by an actively growing plant. The small amount of boron in the plant cell which is available for plant functions is the un-bound (dialyzable) portion in the supernatant fraction. When this is depleted, boron deficiency symptoms promptly appear. It is needed for the formation of tissues but does not appear to be required for the maintenance of fully matured tissues.

The capacity of the borate ion to complex with various polyhydroxy and related compounds appears to be related to the physiological function of boron, but the nature of this relationship is not clear. It is likely that the apparent effect of boron on sugar translocation is an indirect one, related to the effect of boron on growth and cellular activity rather than to a direct enhancement of diffusion through membranes through formation of a sugar-borate complex.

A major function of boron appears to be in relation to the maturation and differentiation of the cell rather than to cell division. It seems to be involved in the formation of some cellular structure or structures such as the cell wall, cell wall constituents, or other cellular entities.

It has not been demonstrated rigorously that boron is indispensable for the action of an enzyme or that it is a constituent of an enzyme. It is possible but not proven that (1) boron is a component of an enzyme or is indispensable for the activation of an enzyme, or (2) that boron is not part of an enzyme system itself but that, in this case, its utilization or incorporation into the plant cell is mediated through an enzyme or enzymes. On the basis of available information, the latter possibility appears more probable to the writer.

A useful step toward gaining more information about the exact manner in which boron is utilized by the plant would be to determine the form or forms in which the bound boron is associated in the cell constituents.

REFERENCES

Agulhon, H. 1910. Thèse de l'Université de Paris, 158 pp.
Alexander, T. R. 1942. *Botan. Gaz.* **103**, 475–491.
Allen, P. J. 1954. *Ann. Rev. Plant Physiol.* **5**, 225–248.
Arnon, D. I., and Stout, P. R. 1939. *Plant Physiol.* **14**, 371–375.
Baker, J. E., Gauch, H. G., and Dugger, W. M., Jr. 1956. *Plant Physiol.* **31**, 89–94.
Berger, K. C. 1949. *Advances in Agron.* **1**, 321–351.
Boynton, D. 1954. *Ann. Rev. Plant Physiol.* **5**, 31–54.
Brandenburg, E. 1931. *Phytopathol. Z.* **3**, 499–517.
Brenchley, W. E. 1914. *Ann. Botany (London)* **28**, 283–301.
Chandler, F. B. 1941. *Maine Agr. Expt. Sta. Bull.* **404**, 305–400.
Chilean Nitrate Educational Bureau, Inc. 1948, 1951, 1953. "Bibliography of the Literature on the Minor Elements and Their Relation to Plant and Animal Nutrition," 4th ed., Vols. I, II, III. New York.
Dugger, W. M., Jr., Humphreys, J. E., and Calhoun, B. 1957. *Plant Physiol.* **32**, 364–370.
Eaton, F. M. 1944. *J. Agr. Research* **69**, 237–277.
Eaton, S. V. 1940. *Plant Physiol.* **15**, 95–107.
Eyster, C. 1952. *Nature* **170**, 755.
Gauch, H. G., and Dugger, W. M., Jr. 1953. *Plant Physiol.* **28**, 457–466.
Gauch, H. G., and Dugger, W. M., Jr. 1954. *Maryland Univ. Agr. Expt. Sta. Bull.* **A-80** (Tech.).
Haselhoff, E. 1913. *Landwirtsch. Ver.-Sta.* **79–80**, 399–429.
Hewitt, E. J. 1951. *Ann. Rev. Plant Physiol.* **2**, 25–52.

Hoagland, D. R. 1948. "Lectures on the Inorganic Nutrition of Plants," p. 31. Chronica Botanica, Waltham, Massachusetts.

Isbell, H. S., Brewster, J. F., Holt, N. B., and Frush, H. L. 1948. *Natl. Bur. Standards (U.S.) Paper RP 1862* 40, 129–149.

Johnson, E. S., and Dore, W. H. 1929. *Plant Physiol.* 4, 31–62.

Lorenz, O. A. 1942. *Cornell Univ. Agr. Expt. Sta. Mem.* 246.

Marsh, R. P. 1942. *Soil Sci.* 53, 75–78.

Marsh, R. P., and Shive, J. W. 1941. *Soil Sci.* 51, 141–151.

Mazé, P. 1915. *Compt. rend.* 160, 211–214.

McElroy, W. D., and Nason, A. 1954. *Ann. Rev. Plant Physiol.* 5, 1–30.

McIlrath, W. J., and Palser, B. F. 1956. *Botan. Gaz.* 118, 43–52.

McIlrath, W. J., and Skok, J. 1957. *Plant Physiol.* 32, Suppl., XIII.

Ordin, L., and Bonner, J. 1957. *Plant Physiol.* 32, 212–215.

Palser, B. F., and McIlrath, W. J. 1956. *Botan. Gaz.* 118, 53–71.

Presley, H. J., and McIlrath, W. J. 1956. *Trans. Illinois State Acad. Sci.* 49, 36–42.

Purvis, E. R., and Ruprecht, R. W. 1937. *Univ. Florida Agr. Expt. Sta. Bull.* 307.

Reed, H. S. 1947. *Hilgardia* 17, 377–411.

Reeve, E., and Shive, J. W. 1944. *Soil Sci.* 57, 1–14.

Schmucker, T. 1934. *Planta* 23, 264–283.

Shive, J. W. 1941. *Plant Physiol.* 16, 435–445.

Siegel, S. M. 1953. *Physiol. Plantarum* 6, 134–139.

Siegel, S. M. 1954. *Physiol. Plantarum* 7, 41–50.

Sisler, E. C., Dugger, W. M., Jr., and Gauch, H. G. 1956. *Plant Physiol.* 31, 11–17.

Skok, J. 1941. *Botan. Gaz.* 103, 280–294.

Skok, J. 1957a. *Plant Physiol.* 32, 308–312.

Skok, J. 1957b. *Plant Physiol.* 32, 648–658.

Skok, J., and McIlrath, W. J. 1957. *Plant Physiol.* 32, Suppl., XIII.

Smith, M. E. 1944. *Australian J. Exptl. Biol. Med. Sci.* 22, 257–263.

Sommer, A. L., and Lipman, C. B. 1926. *Plant Physiol.* 1, 321–349.

Spurr, A. R. 1957. *Science* 126, 78–80.

Steinberg, R. A. 1945. *Soil Sci.* 60, 185–189.

Stiles, W. 1946. "Trace Elements in Plants and Animals." Cambridge Univ. Press, London and New York and Macmillan, New York.

Tchakirian, A. 1943. *Bull. soc. chim. France* 10, 98–102.

Torssell, K. 1956. *Physiol. Plantarum* 9, 652–664.

Torssell, K. 1957a. *Arkiv Kemi* 10, 513–521.

Torssell, K. 1957b. *Arkiv Kemi* 10, 529–540.

Torssell, K. 1957c. *Arkiv Kemi* 10, 541–547.

Torssell, K. 1957d. *Svensk Kem. Tidskr.* 69, 34–44.

Warington, K. 1923. *Ann. Botany (London)* 37, 629–673.

Winfield, M. E. 1945a. *Australian J. Exptl. Biol. Med. Sci.* 23, 111–117.

Winfield, M. E. 1945b. *Australian J. Exptl. Biol. Med. Sci.* 23, 267–272.

Zittle, C. A. 1951. *Advances in Enzymol.* 12, 493–527.

CHAPTER 16

The Accumulation of Boron in Margins of Corn Leaves

J. D. SAYRE

Agricultural Research Service
United States Department of Agriculture
and the Ohio Agricultural Experiment Station
Wooster, Ohio

	Page
I. Introduction	245
II. Materials and Methods	246
III. Results	246
A. Seasonal Accumulation	246
B. Inbred Lines	248
C. Gravel Culture	249
IV. Summary and Conclusions	250
References	250

I. INTRODUCTION

The accumulation of mineral elements in the tips and margins of leaves has been noticed by many investigators reporting toxicity and deficiency symptoms of various elements. In the literature these tip burns or marginal burns, however, have been associated with deficiencies, and not many observations have been made in which the elements were higher in the margins than in the rest of the leaf. Tip burns and marginal dying are common symptoms of both mineral element relationships and diseases in many plants (Hambridge, 1941). In recent years the high accumulation of elements in the margins of leaves, particularly corn leaves (Sayre, 1952), has been observed through the use of radioisotopes. This paper reports the accumulation of elements in the margins of corn leaves under field conditions and in gravel culture in the greenhouse.

II. Materials and Methods

The samples analyzed consisted of corn leaves with the midribs removed. The margins, about one-eighth inch wide, were cut off from fresh leaves with shears, and the rest of the leaf was considered blade tissue. In the first experiment, 10 plant samples were collected at random every week during the summer for the dissection.

Early in the season all the leaves from a plant were included in the sample, but later the upper leaves were separated from the lower ones. At tasseling, the upper, middle, and lower leaves of the plant were collected separately. The middle leaves consisted of the ear leaf and one or two leaves above or below it. As the season progressed the lowest leaves, of course, died and disintegrated. During the latter part of the season it was impossible to separate the margins from the rest of the blades, and the entire leaf blade was put in one sample.

The boron in the dried, finely ground tissue from the leaves of the corn plant was determined spectrographically. The dried, powdered plant tissue was ashed and mixed with lithium fluoride as a diluent or buffer, and the mixture was arced in an open-air A.C. arc at 2200 volts and 2.2 amperes. The spectrograms were recorded on spectrum analysis No. 2 plates for 100 seconds.

The spectrum analysis No. 2 plates were calibrated by proper techniques, and working curves for boron were made from synthetic mixtures of known amounts of plant ash and boron. A lithium line of the buffer or major constituent was used as the internal control line and all line densities were read on a densitometer. The quantities of boron obtained from line density readings of the boron line at 2497 A. were expressed in micrograms per gram of dried plant tissue.

III. Results

A. Seasonal Accumulation

The double cross Ohio W64 was sampled weekly from July 1 to October 7. The dry weight of the leaf blades and margins is shown in Table I. Since the margin is not a definite morphological part of the leaf, there is considerable variation in its dry weight. The data show the proportion of blade tissue represented by the margins and the increase in dry matter over the season. The micrograms of boron per gram of dried plant tissue are shown in Table II. The boron content of the margins was from 1 to 11 times that of the remainder of the leaf blade. In another test, 6 double crosses including W64, the boron content of the leaf margin was always much higher than that of the remainder of the blade.

TABLE I

Dry Weight of Margins and Blades of Leaves of 10 Corn Plant Samples at Weekly Intervals (W64)

Date (1952)	Margin (g.)	Blade (g.)	Margin (g.)	Blade (g.)	Margin (g.)	Blade (g.)	Total (g.)
	All leaves						
July 1	3.1	14.4					17.5
July 8	6.7	37.1					43.8
	Upper leaves		Lower leaves				
July 15	7.1	44.5	6.1	22.6			80.3
July 22	8.5	62.5	7.9	42.4			121.3
July 29	11.7	76.0	8.0	48.2			143.9
	Upper leaves		Middle leaves		Lower leaves		
Aug. 4	10.1	63.8	7.2	45.9	5.5	27.2	159.7
Aug. 12	9.5	53.4	7.3	45.9	4.8	23.6	140.2
Aug. 19	11.0	67.0	7.5	50.3	5.1	29.4	170.3
Aug. 26	13.1	82.6	8.2	47.0	5.5	23.4	179.8
Sept. 2	9.5	57.0	7.1	40.8	48.3		162.7
Sept. 9	11.9	66.8	7.7	49.1	42.9		178.4
Sept. 16	11.4	54.2	7.6	37.8	28.4		139.4
Sept. 23	9.9	67.5	6.1	42.2	29.3		155.0
Sept. 30	11.1	61.7	7.3	41.8	38.9		160.8
Oct. 7	9.4	46.7	58.4		19.5		134.0
Totals	144.0	855.2	88.0	509.7	20.9	103.6	
Grand totals	999.2		656.1		331.8		1987.1

In another study, samples were obtained from corn grown on soil of different pH values, of 5.5, 6.0, 6.5, 7.0. 7.5, with and without manure, and following alfalfa or timothy in the rotation. There was an accumulation of boron in the margin of the corn leaves in these samples as in previous tests. A careful study of the data showed that the different soil pH values had no effect on the accumulation of boron in the blade or the margin. The plants grown on the manured end of the plot were slightly higher in boron than those without manure, and all of the samples from the corn following alfalfa showed slightly higher boron content than those from corn plants following timothy in the rotation.

Samples also were obtained from corn plants grown on continuous culture plots. The corn plants from these plots were very small and non-vigorous, but the accumulation of boron in the margin was just as evident as in the tests of larger and more vigorous corn plants.

TABLE II

Concentration of Boron (Micrograms per Gram of Tissue) in Margins and Blades of
Corn Leaves, Sampled at Weekly Intervals

	Margin (µg.)	Blade (µg.)	Margin (µg.)	Blade (µg.)	Margin (µg.)	Blade (µg.)
	All leaves					
July 1	15	14				
July 8	49	9				
	Upper leaves		Lower leaves			
July 15	57	10	76	12		
July 22	83	12	49	9		
July 29	140	12	88	12		
	Upper leaves		Middle leaves		Lower leaves	
Aug. 4	140	14	97	12	70	14
Aug. 12	110	13	81	10	54	14
Aug. 19	97	17	58	14	58	14
Aug. 26	146	30	81	23	71	22
Sept. 2	105	17	76	13	24	
Sept. 9	100	20	100	17	33	
Sept. 16	81	16	62	14	19	
Sept. 23	52	17	48	13	14	
Sept. 30	66	19	60	16	16	
Oct. 7	51	18	14		19	

B. Inbred Lines

Leaf samples of 19 inbred lines were analyzed for boron content. Ten
ear leaves from each of 4 replications were obtained, the margins and
blades separated, and the 40 leaves composited for spectrographic analysis. The results are shown in Table III.

Considerable variation in the boron content of the margins and blades
among the inbred lines is shown. Again the boron content of the margin
was from 3 to 11 times as much as in the remainder of the blade. In many
plants the margins of the leaves were badly discolored and dying, but
the rest of the plant did not seem to be injured by the high amount of
boron in the tissues.

Many of the inbred lines were grown in rich greenhouse soil following
tomato culture, and the marginal accumulation studied. In these tests
there was even higher boron accumulation in the margins than under
field conditions. In some plants many of the margins were discolored and
dying, while the rest of the leaf showed no apparent injury or toxicity.

TABLE III

Dry Matter and Boron Content (Micrograms per Gram) in Field-Grown Inbred Lines of Corn

Inbred	Boron		Dry matter	
	Margins (μg.)	Blade (μg.)	Margins (g.)	Blade (g.)
Oh02	110	18	7.0	34.8
Oh04	91	18	10.8	54.6
Oh07	110	15	5.2	38.4
Oh7B	90	14	7.1	37.1
Oh26	150	15	6.2	32.4
Oh28	86	13	7.4	38.4
Oh29	140	19	8.2	51.3
Oh33	102	18	7.2	36.3
Oh40B	230	22	4.7	35.6
Oh41	117	15	6.7	34.9
Oh42	132	15	6.5	32.4
Oh43	212	29	6.6	43.1
Oh45	196	20	6.8	45.5
Oh51	62	10	5.5	26.2
Oh51A	85	8	6.1	27.9
Oh56	124	22	6.4	31.8
Oh56A	78	19	6.4	29.8
Oh65	131	19	5.3	30.1
Oh84	106	40	6.0	36.2

C. Gravel Culture

Boron accumulation in the leaf margins of corn plants grown in gravel culture also was investigated. In these experiments the plants were grown to the silking stage under controlled nutrition and water supply in gravel culture. Boron (1.6 g. H_3BO_3) was added to each culture, except the control on February 28, and samples of the leaves were obtained every 3 days thereafter until the last part of March. These samples were dissected, dried, and analyzed as in the other tests. In this experiment boron moved into the margins of the leaves very rapidly, as shown by data in Table IV. The boron content increased more than 15 times at the end of 3 days. At the end of 6 days, it increased about 20 or 30 times what it had been before the boron was added to the culture. After the sixth day there seemed to be no further boron accumulation in the plant, and the variations shown were apparently due to sampling and other conditions. Apparently the 3-day sampling interval was too long to show the actual rate of movement into the corn plant. In this experiment the margins of

TABLE IV

Dry Matter Content and Boron Concentration in Microgram per 100 mg. of Tissue in Margins and Blades of Corn Plants Grown in Gravel Cultures in the Greenhouse

Date (1956)	Boron content			Dry matter	
	Margins (μg.)	Blade (μg.)		Margins (g.)	Blade (g.)
February 28[a]	14	3	No boron	2.8	15.5
March: 2	234	9	Boron	2.6	18.0
5	540	32	Boron	2.7	18.4
8	650	74	Boron	2.6	16.2
11	615	64	Boron	2.7	17.5
14	520	42	Boron	3.6	16.2
17	670	50	Boron	3.5	15.5
20	540	47	Boron	3.5	17.0
20	21	5	No boron	3.3	18.0

[a] 1.60 g. H_3BO_3 added to each culture at 3:00 P.M. on February 28, 1956.

the corn leaves died after the twelfth or fifteenth day, but the rest of the plant showed no apparent boron injury. This test indicates that corn plants can tolerate a rather high amount of boron in their tissues. The effects of the high boron content are shown first in the dying of the margins of the leaves.

IV. SUMMARY AND CONCLUSIONS

Spectrographic analysis showed that boron accumulates in the margins of corn leaves. The boron content ranged from 3 to 11 times higher in the margins than in the rest of the leaf. Boron accumulation in field grown plants shows a seasonal high point in the margins about midsummer with decreases in the older leaves. Lower (older) leaves have less boron in the margins than upper ones. Inbred lines differed somewhat in the boron content of the leaf margins. Similar accumulations occur in corn under greenhouse conditions in rich soil, the amount being even higher than under field conditions. The leaf margins where boron accumulates has many small vein endings and is the region where guttation occurs. These facts may in some way help explain the marginal accumulation of boron in corn leaves.

REFERENCES

Hambridge, G., ed. 1941. "Hunger Signs in Crops," 327 pp. National Fertilizer Association, Washington, D.C.

Sayre, J. D. 1952. *Ohio Agr. Expt. Sta. Research Bull.* **723**, 30 pp.

CHAPTER 17

Boron for Alfalfa and Other Crops on Ohio Soils

E. O. McLEAN AND G. W. VOLK

Ohio Agricultural Experiment Station
Wooster, Ohio, and Ohio State University
Columbus, Ohio

Boron deficiencies for plant growth have been reported in soils throughout the humid sections of the United States and some of the arid sections. In fact, according to Russel (1957) in a very recent report, boron deficiencies have been found in every State east of the Mississippi River and generally in the first two tiers of States west of the Mississippi as well as the Pacific States, with only seven Western States reporting no deficiencies of boron in their soils.

Ohio is in the humid region and therefore is located in the general area where deficiencies of boron may exist. To date no areas of *pronounced* deficiency are known in the State. This does not rule out the fact that extra boron may be needed on certain soils for optimum plant growth and maximum yields under specified conditions. Neither does it imply that all soils of Ohio are equally well supplied with total and available boron, but it does imply that indiscriminate applications of boron are not recommended for all soils even when one specific crop is to be grown.

Since Berger (1949) and Russel (1957) have recently given rather comprehensive reviews of the boron situation from the agronomic viewpoint, the present paper is largely confined to boron studies of Ohio soils, with main emphasis on alfalfa. Other work has been cited only as it has close connection with studies made here.

McVickar (1939) determined the total and available boron contents of 14 soil types of Ohio, representing mainly medium to fine-textured mineral soils under the various weathering conditions of the State. His data indicated considerable variation among soils but that those lowest in available boron were still several times the minimum threshold value of

0.5 p.p.m. suggested by Berger (1949) as the level below which deficiency symptoms might be expected to occur on alfalfa.

Berger (1949) recognized that plants differ greatly in their boron contents or needs and in their abilities to take up sufficient boron for normal growth when grown in soils with various levels of boron. Under normal conditions corn, small grains, and grasses generally contain 5 p.p.m. of boron or less. Alfalfa, the clovers, and soybeans may contain from 20 to 40 p.p.m. when growing normally. Similarly, radish and beet plants may contain as much as 65 to 75 p.p.m., while the onion in contrast may contain only 4 p.p.m. The plant with the highest boron content so far reported is the poppy with 95 p.p.m.

Berger (1949) has classified crops on the basis of their abilities to grow normally on soils of various levels of boron. Generally those plants which may be expected to grow normally on soils of < 0.1 p.p.m. of available boron include the cereals and grasses with a few others such as soybeans, peas, beans, potatoes, small fruits, and buckwheat. Those which generally require from 0.1 to 0.5 p.p.m. include tobacco, cotton, peanuts, the tree fruits except for apples, and the vegetables: tomatoes, lettuce, carrots, and onions. Crops requiring > 0.5 p.p.m. of available boron include apples, alfalfa, the clovers, sugar and red beets, and a goodly number of vegetables, including the root crops and cabbage and its close relatives. Vegetable crops are frequently grown under conditions of high productivity on sandy soils which are subject to considerable leaching. Omission of boron from the fertilization program under these conditions would sooner or later be expected to bring about boron deficiency. The sandy soils of the Atlantic Coastal Plain are particularly noted for their deficiencies of trace elements for vegetable crops. However, we shall confine our remarks here to agronomic crops.

There are several factors which affect the amount of boron available to plants in soils. The total amount present would obviously have an effect on the amount available. Berger and Truog (1940) indicated that the available boron is generally less than 5 per cent of the total. Presumably most of the boron present in soils initially was contained in the mineral tourmaline. Berger and Truog (1940) have demonstrated the stability of this mineral by showing that sunflowers cannot obtain sufficient boron from finely ground tourmaline for more than meager growth. However, it is known that boron is found in other mineral forms in soils. As boron is slowly released by weathering from minerals such as tourmaline, it may be leached away by percolating water or it may be tied up in insoluble inorganic compounds or in chelated form with organic matter. Additions to the soil of soluble boron compounds may likewise be tied up in one of these forms. Hence on soils deficient in boron the need for continued applications of boron is closely analogous to the need for systematic applications of the major element, phosphorus.

The relatively low availability of boron to plants generally is rather intimately tied up with the lime status of soils. Under acid conditions, it tends to become soluble and may then be leached out or removed by cropping. Under alkaline conditions the boron may be tied up chemically with the associated calcium. Deficiency of boron on sandy or highly weathered loam soils would undoubtedly be due to actual removal of the limited supply made soluble or added. Deficiencies in alkaline soils are probably due to lack of availability, while those in peats and mucks probably result from both low total quantity and low availability. Parks and Shaw (1941) reported that boron was fixed by calcium bentonite progressively more as the pH was increased. Likewise in calcium humus, boron was fixed in greater quantities than in the bentonite and increasingly more as the pH increased. They also found increased fixation in the humus system as the pH decreased below 6. Presumably any boron the organic matter; however, the fact that humic materials do fix boron fixed in organic form would be released again upon decomposition of may sometimes make necessary the addition of boron to such soils even when relatively high in total boron content. Parks and Shaw (1941) also showed that boron was fixed by a synthetic aluminosilicate as well as the bentonite and suggested that fixation may account for the fact that under field conditions boron deficiencies are generally observed on highly weathered soils with high contents of free alumina and/or silica. Since their data showed maximum fixation of boron with both high calcium and high aluminum, it is questionable whether natural soils high in aluminum, such as those reported by McLean et al. (1958) for soils of northeast Ohio, would fix more than normal amounts of boron because of their inherent acidity and concomitant low calcium status.

Parks (1944) showed that drying increased boron fixation, but it is generally believed that the occasion would be rare when soils would dry out deep enough to fix significant amounts of boron as a result of drying. However, it is recognized (see Berger and Truog, 1945) that most of the boron in mineral soils in humid areas is in the topsoil associated with organic matter. Thus during periods of dry weather, roots are forced to feed in the lower horizons of the soil where the boron content is less plentiful. This may account for the greater occurrence of boron deficiency during the drier summer months observed by Latimer (1941).

It is known[1] that the boron contents of many Ohio and Indiana coals are relatively high. An average of 118 p.p.m. of boron was obtained in 158 samples from the two States. A few samples contained as much as

[1] Unpublished data from U.S. Geological Survey, courtesy of Taisia Stadnichenko.

300 p.p.m. This reflects the general occurrence of boron in the earth's crust as well as the tendency for it to accumulate in organic form. In addition, it points to the distribution of boron via smoke contamination of the atmosphere. Unpublished data by Dr. J. D. Sayre of the Ohio Agricultural Experiment Station and U.S. Department of Agriculture indicate that the "fly ash" from coal furnaces may contain up to 50 p.p.m. of boron. One would certainly expect this finely divided material to be widely distributed over the countryside as an ingredient of smoke. In addition, there undoubtedly would be some boron expelled into the atmosphere from the exhausting of ignited petroleum products—particularly unrefined industrial and automotive fuels, as well as those refined but enriched with added boron for antiknock purposes. Since the amounts of coal and petroleum consumed by industry in Ohio are tremendous, it seems likely that possible shortages in supply of boron in the soil often may be adequately supplemented from the boron-containing impurities in the air. This would seem to be a fruitful area of investigation for the future—not only with regard to boron, but also with regard to other trace elements.

In regard to its possible distribution as an impurity in the atmosphere, boron may well be comparable with sulfur. The supply of the latter in a given soil is known to be supplemented by that brought down from the impurities of the atmosphere by the various forms of precipitation. The actual amount of sulfur deposited on a given area from the atmosphere depends on the proximity to cities—particularly industrial plants, kind and amount of industry, and location of site area with respect to direction of prevailing winds.

Most of the investigations that have been done with agronomic crops in the field in Ohio were on alfalfa with lesser amounts on sugar beets, ladino clover, corn, oats, wheat, and soybeans. In unpublished studies, borax was applied to alfalfa on experimental fields throughout Ohio. No pronounced increases in yields were obtained on any soils. Under certain conditions slight responses were obtained. On a highly weathered Planasol soil, i.e., Clermont silt loam, the added boron appeared to improve the alfalfa, but significant increases in yield were not obtained. On an old stand of alfalfa at Wooster where boron removal had been appreciable, response to boron was observed. Also at Wooster, (Anon. 1951) liming the soil to pH 7 increased the apparent response of corn and oats to borax application compared to soil limed only to pH 6. Little response was obtained to boron on any of the other crops, including wheat, soybeans, mixed hay, and sugar beets. Response to boron on soils in the greenhouse has been observed in cases where the same soil evidently did not respond in the field.

More recently, Stackhouse *et al.* (1956) reported the results of a considerable number of field and greenhouse studies of boron applied to alfalfa in Ohio. Field plot studies in 1951 at 26 locations in six counties of Ohio and eight studies in 1953 at a like number of locations were included. Also included was a report on a potash-borax interaction study with alfalfa, running from 1951 to 1954 at Wooster. In addition, in 1952, tissue samples were taken and analyzed from alfalfa fields from 61 locations. A greenhouse investigation was made of five soils. On the basis of all the results obtained in these various studies, they concluded that: (1) no general recommendation could be made for boron applications to alfalfa on Ohio soils, (2) if there are boron deficient fields of alfalfa, they do not occur often, and many so-called boron deficiency symptoms evidently were the result of other causes, (3) boron added to grass-legume meadows may actually decrease yields, while addition to pure legume stands is less likely to do so, and (4) the water-soluble boron is evidently not a good index of need for boron fertilizer for alfalfa.

The Soil Testing Laboratory of Ohio State University tests soils for the farmers of Ohio. If the farmer requests it (and is willing to pay the extra cost to have it done), he may have his soils tested for boron, manganese, and magnesium. During the period March 1, 1955 to July 1, 1956 this laboratory tested 31,000 samples for the major fertility element needs. During this same period, 687 samples were tested on the above mentioned optional basis for available boron content.[2] These samples came from counties throughout the State, but fewer came from eastern and southern Ohio than from other sections. The analyses revealed that 16 per cent of the samples tested contained less than 0.5 p.p.m. of available boron as measured by the hot water extraction technique of Berger and Truog (1944). It will be noted that 0.5 p.p.m. of boron is considered necessary for alfalfa by Berger (1949). Fifty-six per cent of the samples contained 0.5 to 1.0 p.p.m., and 28 per cent contained more than 1 p.p.m. of available boron.

Even though the number of samples is small, a few generalizations may be permissible as regards the soils testing low in available boron, i.e., < 0.5 p.p.m. Approximately one-third of them were of coarse texture, i.e., fine sandy loam or coarser; two-thirds of the soils were of medium texture, i.e., loams to silty clay loams; and practically none were finer than silty clay loam.

Those testing low in boron were not confined to any one section of the State. Samples testing low from the three tiers of counties along the north boundary of the State were predominately sands. Samples testing

[2] Appreciation is hereby expressed to O. L. Musgrave, Director of the Soil Testing Laboratory for supplying this information.

low from the central counties were both sandy and silt loams. Those low in available boron from the south and southeast counties were predominately silt loams. These results lend support to the notion that the younger glaciated soils in the northern and western parts of Ohio are generally well supplied with boron. An exception would be the sands which are predominately lacustrine in origin and which may have had the available boron removed by cropping or leaching. On the other hand, in the southern and eastern parts of the State, weathering has been so severe that boron may be approaching a limiting value even on soils containing considerable clay such as the silt loams.

Application of boron (or borax) is currently recommended on the basis of soil test for available boron. If the soil test indicates less than 1 p.p.m. (2 pounds per acre), an application of 25 to 35 pound per acre of sodium tetraborate is recommended. This is recognized as an "insurance" practice with little field data to substantiate it. Obviously, it points to the need for vigilance in getting more soils tested, in correlation of soil tests with response to boron applications, and in continuation of efforts to ferret out those soils on which plants will respond to applied boron.

REFERENCES

Anonymous. 1951. "Handbook of Ohio Experiments in Agronomy." *Ohio Agr. Expt. Sta. Book Series* **B–1**, 69.
Berger, K. C. 1949. *Advances in Agron.* **1**, 321–351.
Berger, K. C., and Truog, E. 1940. *J. Am. Soc. Agron.* **32**, 297–301.
Berger, K. C., and Truog, E. 1944. *Soil Sci.* **57**, 25–36.
Berger, K. C., and Truog, E. 1945. *Soil Sci. Soc. Am. Proc.* **10**, 113–116.
Latimer, L. P. 1941. *Proc. Am. Soc. Hort. Sci.* **38**, 63–69.
McLean, E. O., Heddleson, M. R., Bartlett, R. J., and Holowaychuk, N. 1958. *Soil Sci. Soc. Am. Proc.* **22**, In press.
McVickar, M. H. 1939. Ph.D. Thesis. Ohio State University, Columbus, Ohio.
Parks, R. Q. 1944. *Soil Sci.* **57**, 405–416.
Parks, R. Q., and Shaw, B. T. 1941. *Soil Sci. Soc. Am. Proc.* **6**, 219–223.
Russel, D. A. 1957. *Yearbook Agr. (U.S. Dept. Agr.)* pp. 121–128.
Stackhouse, J. M., Pratt, P. F., and Volk, G. W. 1956. *Ohio Agr. Expt. Sta. Research Circ.* **33**.

Chapter 18

Enzyme Systems Concerned with the Synthesis of Monoiodotyrosine: I. The Occurrence and Behavior of Soluble and Mitochondrial Systems*

G. S. Serif and S. Kirkwood

Department of Agricultural Biochemistry
University of Minnesota
Saint Paul, Minnesota

	Page
I. Introduction	257
II. Methods	258
A. Soluble System	258
B. Mitochondrial System	258
C. Methods of Paper Chromatography and Radioautography	258
D. Quantitative Estimation of Radioactivity Present in Chromatographic Spots	259
E. Estimation of Proteolytic Activity	259
III. Results	259
A. Occurrence of the Enzyme Systems in Different Tissues	259
B. Behavior of the Insoluble System in Extrathyroidal Sites	260
C. Attempts to Liberate Protein-Bound MIT from Thyroid Mitochondria by Procedures that Do Not Disrupt Peptide Bonds	261
D. Investigation of the Action of Pure Proteolytic Enzymes upon Protein-Bound MIT	262
E. Proteolytic Activity in Mitochondria Prepared from Different Tissues	263
F. Nature of the "Front" Material Formed in Mitochondrial Preparations	264
IV. Discussion	265
V. Summary	267
References	267

I. Introduction

Recently two enzyme systems have been obtained from thyroid tissue which catalyze the synthesis of organically bound iodine. Fawcett and Kirkwood (1953, 1954) have described a cupric ion dependent, soluble,

* This work was supported by a grant from the National Science Foundation.

enzyme system in thyroid and salivary gland tissue (hereafter referred to as the "soluble system") which catalyzes the formation of monoiodotyrosine (MIT), one of the intermediates in thyroxine synthesis in the gland. More recently Taurog et al. (1955) have described an enzyme system associated with thyroid mitochondria which catalyzes the formation of MIT. This MIT, unlike that formed by the soluble system, is apparently protein-bound since it is immobile on paper chromatograms but runs as free MIT after being treated with a crude preparation containing proteolytic enzymes (pancreatin). It is the purpose of this paper to report further studies on the behavior and extrathyroidal occurrence of both the soluble system and the Taurog, Potter, and Chaikoff system (hereafter referred to as the "mitochondrial system").

II. Methods

A. Soluble System

All experiments involving the soluble system were carried out as previously described (Fawcett and Kirkwood, 1954) with the exceptions that 1.0 cc. of 5 per cent homogenate of the appropriate tissue was used and the incubation time was reduced to 0.5 hours.

B. Mitochondrial System

Experiments with the mitochondrial system were carried out according to the procedures of Taurog et al. (1955). The appropriate tissue was homogenized in ice-cold Krebs-Ringer bicarbonate buffer using a glass homogenizer. The homogenate was centrifuged at $600 \times g$ for 10 minutes at $0°C.$ to remove cell debris and nuclei, and the supernatant solution was then centrifuged at $25,000 \times g$ for 30 minutes at $0°C.$ The mitochondria were resuspended in fresh Krebs-Ringer bicarbonate buffer (3 cc. for each 1.5 g. of original tissue). This preparation will be referred to as the "mitochondrial system," but it should be kept in mind that it contains microsomes (Taurog et al., 1955). These suspensions were incubated as described by Taurog et al. (1955). After incubation, reaction was stopped by the addition of thiouracil and an aliquot of the reaction mixture treated with the appropriate enzyme preparation prior to chromatography while a control aliquot was kept at $0°C.$ and chromatographed directly.

C. Methods of Paper Chromatography and Radioautography

All preparations were chromatographed on Whatman No. 1 paper which had been pretreated with buffer. The general techniques have been described elsewhere (Fawcett and Kirkwood, 1954, 1955).

D. Quantitative Estimation of Radioactivity Present in Chromatographic Spots

In order to determine the proportion of iodine in the different chemical forms present at the end of each experiment, the corresponding spots on the chromatograms were cut out, folded into small squares (approximately 5×5 mm.), and counted with a scintillation counter. The radioiodine present in MIT was expressed as a percentage of the total radioiodine present on the chromatogram. This corrects for decay and for any small variation in the aliquot dried on the paper.

E. Estimation of Proteolytic Activity

All estimations of proteolytic activity were made using the method of Anson as described in Sumner and Somers (1953), with the modifications that the pH was adjusted to 7.4 and the time of incubation was increased to 30 minutes.

III. Results

A. Occurrence of the Enzyme Systems in Different Tissues

Fawcett and Kirkwood (1954) investigated a number of tissues and reported that the soluble system occurs in the thyroid and also in the parotid and submaxillary salivary glands. Taurog et al. (1955) investigated the occurrence of the mitochondrial system in three tissues, thyroid, liver, and kidney. It was present in the thyroid but absent from the other two tissues. In a later investigation, Taurog et al. (1956) found the mitochondrial system to be present in rat mammary gland, submaxillary, and spleen. In view of a possible connection between the two systems, it was decided to investigate their occurrence in a wide variety of tissues. The results of this investigation are shown in Table I. While the per cent incorporation of radioiodine into MIT cannot be considered an absolute index of the concentration of the enzyme systems in different tissues, it can probably be taken as a semiquantitative measure of the concentration. It is apparent that all tissues that possess the soluble system also contain the mitochondrial system. Five tissues show activity for the mitochondrial system, while the soluble system either cannot be shown to occur in them, or the per cent incorporation of iodide is so near to the control value as to have doubtful significance.

This work has also led to the discovery of the soluble system in a new site, the intraorbital and extraorbital lacrimal glands. The extraorbital lacrimal gland of the rat possesses fully as much activity for the soluble

TABLE I

Enzyme Activity in Various Tissues

Tissue[a]	Enzyme activity present[b]	
	Soluble system	Mitochondrial system
Thyroid		
Rat	+++	NI
Beef	++	+++
Sheep	NI	+++
Human	+++	NI
Submaxillary Salivary		
Rat	+++	++
Beef	+++	+
Guinea pig	++++	NI
Lacrimal		
Rat (intraorbital)	++	NI
Guinea pig (intraorbital)	+	NI
Human	++	NI
Extraorbital lacrimal (rat)	+++	+++
Stomach (rat)	+	++
Thymus (rat)	−	+
Spleen (rat)	−	++
Lymph node (rat)	NI	+
Lymph node (guinea pig)	−	+
Small intestine (rat)	−	+
Lung (rat)	−	+

[a] The following rat tissues were completely devoid of activity for both systems: liver, kidney, brain, skeletal muscle, heart muscle, testis, pancreas.

[b] The scale of enzyme activity was based on the per cent incorporation of radioiodine into monoiodotyrosine, in excess of that which takes place in boiled controls. For the soluble system a 5 per cent homogenate of the appropriate tissue was incubated for 0.5 hr. under the conditions described in Section II,A. For the mitochondrial system the conditions specified in Section II,B were used.

The scale of activities is:
0–2 per cent incorporation	−
2–10 per cent incorporation	+
10–25 per cent incorporation	++
25–50 per cent incorporation	+++
50 per cent and over	++++
Tissue not investigated	NI

system as does the rat thyroid, while its mitochondrial system activity is equal to that found in beef thyroid.

B. Behavior of the Insoluble System in Extrathyroidal Sites

Mitochondria from rat and beef submaxillary gland and rat extraorbital gland, unlike those from beef and sheep thyroid, form considerable amounts of free MIT as well as protein-bound MIT. The results of a typical experiment with salivary gland mitochondria are shown in Fig. 1. It is obvious that an appreciable amount of the MIT formed by these mitochondria is in the free state, while at the same time a considerable amount of protein-bound MIT is also formed. This is in contrast to the observation of Taurog *et al.* (1956) that no free MIT is formed by rat submaxillary mitochondria. We have no explanation for this discrepancy but have repeatedly found free MIT in experiments with rat and beef submaxillary mitochondria and with rat extraorbital lacrimal mito-chondria. The following facts indicate that the free MIT is formed within the mitochondria and then diffuses into the surrounding medium. Super-natant solutions prepared by centrifuging the mitochondrial suspensions at 25,000 × g do not synthesize MIT when supplemented with radio-iodide. Submaxillary mitochondria can be washed free of soluble MIT by repeated centrifugations and resuspensions in Krebs-Ringer bicarbonate buffer. When these washed mitochondria are allowed to stand, under toluene, in buffer for 12 hours at 38°C., free MIT is easily demonstrated in the supernatant solution.

C. Attempts to Liberate Protein-Bound MIT from Thyroid Mitochondria by Procedures that Do Not Disrupt Peptide Bonds

The formation of appreciable amounts of free MIT in salivary gland mitochondria opens the possibility that the protein-bound MIT formed in thyroid and salivary gland mitochondria is not bound by a peptide link-age, but rather is retained within the mitochondria by other means. If this were the case, then the steady release of free MIT by salivary gland mitochondria could be explained on the basis that they did not retain the MIT so tenaciously as thyroid mitochondria. In order to bring evidence to bear on this point, several types of procedure were tried. Thyroid mitochondria were submitted to the action of ultrasonic vibra-tions (0.5 megacycles per second) to disrupt the mitochondrial mem-brane; they were treated with a reducing agent (thioglycollic acid) to disrupt protein structure by breaking –S–S– linkages; they were submitted to the action of surface active agents (Tween 80 and a mixture of the sulfonated higher alcohols), and they were also treated with various enzymes which attack structures other than the peptide bond. The enzymes tried were: crystalline ribonuclease that had been prepared according to Kunitz (1940) and McDonald (1948), crystalline de-oxyribonuclease that had been prepared according to Kunitz (1950), lipase that had been prepared according to Singer (1948), and α- and β-amylases from a commercial source (General Biochemicals, Chagrin Falls, Ohio). None of these treatments caused the release of free MIT from beef thyroid mitochondria. In a few cases there was liberation after treatment with nonproteolytic enzymes. It was found, however, that the enzyme preparations were invariably contaminated with proteolytic activity and when preparations free of this activity were obtained, there was no liberation of MIT.

D. Investigation of the Action of Pure Proteolytic Enzymes upon Protein-Bound MIT

Since the work of Taurog et al. (1955) and the results reported in this paper both support the concept that the MIT formed in mitochondrial systems is bound by peptide bonds, it becomes of considerable interest to determine the action of specific peptidases on the iodoprotein formed by the mitochondrial system. In this way it might be possible to come to some conclusion as to the nature of the iodoprotein formed. Roche et al. (1954) have shown that it is possible to distinguish thyroglobulin from artificially iodinated proteins through the action of purified trypsin and pepsin. The MIT bound in thyroglobulin is remarkably labile to the action of trypsin, a high proportion of it being liberated in the free form by the action of this enzyme. Pepsin, on the other hand, liberates a

TABLE II [a]

The Action of Proteolytic Enzymes on Mitochondrial Iodoproteins

Source of mitochondria	Proteolytic enzyme	Liberation of protein-bound MIT[a] (%)
Beef thyroid gland	No enzyme	11.3
	Pepsin	11.5
	Trypsin	70.0
	Pancreatin	92.6
Rat salivary gland	No enzyme	49.1
	Pepsin	40.9
	Trypsin	92.0
	Pancreatin	88.3
Rat extraorbital lacrimal gland	No enzyme	37.2
	Pepsin	31.1
	Trypsin	76.3
	Pancreatin	77.4

[a] Mitochondria from the above sources were incubated with radioiodine as described in Section II,B. All free MIT was then extracted from the mitochondria by washing with Krebs-Ringer bicarbonate solution. The mitochondria were incubated, under toluene, with the above proteolytic enzymes for a 10-hr. period and the preparations analyzed to determine the per cent conversion of protein-bound MIT to free MIT.

high proportion of the MIT in trichloroacetic acid-soluble form, but this is largely MIT-containing peptides rather than free MIT.

In view of this, the iodoprotein formed in thyroid, extraorbital lacrimal, and submaxillary gland mitochondria was submitted to the action of crystalline preparations of pepsin and trypsin (Worthington Biochemical Corporation, Freehold, New Jersey) at their pH optima. The results of this investigation are shown in Table II. It is evident that the iodinated proteins formed in thyroid, salivary, and extraorbital lacrimal gland mitochondria have the characteristic in common with thyroglobulin, that the MIT contained in them is extremely labile to the action of trypsin. Also, like thyroglobulin, they show the characteristic that very little free MIT is liberated by the action of pepsin although, like Roche et al. (1954), we observe what appear to be MIT peptides. These results, in the case of salivary and lacrimal gland mitochondria, are somewhat obscured by the spontaneous hydrolysis that occurs in these tissues. However, it is quite clear that both trypsin and crude pancreatin markedly accelerate the release of free MIT in these preparations, while pepsin does not raise the rate of spontaneous hydrolysis.

E. Proteolytic Activity in Mitochondria Prepared from Different Tissues

Since the free MIT formed in the mitochondria of salivary gland tissue might arise as a result of the action of a proteolytic enzyme on protein-bound MIT, it was thought of interest to determine the level of

TABLE III

Proteolytic Activities of Mitochondrial Suspensions

Source of mitochondria	Relative proteolytic activity[a] moles $\times 10^7$
Rat submaxillary	9.1
Beef extraorbital lacrimal	3.0
Beef thyroid	Not detectable

[a] The relative proteolytic activity is expressed as the number of moles of tyrosine $\times 10^7$ that produce a color, with the Folin-Ciocalteu reagent, equivalent to that produced by the hydrolytic products that are formed from bovine hemoglobin during the incubation period (see Section II,E).

proteolytic activity in mitochondrial preparations from different tissues. The results of this investigation are shown in Table III. It would appear that there is a correlation between the observed proteolytic activity and the proportion of free MIT formed by the mitochondrial preparation.

F. Nature of the "Front" Material Formed in Mitochondrial Preparations

All mitochondrial preparations that synthesize protein-bound MIT, regardless of the source of the tissue, show a component that, upon chromatography, runs just behind the solvent front in the solvent system used in this work. Taurog *et al.* (1955), who drew attention to this

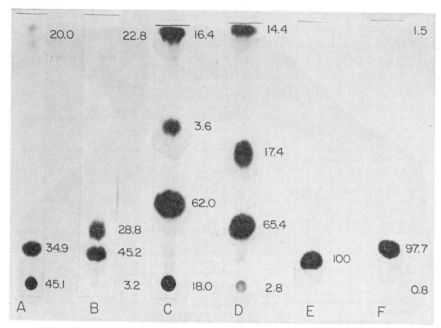

Fig. 1. Organic binding of radioiodine by beef thyroid and rat submaxillary mitochondria. Reproductions of radioautographs of paper chromatograms. (A) Beef thyroid mitochondria incubated with radioiodide ion. The components, in order from origin to solvent front are: protein-bound material, iodide ion, and unknown front components. (B) Mitochondria from (A) after pancreatin hydrolysis. The material at the origin has been replaced by MIT running directly in front of the iodide ion. Both (A) and (B) were run at a reduced temperature to show the multiple nature of the front components. (C) Rat submaxillary mitochondria incubated with radioiodide ion. The components in order from origin to solvent are: protein-bound material, iodide ion, MIT, and unknown front components. The higher R_f values and the failure of the front components to resolve are due to the chromatogram being run at a higher temperature than was the case with (A) and (B). (D) Mitochondria as in (C) but after pancreatin hydrolysis. (E) Beef thyroid mitochondria boiled prior to incubation with radioiodide. (F) Supernatant solution from beef thyroid mitochondria which had been incubated with radioiodide and then centrifuged at 25,000 × g. Faint spots for origin and front components are visible on the radioautograph but do not appear on this reproduction. The numerical values opposite the radioactive spots represent the percentage of the total activity on the chromatogram present in each spot. The experiments were conducted as described in Section II on methods.

material, observed that it was not affected by pancreatin. We have found that it is associated with the mitochondria since centrifugation at $25,000 \times g$ precipitates it (Fig. 1). Chromatography with the butanol-acetic acid-water system, carried out at reduced temperatures, shows that this "front" material consists of at least three distinct components. We are as yet unaware of their identity.

IV. Discussion

The relationship between, and the function of, the soluble and mito-chondrial enzyme systems is puzzling. That there is some relationship is indicated by their occurrence in the same tissues. An examination of Table I shows that all tissues that show appreciable activity for the soluble system also contain the mitochondrial system in considerable amounts. While the reverse is not true, it should be borne in mind that experiments with the mitochondrial system involve an enzyme preparation equivalent to 50 per cent original tissue, while those with the soluble system involve only the equivalent of 2 per cent of original tissue. It is entirely possible that the soluble system occurs in thymus, spleen, lymph node, intestine, and lung, but for the above reason is not detectable in these tissues.

If there is a connection between the two enzyme systems, there would appear to be two possible explanations for this relationship. The first is that the soluble system may be the result of the mitochondrial system passing into solution. Since the soluble system requires cupric ion, the copper presumably replaces something that is destroyed when the enzyme system passes into solution, or it could also replace a factor which is essential for the action of both systems but which does not pass into solution from the mitochondria. The soluble system will not accept protein (casein) as substrate (Fawcett and Kirkwood, 1953), and this would appear to argue against the identity of the two systems. However, the results observed with crystalline trypsin, which will be discussed below, indicate that the mitochondrial system is iodinating tyrosine located at specific points within the protein molecule; casein may not possess tyrosine in this specific combination. Although the best substrate for the soluble system yet reported is free tyrosine, it will also accept a tyrosine compound with the amino nitrogen in an amide link (Fawcett and Kirkwood, 1954). It is therefore possible that the soluble system will iodinate tyrosine located at the end of peptide chains.

The second possibility is that the mitochondrial system consists of the soluble system plus a mechanism for incorporating the free MIT formed into protein. If this is the case, the incorporation could proceed via *de novo* protein synthesis since the mitochondrial preparations contain microsomes which are necessary for this process (Tarver, 1954), or it could proceed by a transpeptidation reaction (Fruton and Simmonds, 1953). This type of exchange reaction is readily carried out by intracellular proteases. It will require much more evidence than is presently available to decide which one, if either, of these possibilities is the correct one.

The origin of the free MIT formed by salivary and extraorbital lacrimal gland mitochondria would appear to be the proteolytic activity present in these tissues. This is indicated both by the levels of proteolytic activity reported in Table III and by the fact that there is a continuous liberation of free MIT in washed mitochondrial preparations from salivary and extraorbital lacrimal gland tissue.

The formation, in mitochondria from a number of extrathyroidal sites, of an iodoprotein similar to thyroglobulin is very puzzling. The formation of such an iodoprotein *in vivo* would lead to extensive iodine storage and would almost certainly have been detected in experiments such as those reported by Pitt-Rivers and Trotter (1953) and by Cohen *et al.* (1955). It would appear that the storage of protein-bound iodine does not normally occur *in vivo* other than in the thyroid gland. In all experiments with both the soluble and mitochondrial systems, the possibility has to be kept in mind that the iodination observed may be of the type first reported by Keston (1944). If there is enzymatic generation of hydrogen peroxide then the possibility is opened that iodide will be oxidized to iodine which can then iodinate protein spontaneously. If this should prove to be the case, the possibility is opened that both enzyme systems have no physiological significance. However, experiments conducted with peroxide-generating enzyme have not as yet resulted in nearly as high a proportion of the available iodine being bound as is the case in experiments with both the soluble and mitochondrial systems (McQuillan *et al.*, 1954). Also, the specificity of the soluble system has been studied (Fawcett and Kirkwood, 1954) and is of a type indicating an enzyme catalysis of the iodination reaction.

The extreme lability of the protein-bound MIT toward trypsin allows some conclusions to be drawn regarding its position in the peptide chain. Trypsin has been shown to catalyze, specifically, hydrolytic cleavage and transpeptidation reactions involving the carboxyl group of either arginine or lysine (Fruton and Simmonds, 1953, p. 60; Waley and Watson, 1951). Thus the MIT formed by mitochondrial preparations appears to be at the end of peptide chains with its amino group linked to the carboxyl group of either lysine or arginine. Judging from the observations of Roche *et al.* (1954), this is also true of the iodinated amino acids in thyroglobulin, but is not true of those formed by the spontaneous iodination of casein.

V. Summary

(1) A number of tissues have been investigated for the presence of two enzyme systems that synthesize monoiodotyrosine.

(2) Salivary and extraorbital lacrimal gland mitochondria, unlike thyroid mitochondria, form appreciable amounts of free monoiodotyrosine. It would appear that this free monoiodotyrosine originated from iodoprotein.

(3) A series of studies confirms the idea that the bound monoiodotyrosine formed in thyroid mitochondria is in peptide combination.

(4) The action of pure crystalline pepsin and trypsin on the protein-bound monoiodotyrosine produced by mitochondrial preparations indicates that the major part of the monoiodotyrosine is located at the ends of peptide chains and is presumably linked to the carboxyl group of either lysine or arginine.

References

Cohen, B., Logothetopoulos, J. H., and Myant, N. B. 1955. *Nature* 176, 1268.

Fawcett, D. M., and Kirkwood, S. 1953. *J. Biol. Chem.* 205, 795.

Fawcett, D. M., and Kirkwood, S. 1954. *J. Biol. Chem.* 209, 249.

Fruton, J. S., and Simmonds, S. 1953. "General Biochemistry," p. 626. Wiley, New York.

Keston, A. S. 1944. *J. Biol. Chem.* 153, 335.

Kunitz, M. 1940. *J. Gen. Physiol.* 24, 15.

Kunitz, M. 1950. *J. Gen. Physiol.* 33, 349.

McDonald, M. R. 1948. *J. Gen. Physiol.* 32, 39.

McQuillan, M. T., Morton, R. K., Stanley, P. G., and Trikojus, V. M. 1954. *Nature* 173, 305.

Pitt-Rivers, R., and Trotter, W. R. 1953. *Lancet* 265, 918.

Roche, J., Michel, R., Lissitzky, S., and Yagi, Y. 1954. *Bull. soc. chim. biol.* 36, 143.

Singer, T. P. 1948. *J. Biol. Chem.* 174, 11.

Sumner, J. B., and Somers, G. F. 1953. "Chemistry and Methods of Enzymes," 3rd ed., p. 167. Academic Press, New York.

Tarver, H. 1954. *In* "The Proteins" (H. Neurath and K. Bailey, eds.), Vol. II, Part B, p. 1259. Academic Press, New York.

Taurog, A., Potter, G. D., and Chaikoff, I. L. 1955. *J. Biol. Chem.* 213, 119.

Taurog, A., Potter, G. D., Tong, W., and Chaikoff, I. L. 1956. *Endocrinology* 58, 132.

Waley, S. G., and Watson, J. 1951. *Nature* 167, 360.

CHAPTER 19

The Metabolic Role of Vanadium and Molybdenum in Plants and Animals*

ALVIN NASON

McCollum-Pratt Institute
The Johns Hopkins University
Baltimore, Maryland

	Page
I. General Chemical and Biological Aspects	269
II. Vanadium in Animals	271
A. In Tunicates	271
B. Localization, Properties, and Function of Vanadium in the Tunicates	272
C. Vanadium in Other Animals	274
D. Possible Role of Vanadium in Animals	275
III. Vanadium in Plants	276
A. Occurrence in Plants	276
B. Vanadium in Nitrogen-Fixing Organisms	277
C. Essentiality and Function of Vanadium in Plants	277
IV. Molybdenum in Animals	279
A. In Animal Nutrition	279
B. Molybdenum as a Component of Certain Animal Enzymes . . .	280
C. Is Molybdenum an Essential Trace Element for Animals? . . .	282
V. Molybdenum in Plants	282
A. In Nitrogen Fixation	282
B. Molybdenum in Nitrate Assimilation and Plant Nutrition	285
C. Role of Molybdenum as a Component of Nitrate Reductase . . .	286
D. Function of Molybdenum in Other Biological Processes	291
References	292

I. GENERAL CHEMICAL AND BIOLOGICAL ASPECTS

The elements vanadium and molybdenum have somewhat similar chemical properties. In the periodic system of the elements they are both classified as members of the transition metals, vanadium belonging to group Va and the first long period, and molybdenum belonging to the adjacent group VIa and the second long period. Vanadium forms compounds representing the oxidation states +2, +3, +4, +5, and

---

* Contribution No. 222 of the McCollum-Pratt Institute.

molybdenum forms compounds corresponding to oxidation states $+2$, $+3$, $+4$, $+5$, and $+6$.

The pentoxides of the two metals place them near nitrogen and phosphorus. The tetrachlorides, however, relate them to the carbon group, and the formation of complex anions tend to relate the two elements to each other and to chromium. The salts of vanadium and molybdenum possess very marked catalytic properties which have been used to some extent in the laboratory and in industry. The average concentrations of vanadium and molybdenum in the lithosphere are 100 p.p.m. and 10 p.p.m., respectively. Vanadium is the twentieth most prevalent element in the earth's crust.

From the biological standpoint, there appears to be a somewhat tenuous relationship between the two metals in the nitrogen fixation process. Molybdenum is indispensable for the assimilation of gaseous nitrogen, and vanadium has been reported by some workers to serve in place of molybdenum in nitrogen fixation by various organisms. Here the biological relationship between the two metals appears to end, due in large part to our limited knowledge of the mechanism of action in the living cell of these metals, especially of vanadium. Our understanding of the importance and role of molybdenum has been considerably augmented during the last five years.

Vanadium was first implicated at the biological level nearly fifty years ago by the discovery of an organic vanadium compound in the blood of certain marine organisms (Henze, 1911). Actually, the metal was found in the ash of plants much earlier (Bechi, 1879). Although it has since been reported to be present in different organisms, vanadium has not been established thus far as an essential element for animals. The fact that an element is found in living cells does not necessarily mean that it is essential. Rather it is necessary to show that it is required by a living form for normal growth and development. The essentiality of the trace metals has been established for the most part through the use of painstaking purification techniques and long term experiments, often over a number of generations, in order to induce deficiency states which may finally be accompanied by characteristic deficiency diseases. Deficiency symptoms together with the fulfillment of criteria that the action of the given metal is specific and direct have ultimately provided a sound basis for our knowledge of micronutrient element nutrition. With reference to plants, it is only very recently, using the above criteria, that vanadium was shown to be an essential micronutrient element for a species of green algae (Arnon and Wessel, 1953).

Molybdenum, on the other hand, was first indicated to be of biological importance almost thirty years ago in the biological process of fixation of gaseous nitrogen (Bortels, 1930). Since that time the metal has also been firmly established as an essential trace element for fungi and higher plants in the process of nitrate assimilation; its electron carrier role as the metal component of nitrate reductase has been elucidated, and its function has been indicated as a metal component of a number of enzymes of animal origin, suggesting that it may possibly be an essential micro-nutrient element for animals. The fact that molybdenum is a metal component of the xanthine oxidase and aldehyde oxidase of animals does not necessarily make molybdenum an essential element. It is important to show that molybdenum-containing enzymes are necessary for the well-being or normal physiology of the animal, and this has not been con-clusively established.

II. Vanadium in Animals

A. In Tunicates

The first report of the presence of vanadium in the animal kingdom was made by Henze (1911) who found 42,000 p.p.m. of the metal in the blood of an ascidian or marine worm belonging to the tunicates, a subphylum of the Chordata. Within two years, he produced evidence indicating that the metal was probably in the form of a vanadium-protein complex and that it was present in the blood of 4 other ascidians (Henze, 1912, 1913). Despite these early discoveries and investigations by other workers, proof of the essentiality and function of vanadium in these organisms has continued to elude subsequent studies. Hecht (1918) observed that the green blood cells of *Ascidia aetra* contained a vanadium compound, presumably the same as that reported by Henze, and postu-lated that the metal was functioning in some catalytic role. The presence of vanadium was further confirmed in various ascidians by Portes and Benoit (1923), Pied and Azéma (1930), Cantacuzène and Tchekirian (1932), and Vinogradov (1934), indicating that the tunicates tend to accumulate vanadium (see reviews by Bertrand, 1950 and Webb, 1956).

Vinogradov (1934) reported that the concentration of vanadium in most animals and plants is about 0.13 per cent, whereas in the tunicate marine worms that he had examined, comprising 13 ascidians, it was unusually rich, ranging as high as 1.5 per cent. He suggested that marine muds are the probable source of vanadium and that oils containing vanadium very likely formed from *Ascidia*. Webb (1939) examined the vanadium content in 8 species of the tunicates, including members of the families *Cionidae, Diazonidae,* and *Ascididae,* and found the metal to be present in large quantities ranging up to 1900 p.p.m. on a dry weight basis. Bertrand (1950) has summarized his analysis of a large number of tunicates and demonstrated the presence of vanadium in all 14 species which he examined. His data showed that the vanadium content of the tunicates in comparison with the figures for other animals is relatively high, never falling below 2.5 p.p.m. dry weight. With a few exceptions the majority of invertebrates showed a concentration between 0.2 and 2 p.p.m. The wide range of vanadium concentration, 2.5 to 1900 p.p.m., reported for tunicates is of interest and warrants a study of its effect on the morphological and physiological characteristics of the organism. There seems to be little question that the tunicates have the unusual characteristic of accumulating vanadium. Subsequent analysis by other workers (Noddack and Noddack, 1940; Kobayashi, 1949; Goldberg et al., 1951; and Ciereszko, 1954) are in general agreement with this pattern.

B. *Localization, Properties, and Function of Vanadium in the Tunicates*

The early work of Henze (1912) indicated that vanadium is present in the blood of tunicates in the form of a vanadium-protein complex. Hecht (1918) observed that vanadium was found in the green blood cells of *Ascidia aetra,* and Webb (1939) showed that the vanadium chromogen in the blood of ascidians is always found in special blood cells which he called vanadocytes. The vanadium chromogen was named hemovanadin by Califano and Caselli (1948) and was reported to exist in the vanadium-containing corpuscles as a pale green solution. Hemovanadin had been reported earlier (Webb, 1939) to contain pyrrole rings, not as a porphyrin complex, in view of the absence of well-defined absorption bands in the visible spectrum, but probably as a straight chain comparable to bile pigments. The studies of Califano and Caselli (1948, 1950), Califano and Boeri (1950), and Bielig et al. (1954) indicated that hemolysis of the vanadocytes yields an opalescent red-brown solution ("red hemovanadin") containing a protein which can be separated from hemovanadin by dialysis or precipitation. It is not certain whether the protein is independent or weakly linked with the hemovanadin in the corpuscle. According to these investigators, maintenance of the hemolysate at a low pH (2.4) permits a solution of "red hemovanadin" to remain stable for long periods. Neutralization, however, results in oxidation and the appearance of blue and green precipitates ("blue hemovanadin"). They suggested that vanadium is trivalent in the corpuscles and in the red-brown solution, and tetravalent in the blue and green precipitates. Borei and Ehrenberg (1954) reported on the basis of magnetic, spectrophotometric, and ultracentrifugation experiments that the vanadium in the red-brown hemolysates is present as trivalent

$V_2(SO_4)_3$. They questioned whether vanadium is indeed a part of an organic compound within the vanadocyte or bound as the inorganic ion to the cell membrane or some protein. Apparently the entire problem of the physical and chemical state of vanadium in the corpuscles of the blood of tunicates is still unsettled and in need of considerable clarification.

No generalization can be made concerning the distribution of vanadium in tunicates. The work of Webb (1939) showed that in *Phallusia mamillata* 80 per cent of the vanadium is in the blood. However, Bertrand (1950) found that in *Ascidia mentula,* which also possesses vanadocytes, there was about 560 micrograms of vanadium in the animal without its tunic as compared to the 1600 micrograms in the entire animal, whereas the blood contained approximately 10 per cent of the total, virtually all of it being present in the corpuscles. Webb's findings that in *Phallusia mamillata* most of the vanadium exists as hemovanadin in the blood has been confirmed by Baltscheffsky and Baltscheffsky (1953). On the other hand, Kobayashi (1949) reported that in *Chelyosoma siboja* 25 per cent of the vanadium is in the blood, 50 per cent in the gut and associated tissues (also shown by Goldberg *et al.* (1951) for *Ciona intestinalis*), and the remaining 25 per cent in other tissues. Vanadocytes are apparently lacking in *Chelyosoma* and *Ciona,* although they are present in *Ascidia mentula,* which also showed a low percentage of vanadium (Bertrand, 1950).

The function of the vanadium chromogen of the blood of tunicates is unknown. Henze *et al.* (1932), examining the possible role of the metal chromogen as a respiratory carrier, demonstrated that the combination of oxygen with the pigment was not comparable with that of oxygen with hemoglobin since in the former case the gas was not released under lower oxygen tension. They concluded that the vanadium chromogen was not a respiratory pigment but was capable of serving in reduction processes, perhaps in the reduction of carbon dioxide for the production of the celluloselike substance of the tunic. Hemovanadin has since been shown to reduce cytochrome c (Califano and Boeri, 1950) as further evidence of its reducing power.

An Australian tunicate species, *Pyura stolonifera,* has recently been reported to contain large quantities of an organic compound of iron in blood corpuscles similar to vanadocytes (Endean, 1953, 1954). No vanadium could be detected in the blood cells. The iron compound appears to be chemically unrelated to heme or other iron-porphyrin compounds and is, like hemovanadin, a strong reducing agent with the iron in the ferrous condition. It is possibly associated with a protein in the corpuscles and upon hemolysis passes out as a yellow solution. The fluid in these cells as well as in the vanadocytes is high in concentration of sulfuric acid.

There is no agreement as to the source from which the tunicates accumulate their vanadium. Bertrand (1950) feels that the concentration of vanadium in sea water is too small to account for this accumulation, especially since he (1943) and Noddack and Noddack (1940) failed to detect any vanadium in sea water. However, Ishibashi (1951) found 3 to 4 mg. per cubic meter. Bertrand instead concludes that the food of these animals serves as the source from which they obtain the metal, having also dismissed the marine muds as a possibility. Webb (1939), on the other hand, presents some strong arguments in favor of sea water as a possible source of vanadium. This seems to be the more likely possibility by analogy with established phenomena of accumulation of inorganic nutrients by other organisms from very dilute solutions (e.g., copper).

C. Vanadium in Other Animals

It is still too early to state categorically that the tunicates are the only group in the animal or plant kingdom which consistently accumulates vanadium in relatively large quantities. Phillips (1918) reported a vanadium concentration of 1200 p.p.m. on a dry weight basis in a holothurian (phylum Echinodermata) *Stichopus mobii.* Vinogradov (1934) has also indicated the presence of large concentrations of the metal in S. *japonicus* and some other holothurians, and Noddack and Noddack (1940) reported 57 p.p.m. in S. *tremulus,* a much higher value than that found in most marine invertebrates. On the other hand, vanadium accumulation does not appear to hold for all the holothurians, since Webb (1939) and Bertrand (1943) found low vanadium accumulation in other genera.

The earlier reports of vanadium in various animal tissues and natural products such as milk (Wright and Papish, 1929; Zbinden, 1931), eggs, milk, and chicken (Drea, 1934, 1935), human pancreas, liver, and kidney (Boyd and De, 1933), and teeth (Lowater and Murray, 1937) are somewhat in doubt in view of the use of carbon-arc spectrography. The presence of vanadium in graphite electrodes was pointed out by Newell and McCollum (1931), and Blumberg and Rask (1933) and again by Webb and Fearon (1937), who showed that metallic electrodes were free of vanadium. Webb (1937) found up to 150 p.p.m. of vanadium on a dry weight basis in a single mollusk species, *Pleurobranchus plumula.* Daniel and Hewston (1942) were uncertain about the presence of the metal in normal rat tissues (at most 1 to 5 p.p.m.) and did not consider it to be widely distributed in living organisms. Noddack and Noddack

(1940), in a carefully controlled spectrographic assay, found vanadium (5 to 57 p.p.m.) in a number of species of the porifera, coelenterates, and echinoderms. Bertrand (1943, 1950), using a chemical assay for vanadium with a demonstrated ability to determine as little as 0.02 p.p.m. vanadium in the dry organism, surveyed a large number of plants and animals. He found the concentration of vanadium on a dry weight basis in the invertebrates to range from 0.1 to 3.0 p.p.m. with 1.2 p.p.m. as the mean, whereas that in the vertebrates was considerably lower, ranging from 0.02 p.p.m. to 0.3 p.p.m. with a mean of 0.1 p.p.m. One invertebrate, *Plumatella fungosa* (a Bryozoan), had the unusually high vanadium concentration of 16.8 p.p.m. In the vertebrates, the highest values were obtained for liver, previously shown to accumulate metals, including manganese and vanadium (Luzzato, 1902; Reiman and Minot, 1920). Of all the vertebrates examined, fish showed the highest concentration of vanadium.

D. Possible Role of Vanadium in Animals

As indicated above, the role of vanadium in the tunicates is unknown. There are a number of reports in the literature concerning the effects of vanadium salts on the development of cells, on hemoglobin formation, and at high concentrations when administered in the diet or intraperitoneally (see Bertrand, 1950). None of these studies has pointed to a function for vanadium.

At the enzymatic level, vanadium was shown earlier to inhibit trypsin and pepsin (Lyonnet, 1899) and to accelerate the hydrolysis of hexose diphosphate by yeast extracts (Neuberg and Kobel, 1926). The fact that vanadium salts can act as catalysts in the oxidation of certain organic compounds prompted a study of the effects of the metal on oxygen uptake of various tissues. The addition of 20 to 40 micrograms of vanadium as sodium metavanadate or as vanadium acetate markedly increased oxidation of phospholipide by washed rat or guinea pig liver suspensions (Bernheim and Bernheim, 1939a). This vanadium stimulation, however, was inhibited by manganese, whereas iron, nickel, and titanium had no effect (Bernheim and Bernheim, 1939b). Curran (1954), using rat liver cell clusters, observed that salts of elements of atomic numbers 23 to 26 influence cholesterol synthesis. Vanadium (VO^{++} and VO_3^- were equally active) and iron decreased, whereas chromium and manganese increased, incorporation of labeled acetate into cholesterol. The fact that manganese nullified both the stimulatory effect of vanadium on phospholipid oxidation and the depressant action of vanadium on cholesterol synthesis suggested to Curran a possible link between the metabolism of cholesterol and liver phospholipides. Mountain et al. (1956) recently reported that dietary vanadium lowered the free cholesterol and phospholipide content of the liver of rabbits and prevented the elevation of free and total plasma cholesterol. This appeared to involve both an inhibition by vanadium of cholesterol synthesis and an acceleration of cholesterol catabolism.

In terms of its physiological effects on tissues and whole organisms, it has been reported that tetravalent vanadium, as $VOCl_2$, when added to the culture medium, caused a marked increase in the frequency of division of *Chlomonas paramecium* (Bowen, 1940). Pentavalent vanadium, as Na_3VO_4, manganese, and iron had no effect. A possible relationship between vanadium and the mineralization of teeth and bone appears to be emerging. Using carbon electrodes, which have since proven to be questionable as indicated in Section II,C, Lowater and Murray (1937) always found vanadium present in human teeth. They pointed out that the metal is isomorphous with phosphorus and can replace it in the apatite molecule.

Approximately a decade later it was reported that the addition of vanadium, as well as strontium, to the purified diets of rats and guinea pigs caused a marked stimulation of mineralization of bone and teeth during development of the animals (Rygh, 1949a,b, 1953). The greatest frequency of carious teeth were observed in the vanadium- and strontium-deficient animals. Subsequently, Geyer (1953), working with hamsters on a caries diet without vanadium, showed that the administration of the metal orally or subcutaneously resulted in a marked decrease of new enamel caries and a cessation of progress of dentine caries. The possibility that vanadium might be functioning by increasing the hardness of the apatite structure as well as serving as a binding substance between the organic and inorganic matter in enamel and dentine was suggested.

III. VANADIUM IN PLANTS

A. Occurrence in Plants

In view of the presence of vanadium in the lithosphere, one would expect, as in animals, that it would also be widely distributed in plants. Bertrand (1950) has reviewed the literature on the ubiquity of the metal in plants starting with the first reports in the 19th century. Bertrand (1942a,b) reported vanadium present in every sample of 62 species of plants analyzed and found that plants growing in soils that were richest in vanadium had greater amounts than those growing in poorer soils. Higher plants had a mean concentration of 1 p.p.m. on a dry weight basis with the roots appearing to be richer than the aerial parts. Most of the fungi had less than 0.5 p.p.m. except for *Amanita muscaria,* believed to live on the roots of certain conifers, which had a mean concentration of 112 p.p.m. vanadium. The root nodules of most leguminous plants had 3 to 4 p.p.m., which is 3 to 4 times higher than most plants, while that of the broad bean, *Vicia faba,* contained as much as 12 p.p.m. vanadium.

B. Vanadium in Nitrogen-Fixing Organisms

That vanadium might be implicated in nitrogen fixation was suggested by the work of Konishi and Tsuge (1933a,b), Shibuya and Saeki (1934), Burk (1934), Van Neil (1935), Burk and Horner (1935, 1937), and Bortels (1936, 1937), who found that the addition of molybdenum or vanadium to soils may increase bacterial numbers and nitrogen fixation. The studies of Bortels (1933), Burk (1934), and Burk and Horner (1935) demonstrated a stimulation of *Azotobacter* nitrogen fixation and growth by vanadium in cultures where nitrogen was not added in a combined form. Bortels (1937) extended these observations to other nitrogen-fixing microorganisms and showed only a small effect of vanadium salts on leguminous plants. Horner *et al.* (1942) reported that molybdenum or vanadium was essential for nitrogen fixation by a number of *Azotobacter* species with similar concentration ranges for both metals. The maximum effect by vanadium was 50 to 80 per cent of that produced by molybdenum. They found that the responses to tungsten were due to a molybdenum impurity.

The above studies tend to indicate that vanadium can replace molybdenum as a catalyst in nitrogen fixation by a number of soil bacteria, although there is no evidence that vanadium is required in the presence of molybdenum. On the other hand, it has been shown that although tungstate is a competitive inhibitor of molybdate in nitrogen fixation and nitrate assimilation by *Azotobacter* (Takahashi and Nason, 1957; Keeler and Varner, 1957), vanadate did not compete with tungstate, thus suggesting that vanadium cannot replace the molybdenum requirement. It has also been reported by Allen (1956) that vanadium cannot substitute for the molybdenum requirement of the blue-green algae *Anabaena.*

C. Essentiality and Function of Vanadium in Plants

Extensive studies have been made of the effect of vanadium salts on the growth of higher plants and microorganisms starting with the work of Witz and Osmond in 1886. Most of these investigations (reviewed by Bertrand, 1950) reported that vanadium concentrations of 10 to 20 p.p.m. or greater were generally toxic to higher plants, whereas in a number of cases lower concentrations proved to be stimulatory. The stimulatory effect on growth appeared to be more consistent for microorganisms.

During the last twenty years there has been an upsurge in the number of investigations concerned with vanadium as an essential trace element for plants. Bertrand (1941) found that vanadium acted as a growth factor in concentrations of the order of 2×10^{-9} M for *Aspergillus niger* and concluded that it was an essential micronutrient element.

Earlier Arnon (1938) had reported that increased growth of asparagus and lettuce plants in nutrient solution resulted from the addition of 0.01 p.p.m. of vanadium, and Mazé and Mazé (1939) concluded that the metal was favorable for corn. Dimitriev (1939), however, considered that vanadium had no effect on the growth of clover in soils. Gericke and Von Rennenkampff (1939–1940, 1940) found a more favorable effect of the anionic form of vanadium (as metavanadate) over the cation (V^{+++}) in barley cultivated on sand and in liquid culture. They reported vanadium to be a growth stimulant for plants up to a certain concentration when toxicity appears. On the other hand, Gericke (1940, 1941) soon afterwards reported that vanadium was unimportant as a fertilizer and that it had little or no effect on the growth of clover and wheat.

The soundest evidence thus far in support of vanadium as an essential trace element is the data of Arnon and Wessel (1953), who obtained a marked increase (as high as 8-fold) in the growth rates of the green alga *Scenedesmus obliquus* upon the specific addition of vanadium to the purified nutrient solution. The initial observation showed that increasing concentrations of iron resulted in increased growth rates. This, however, could be ascribed to an active impurity in the iron which proved to be vanadium. Of 19 different elements tested, only vanadium was capable of this effect. The requirement for vanadium could not be replaced by molybdenum, nor was there evidence for the replacement of molybdenum by vanadium. The authors regard this specificity of vanadium as ". . . supporting its proposed status as an essential for green plants."

There is still no proof that vanadium is an essential micronutrient element for higher plants. Warington (1951) investigated the effects of high and low molybdenum and vanadium levels in combination with toxic and nontoxic amounts of manganese on soybeans, flax, and oats, in nutrient solution and found no indication of the replaceability of molybdenum by vanadium. Low vanadium or molybdenum concentrations (0.1 p.p.m.) had no effect while high concentrations (10–20 p.p.m.) proved harmful. Chiu (1953) has reported an increased growth of rice seedlings by application of vanadium to nursery beds with best results at 150 p.p.m. V_2O_3. In terms of a possible role of vanadium, Arnon (1958) has just reported that the element raises the maximal level of the Hill reaction in photosynthesis by isolated chloroplasts.

IV. Molybdenum in Animals

A. In Animal Nutrition

The first report on the effect of molybdenum in animal nutrition was that of Ferguson *et al.* (1938) who attributed the cattle disease "teart," characterized by severe diarrhea and loss of condition, to the high-molybdenum content of certain pastures in Great Britain. These investigators produced a similar condition by dosing cattle with molybdenum or by raising the molybdenum content of the pasture. Similar toxic effects of high-molybdenum pastures (15 to 300 p.p.m. dry weight) have since been reported in the United States, Canada, New Zealand, and Sweden (see Dick, 1956a). The resemblance of the disease to that in certain copper-deficient areas in Holland led to the use of copper sulfate in its treatment.

The effects of molybdenum toxicity are intimately tied in with copper and sulfur nutrition as well. In the normal metabolism of both ruminant and monogastric animals, there is an antagonism between molybdenum and copper which is markedly affected by the sulfur content of the diet. It was shown (Dick and Bull, 1945) that sheep on a low-molybdenum diet (less than 0.1 p.p.m. dry weight) rapidly accumulated copper in their livers resulting in a typical copper toxicity. Conversely, when the diet is high in molybdenum (5 p.p.m.), sheep may develop a clinical copper deficiency (Wynne and McClymont, 1955). Molybdenum toxicity can be alleviated by increasing the copper in the diet, and copper toxicity by increasing molybdenum (Cunningham *et al.*, 1953). Studies in sheep have shown (Dick, 1953a, 1956a) that both the amount of molybdenum absorbed by the animal and the route of excretion of the metal depend on the amount of inorganic sulfate in the diet. If a sheep on a constant molybdenum intake is given a dose of sulfate, orally or parenterally, excretion of molybdenum in the urine will rapidly rise, and the concentration of the molybdenum in the blood will fall. Sulfate administration also results in an increased excretion of molybdenum in the feces, suggesting a reduction in the rate of molybdenum absorption from the gut. The lower tissue content of molybdenum in sheep on a high sulfate intake reflects the influence of the salt in reducing molybdenum absorption and increasing the loss of stored molybdenum.

The effect of molybdenum in turn on copper retention by tissues is dependent on the amount of inorganic sulfate in the diet (Dick, 1953b). Neither molybdenum nor sulfate alone interfered with copper retention unless the other was present (Dick, 1954). Thus the copper reserves of sheep were made to increase on low copper intakes provided dietary molybdenum and sulfate were low, whereas the animal's copper reserves were depleted despite a high copper intake if molybdenum and sulfate in the diet were also high. The protective effects of copper against molybdenum toxicity have also been observed in a number of nonruminants such as rats and rabbits (see Dick, 1956a, b), and there are indications that sulfate is involved in the same fashion as already indicated for ruminants.

In this respect, Miller et al. (1956) and Mills and Murray[1] have found that sulfate ingestion markedly reduces the storage of molybdenum and excessive accumulation of copper in the livers of rats fed high molybdenum diets. Using rats, Van Reen (1954) could show that molybdenum toxicity resulted in a 9-fold increase in the liver alkaline phosphatase, whereas catalase, cytochrome oxidase, isocitric dehydrogenase, and hemoglobin values were not severely affected. The response of liver alkaline phosphatase has proven to be a sensitive indicator of molybdenum toxicity, for at levels of molybdenum where growth and general appearance were normal, increased liver alkaline phosphatase was still observed. The results of Gray and Daniel (1954) indicated that methionine exhibited a protective action against molybdenum toxicity in rats on a milk powder ration. Subsequently, Van Reen found that both copper and methionine were also effective in correcting the enzyme changes due to molybdenum toxicity.

The proposal of Van Reen and Williams (1956) that methionine exerts its protective effect after oxidation to inorganic sulfate finds support in experiments with other sulfur compounds. Dietary sulfate, thiosulfate, cystine, or methionine had a similar protective effect against the growth depression of high dietary molybdenum (up to 1200 p.p.m.) as well as preventing the elevation of liver alkaline phosphatase associated with molybdenum toxicity in the rat. Mills et al.[2] have recently observed a marked depression in liver sulfide oxidase of molybdenum-toxic rats. It is possible that the earlier studies showing a relationhip between copper and molybdenum may be explained on the basis that copper sulfate was used in the diets. The complexity of the molybdenum-copper-sulfur interrelationship is further emphasized by recent reports (Dick, 1956b) that a high manganese intake antagonizes the effect of molybdenum and sulfate in limiting copper retention.

B. Molybdenum as a Component of Certain Animal Enzymes

Within the last five years molybdenum has been shown to be a metal constituent of a number of enzyme systems. In animal tissues, two en-

[1] Personal communication.

[2] Mills, C. F., Monty, K. J., Ichihara, A., and Pearson, P. B. (in preparation).

zymes which contain molybdenum have been characterized, namely, xanthine oxidase and liver aldehyde oxidase.

The need for adequate dietary molybdenum in order to establish normal levels of xanthine oxidase in rat tissues, especially in the intestine, was shown almost simultaneouly by two different groups of investigators (Richert and Westerfeld, 1953; De Renzo et al., 1953a). The enzyme was subsequently demonstrated to contain molybdenum as one of its components in the ratio of 1 atom of molybdenum per 2 moles of flavin (De Renzo et al., 1953b; Richert and Westerfeld, 1953, 1954; Green and Beinert, 1953; Totter et al., 1953; Mackler et al., 1954).

Molybdenum in xanthine oxidase is present as an anion and is apparently associated with an unidentified chromogen which acts as a dehydrogenase group for purine and aldehyde substrates. The loss in activity resulting from the parallel removal of molybdenum by aging and dialysis is not restored by the addition of MoO_3 (Westerfeld et al., 1956). The loss in activity upon dialysis of cream xanthine oxidase, which is accompanied by a parallel loss of molybdenum and flavin, is reported to be partially restored by addition of the supernatant solution obtained by boiling the undialyzed enzyme (De Renzo et al., 1956). However, about 0.83 γ of molybdenum as $Na_2MoO_4 \cdot 2H_2O$ must be added to produce the same reactivation as $3-4 \times 10^{-5}$ γ molybdenum in the supernatant fluid.

Mackler et al. (1954) reported a solution of MoO_3 to be effective in restoring the activity of xanthine oxidase, whereas solutions of sodium or ammonium molybdate, even at higher concentrations, were inactive. It was subsequently shown (Glenn and Crane, 1956) that both molybdate and MoO_3 are equally effective provided they have undergone alkalization followed by acidification, apparently forming complex molybdates such as silicomolybdates which are the effective agents. As yet the role of molydenum in xanthine oxidase has not been elucidated. Of great interest is the observation that the enzyme from milk and chicken liver contains 8 times as much iron as molybdenum (Richert and Westerfeld, 1954; Remy et al., 1955), thus also establishing xanthine oxidase as an iron system by essentially the same criteria which designated it as a molybdenum enzyme.

Liver aldehyde oxidase is a molybdoprotein which has iron-porphyrin groups as well (Mahler et al., 1954) and can be reactivated by silicomolybdates as already indicated for xanthine oxidase.

Jacobs (1956) has recently reported that the aerobic oxidation of ascorbate by rat liver mitochondria can be mediated by 12-silicomolybdate (or ferricyanide) in catalytic amounts. Under given conditions, the oxidation of ascorbate-reduced silicomolybdate (or ferricyanide) can also be coupled to phosphorylation with the attainment of P/O ratios as high as 3. This system may be of aid as an artificial model in helping to clarify the mechanisms of oxidative phosphorylation.

C. Is Molybdenum an Essential Trace Element for Animals?

There is no evidence to date that the molybdoproteins, xanthine oxidase and aldehyde oxidase, are essential for the well-being or growth of the animal. Approximately three-fourths of the total xanthine oxidase of the rat can be lowered by a low-protein diet or by tungstate feeding (Higgins et al., 1956) without changing its excretion of uric acid and allantoin (Bass et al., 1950). The alternate basis for establishing molybdenum as a necessary trace element is to demonstrate an absolute requirement for the element in animal nutrition. This has proven to be an extremely difficult problem with animals.

The use by De Renzo (1954) of sodium tungstate as a competitive inhibitor of molybdate was applied by Higgins et al. (1956) to produce an apparent molybdenum deficiency in chicks. Such evidence, however, cannot be regarded as final proof of essentiality of molybdenum. The addition of molybdenum (0.0254 p.p.m.) to a purified diet has been reported to stimulate the growth of poults and the activity of intestinal and liver xanthine dehydrogenase (Reid et al., 1957). Growth of chicks was also reported to be significantly improved by the addition of sodium molybdate (Kurnick et al., 1957), further implicating the metal as an essential element.

Westerfeld et al. (1957) have recently used the technique of administering tungstate as a means of removing molybdenum and molybdenum enzymes from tissues in order to assess the role of molybdenum in the reduction of organic nitro groups. The specificity of the tungstate effect was controlled by overcoming it with dietary molybdate. The results indicated that most of the enzymes in rat tissues capable of reducing the nitro group p-nitrobenzene sulfonamide are molybdenum-dependent enzymes. A number of different enzymes capable of reducing organic nitro groups are present in animal tissues, and any one system exhibits some specificity toward different nitro substrates.

V. Molybdenum in Plants

A. In Nitrogen Fixation

The first demonstration of the biological importance of molybdenum was made by Bortels (1930), who showed that the element was indispensable for the assimilation of gaseous nitrogen by the aerobic bacterium *Azotobacter chroococcum.* Bortels' work has since been confirmed by numerous other workers (Burk and Lineweaver, 1931; Birch-Hirschfeld, 1932; Schroder, 1931–1932; Kluyver and Van Reenen, 1933; Burema and Wieringa, 1942; Horner *et al.*, 1942; Mulder, 1948) who further indicated that molybdenum is necessary for other *Azotobacter* species. The anaerobic soil bacteria *Clostridium pasteurianum* and several other clostridium species also require trace amounts of molybdenum for nitrogen fixation (Bortels, 1936; Jensen, 1947). The early reports of a more or less stimulating effect of molybdenum on the growth of leguminous plants (Bortels, 1937; Bertrand, 1940; Bobko and Savvina, 1940) were not regarded as strong evidence for the essentiality of molybdenum in the fixation of nitrogen gas by leguminous plants in symbiosis with rhizobium bacteria (Hoagland, 1945).

The more recent experiments of Jensen (1945, 1948), Anderson and Thomas (1946), Mulder (1948), and others (see reviews by Evans, 1956; Anderson, 1956), including the wide occurrence of molybdenum deficiency symptoms in legumes grown in certain soils of Australia (Anderson, 1956), have definitely established molybdenum as an essential trace element in the symbiotic nitrogen fixation by leguminous plants. There is also good evidence that molybdenum is necessary for the fixation of nitrogen by the algae *Nostoc* and *Anabaena* (Bortels, 1940; Fogg, 1949; Wolfe, 1954). The recent review by Anderson (1956) is recommended for a detailed survey and evaluation of the literature dealing with the essentiality of molybdenum in plant and microbial nutrition.

While the mechanism of the role of molybdenum in nitrate reduction has been considerably elucidated (see Section V,B on nitrate assimilation), the function of molybdenum in nitrogen fixation is still obscure. This has been due in large part to our limited knowledge of the biochemistry of nitrogen fixation. Thus far the process of assimilation of nitrogen gas has not been consistently obtained with cell-free preparations. Until this major hurdle is cleared, characterization of the mechanism of action of molybdenum in this process will probably not be attained.

There is a requirement for considerably more molybdenum by *Azotobacter*, which are fixing nitrogen gas, as compared to those which are utilizing nitrate as a nitrogen source (Bortels, 1930; Burema and Wieringa, 1942; Mulder, 1948). This has also been indicated by the smaller response of *Azotobacter* to molybdenum obtained by Burk (1934) and others when combined nitrogen was provided as compared to that with nitrogen gas as the sole nitrogen source. This special requirement prompted studies on the distribution of molybdenum in cell-free preparations of *Azotobacter vinelandii*. Magee and Burris (1956) purified a molybdenum-protein fraction 150-fold from *Azotobacter* grown on Mo[99].

Although the fraction was stable to dialysis against phosphate buffer, Mo^{99} could be rapidly dissociated by dialysis against cyanide solution. Addition of this molybdenum-protein to cell-free preparations did not stimulate nitrogen fixation. Keeler et al. (1956) demonstrated that a large portion of the Mo^{99} taken up by Azotobacter cells is associated with a particulate fraction but is stable against cyanide dialysis. It has been shown that tungstate is a competitive inhibitor of molybdate in nitrogen fixation (and nitrate assimilation) by Azotobacter (Takahashi and Nason, 1957; Keeler and Varner, 1957). However, 100 p.p.m. tungsten did not seriously inhibit growth whereas it almost completely prevented Mo^{99} uptake by Azotobacter cells grown on N_2 or nitrate suggesting that relatively large quantities of molybdenum taken up and combined with protein by growing cells are apparently not essential for growth (Keeler and Varner, 1957). Vanadium, which has been reported by a number of workers to serve in place of molybdenum in nitrogen fixation, failed to show a competitive antagonism with tungstate, thus adding further support to the contention that vanadium cannot replace the molybdenum requirement.

There appears to be a direct relationship between hydrogenase and nitrogen fixation in Azotobacter in that the hydrogenase content is markedly greater in cells that are fixing nitrogen gas (Lee and Wilson, 1943). Molecular hydrogen is a competitive inhibitor of nitrogen fixation in Azotobacter and other aerobic agents and in symbiotic nitrogen fixation by red clover (see reviews by Gest et al., 1956; Burris, 1956; Shug et al., 1956). Hydrogenase activity has recently been reported in soybean root nodules (Hoch et al., 1957). However, in the case of certain anaerobic nitrogen fixers such as Clostridium pasteurianum molecular hydrogen has no appreciable effect on nitrogen fixation (Rosenblum and Wilson, 1950), and there appears to be no obvious relationship between nitrogen fixation and hydrogenase (Gest et al., 1956).

Rhodospirillum rubrum, the first of the photosynthetic bacteria found to be capable of nitrogen fixation, is an anaerobic nitrogen fixer, however, whose hydrogenase activity is distinctly higher when grown on molecular nitrogen than on glutamate or ammonia (Gest et al., 1956). Although it would appear that in certain organisms hydrogenase is related to nitrogen fixation, the evidence in support of such a relationship is still inconclusive. Hydrogenase has been partially purified from Clostridium pasteurianum and characterized as a flavoprotein whose capacity to reduce cytochrome c or nitrate is specifically restored by the addition of MoO_3 (Shug et al., 1954). Other elements, including vanadium, could not replace molybdenum in this effect.

It was also reported that cell-free preparations of C. pasteurianum showed a 2-banded difference spectrum with maxima at 450 and 390 mμ upon exposure first to 0.2 atmosphere H_2(0.8 atmosphere vacuum) followed by admission of molecular nitrogen to atmospheric pressure (Shug et al., 1956). This was interpreted to mean that the endogenous flavin was reduced by the molecular hydrogen and then subsequently oxidized by the nitrogen gas. The peaks in the Soret region at 405 and 425 mμ are presumed to be the reduced nitrogen products. Whether or not hydrogenase is a molybdoprotein is not entirely clear. It may well be that in the above system the restoration effect of added MoO_3 in the enzymatic transfer of electrons from molecular hydrogen to cytochrome c is an artificial model electron transport system and that hydrogenase is really an iron protein (see review by Gest et al., 1956).

Possible mechanisms for the interaction of hydrogenase and the hypothetical nitrogen-fixing enzyme (nitrogenase) have been proposed by Winfield (1955) and Shug et al. (1956), involving chemisorption of molecular nitrogen to a metalloenzyme (nitrogenase) containing two metal atoms which can form single or double covalent bonds to nitrogen. Another enzyme, presumably a flavoprotein such as hydrogenase, would transfer hydrogen atoms to the chemisorbed nitrogen with the ultimate release of the nitrogen as ammonia.

B. Molybdenum in Nitrate Assimilation and Plant Nutrition

Steinberg (1936, 1937) showed that Aspergillus niger required small amounts of molybdenum when grown on a nitrate medium, whereas the response to molybdenum with ammonium nitrogen was found to be considerably less. Thus the finding eliminated the possibility that molybdenum was needed only for nitrogen fixation, and at the same time provided evidence that the metal was needed for growth apart from nitrogen fixation.

The first clear-cut proof of the essentiality of traces of molybdenum for higher plants was demonstrated by Arnon and Stout (1939) in water culture experiments with tomato plants. They produced a deficiency characterized by mottling of the leaves and involution of the laminae which was prevented specifically by molybdenum, the 19 other elements tested, including vanadium, having no effect. The results were confirmed for other higher plants including oats, lettuce, white mustard, and plum seedlings (Piper, 1940; Arnon, 1940; Brenchley and Warington, 1942; Hoagland, 1945), thus showing the essentiality of molybdenum for plant growth in general. The findings of Hewitt et al. (1947) of high concentrations of nitrate in molybdenum-deficient plants were confirmed by Wilson and Waring (1948), Stout and Meagher (1948), and Mulder (1948).

Mulder's work (1948) was classic in that it confirmed and demonstrated a number of relationships between molybdenum and nitrogen metabolism in various organisms. It confirmed that *Azotobacter* and *Aspergillus* respond more to molybdenum when provided with nitrate nitrogen than with ammonium nitrogen; he used the growth-rate curve and the increasing sporulation of *Aspergillus niger* with increasing amounts of molybdenum to estimate minute quantities of molybdenum in various materials; it showed that molybdenum-deficient tomato plants contained a high concentration of nitrate, and that denitrifying bacteria grown on a molybdenum-deficient medium failed to reduce nitrate.

More recently, molybdenum has been shown to be essential for the growth and cell division of the green alga *Scenedesmus obliquus*, molybdenum-deficient cells failing to assimilate nitrate nitrogen (Arnon *et al.*, 1955; Ichioka and Arnon, 1955). It should be noted that the accumulation of nitrate in plants is not specific for a molybdenum deficiency since plants deficient in manganese (Leeper, 1941) or sulfur (Anderson and Spencer, 1950) also give rise to the same effect.

C. Role of Molybdenum as a Component of Nitrate Reductase

Definite proof of the specific involvement of molybdenum in nitrate assimilation by fungi, higher plants, and certain bacteria was obtained as a result of the isolation and characterization of nitrate reductase. The nitrate reductases from *Neurospora* and soybean leaves (purified approximately 70-fold) are sulfhydryl metalloflavoproteins which catalyze the transfer of electrons from reduced pyridine neucleotides (TPNH[3] for the *Neurospora* enzyme, TPNH and DPNH for the soybean enzyme) to nitrate to form nitrite as follows:

$$\text{TPNH (or DPNH)} + \text{H}^+ + \text{NO}_2^- \rightarrow \text{TPN}^+ \text{ (or DPN+)} + \text{NO}_3^- + \text{H}_2\text{O}$$

FAD is the prosthetic group (Nason and Evans, 1953; Evans and Nason, 1953), and molybdenum is the metal component (Nicholas and Nason, 1954a, b).

In the early stages of these studies, the significant sensitivity of the enzyme to a number of metal-binding agents such as cyanide (but not carbon monoxide), azide, potassium ethyl xanthate, *o*-phenanthroline, and 8-hydroxyquinoline suggested a metal component. Further indirect evidence for a metal component of the enzyme suggestive of molybdenum was the observation that only a molybdenum deficiency resulted in a sig-

[3] The following abbreviations are used: DPN and DPNH, unreduced and reduced diphosphopyridine nucleotide, respectively; TPN and TPNH, unreduced and reduced triphosphopyridine nucleotide respectively; FAD, flavin adenine dinucleotide; FMN, flavin mononucleotide or riboflavin phosphate; FADH₂ and FMNH₂, the corresponding reduced forms of FAD and FMN.

TABLE I

Effect of Nutrient Deficiencies on Nitrate Reductase in Cell-Free Extracts of
Neurospora crassa[a] (Wild Type 146) ·

	Treatment							
	+Ca	−Ca	+N	−N[c]	+Mg	−Mg[c]	+Fe	−Fe
Per cent growth	100	16	100	8	100	20	100	0.7
Nitrate reductase[b]	26	38	43	5	49	41	29	55

	Treatment									
	+Cu	−Cu	+Zn	−Zn	+Mn	−Mn	+Mo	−Mo	+ Biotin	− Biotin
Per cent growth	100	40	100	28	100	30	100	29	100	15
Nitrate reductase[b]	27	79	25	39	30	34	53	10	27	21

[a] Nicholas *et al.* (1954).

[b] Units of enzyme activity per mg. protein.

[c] Nitrogen and magnesium were supplied at one-thirtieth and one-hundredth, respectively, of the level in the controls.

nificant decrease of nitrate reductase (Table I) in cell-free extracts of *Neurospora* (Nicholas *et al.*, 1954). Activity of molybdenum-deficient *Neurospora* was restored to normal 12 hours after the addition of molybdenum. Direct evidence in support of molybdenum as the metal component of nitrate reductase was provided in subsequent experiments. Figure 1 shows that there is a direct relationship in the various *Neurospora* protein fractions between specific activity of the enzyme and molybdenum content, the most purified fractions being a concentration of approximately 0.00015 per cent molybdenum (Nicholas and Nason, 1954a).

Further evidence identifying molybdenum as the metal component of nitrate reductase was obtained by dialysis of the enzyme against cyanide in order to remove the metal component as the metallocyanide complex. This resulted in inactivation of nitrate reductase and a corresponding decrease in molybdenum as shown in Table II (Nicholas and Nason, 1954a). After a 3-hour dialysis against cyanide, the molybdenum content fell to a thirtieth of the control. Subsequent dialysis against a phosphate buffer and glutathione solution to remove the cyanide from the enzyme resulted in increased activity and molybdenum content, due to a molybdenum impurity in the phosphate.

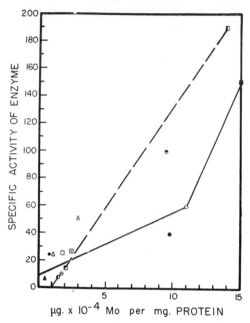

Fɪɢ. 1. Relation between molybdenum content and specific activity of nitrate reductase of various protein fractions from *Neurospora* (Nicholas and Nason, 1954a).

As shown in Experiment 4 of Table II, when the same experiment was performed with redialysis against molybdenum-free phosphate and glutathione there was no recovery of nitrate reductase nor any increase in the negligible molybdenum content of the enzyme. The addition of molyb-

TABLE II

Enzyme Activity and Molybdenum Content of Dialyzed Nitrate Reductase[a]

Treatment and dialyzing solutions		Dialysis time				
		0 hr.	3 hr.	6 hr.	9 hr.	12 hr.
(1) 0.2 M phosphate + 10^{-3} M glutathione	Enzyme[b]	19	17	15	15	14
	Mo	13	13	14	13	13
(2) Same as (1) + 10^{-3} M cyanide	Enzyme	4	3	2	1	1
	Mo	15	0.5	0.5	0.2	0.5
(3) Same as (2), but after 3 hr. dialyzed against (1)	Enzyme	4	3	5	9	11
	Mo	15	0.5	1	5	8
(4) Same as (3), but with Mo-free solutions	Enzyme	4	3	1	1	0
	Mo	15	0.5	0.2	0.2	0.2

[a] Nicholas and Nason (1954a).
[b] Units of enzyme activity per 0.05 ml. of enzyme.

denum trioxide or sodium molybdate reactivated the enzyme to 85 per cent of the original value. Preincubation with other metals including iron, zinc, manganese, nickel, cobalt, mercury, tungsten, uranium, vanadium, or boron were ineffective in place of molybdenum (Table III) (Nicholas and Nason, 1954a).

TABLE III

Effect of Metals on the Reactivation of Cyanide-Dialyzed Nitrate Reductase[a]

(Units of Enzyme Activity per 0.05 ml. Enzyme)

Treatment:	1	2	3	4
Experiment No.	Undialyzed enzyme	Dialyzed for 6 hr. against 0.1 M phosphate + 10^{-3} M glutathione[b]	As for (2) + $10^{-3}M$ cyanide	As for (3) then redialyzed for 6 hr. in (2)
I	18	14	4	4
II	15	11	3	4

Metals added:[c]	MoO_3	Na_2MO_4	$FeCl_3$	$FeSO_4$	$ZnSO_4$	$MnSO_4$	$NiCl_2$
Experiment No.							
I	13	14	5	6	4	3	4
II	12	11	4	4	3	3	2

Metals added:[c]	$AgCl$	$NaWO_4$	$Na_2Cr_2O_7$	Na_3VO_4	$VO_2(NO_3)_2$	$CoSO_4$	$Na_2B_2O_4$
Experiment No.							
I	4	4	5	3	4	3	4
II	3	3	4	3	4	3	4

[a] Nicholas and Nason (1954a).

[b] Reagents freed from molybdenum.

[c] 1 μg. of each metal added to 0.05 ml. enzyme incubated for 10 min. at 25° C. before assay.

In summary, the following lines of evidence were used to establish that molybdenum is the metal constituent of nitrate reductase in *Neurospora* (Nicholas *et al.*, 1954; Nicholas and Nason, 1954a): (*a*) increased enzyme activity in various protein fractions was accompanied by increased molybdenum content; (*b*) dialysis of the enzyme against cyanide resulted in an inactivation of nitrate reductase and a corresponding decrease in the micronutrient element; (*c*) the dialyzed enzyme free from cyanide was specifically reactivated by molybdenum salts, and (*d*) of all the micronutrient element deficiencies, only a molybdenum deficiency resulted in a decreased nitrate reductase activity.

It is of interest that the removal of molybdenum from the nutrient medium results in a decrease in nitrate reductase which is quite different from the loss of activity brought about by removal of molybdenum from the intact enzyme, for example, by cyanide dialysis. In the latter case, the inactivated enzyme can be restored almost completely by adding the metal back to the protein; whereas in the case of molybdenum deficiency the addition of the metal to the cell-free extract is ineffective. Molybdenum appears to be necessary for the adaptive formation of nitrate reductase in the presence of nitrate or nitrite by *Neurospora* during growth, presumably for the synthesis of the protein moiety of the enzyme.

It has also been possible to show (Nicholas and Nason, 1954b) that the flavin and molybdenum function as electron carriers in the nitrate reductase enzyme in the following sequence:

$$TPNH \rightarrow FAD \ (or \ FMN) \rightarrow Mo \rightarrow NO_3^-$$

That flavin precedes molybdenum in the above scheme was indicated by the fact that the molybdenum-free enzyme cannot catalyze the reduction of nitrate to nitrite by TPNH or reduced flavin. The metal-free enzyme, however, will catalyze the reduction of FAD or FMN by TPNH. Addition of molybdenum specifically restored the ability of the enzyme to catalyze the formation of nitrite from nitrate by reduced flavin or TPNH or TPNH plus flavin. The enzymatic oxidation of $FMNH_2$ by molybdate under anaerobic conditions in the absence of nitrate (Table IV) sug-

TABLE IV

Enzymatic Oxidation of $FMNH_2$ by Molybdate[a]

	$\Delta E \ 455 \times 10^3$ per minute			
Experiment No.	Complete	−Enzyme	Boiled enzyme	−Molybdate
1	130	10	20	15
2	150	25	10	20

[a] Nicholas and Nason (1954b).

gested that the metal ion was acting as an electron carrier (Nicholas and Nason, 1954b). Direct evidence for the role of molybdenum as an electron carrier is given by the data in Table V. Reduced molybdate prepared with $Na_2S_2O_4$, enzymatically reduces nitrate to nitrite in the absence of added FAD. The molybdenum appears to be undergoing an oxidation-reduction reaction from an oxidation state +6 to a more reduced

TABLE V

Dithionite-Treated Molybdate as Electron Donor for Enzymatic Nitrate Reduction[a]
(Millimicromoles of Nitrite Formed per 0.5 ml. of Reaction Mixture)

Experiment No.	TPNH, enzyme, FMN, KNO_3	Reduced Mo, enzyme, KNO_3	Mo, enzyme, KNO_3	Reduced blank, enzyme, KNO_3	Reduced Mo, KNO_3	Reduced Mo, boiled enzyme, KNO_3
1	24	19	7	3	1	4
2	30	25	9	8	2	6
3	20	15	2	2	1	2
4	23	20	4	2	2	3

[a] Nicholas and Nason (1954b).

level, probably +5 (Nicholas and Nason, 1954b; Nicholas and Stevens, 1955).

Similar studies identifying molybdenum as the metal component as well as demonstrating the sequence and mechanism of electron transport by molybdenum to be the same as for the *Neurospora* enzyme have also been made with nitrate reductase from soybean leaves (Nicholas and Nason, 1955a). That molybdenum is a component of soybean leaf nitrate reductase has been subsequently confirmed by Evans and Hall (1955). The properties of a pyridine nucleotide reductase in *Escherichia coli* and its identification as a metalloflavoprotein, with molybdenum as the probable metal component, have also recently been shown (Nicholas and Nason, 1955b). This is apparently a distinct system from that described by Taniguchi *et al.* (1956), which allegedly contains iron as the metal component.

D. Function of Molybdenum in Other Biological Processes

Molybdenum is also essential in plant metabolism for processes other than nitrate reduction and nitrogen fixation. There are small but definite indications that molybdenum is required for fungi using ammonium nitrogen as the sole nitrogen source (Mulder, 1948; Vanslow and Datta, 1949; Agarwala, 1952; Nicholas *et al.*, 1954). Cauliflower plants grown on urea and ammonium as nitrogen sources still developed characteristic molybdenum deficiency symptoms known as "whiptail" (Agarwala, 1952). Molybdenum deficiency in higher plants is accompanied by a decreased concentration of ascorbic acid in the tissues (Hewitt, 1951) as well as a lowered capacity to reduce dyes such as methylene blue (Evans *et al.*, 1950) and triplenyltetrazolium chloride (Hewitt and Agarwala, 1954). It has also been reported (Possingham, 1954) that molybdenum-deficient tomato plants convert less inorganic phosphorus to the organic form as compared to the controls. This may be related to the observation that molybdate is an inhibitor of acid phosphatases from the tomato plant (Spencer, 1954). The possibility of an antagonistic effect between copper and molybdenum in the net formation of certain enzymes by *Neurospora* has recently been indicated by Commissiong and Nicholas (1957), although the evidence is inconclusive.

REFERENCES

Agarwala, S. C. 1952. *Nature* **169**, 1099.

Allen, M. B. 1956. *Sci. Monthly* **83**, 100–106.

Anderson, A. J. 1956. *Symposium on Inorg. Nitrogen Metabolism, Baltimore, 1955,* pp. 3–58.

Anderson, A. J., and Spencer, D. 1950. *Australian J. Sci. Research Ser. A* **3**, 431–449.

Anderson, A. J., and Thomas, M. P. 1946. *Australia, Commonwealth, Council Sci. Ind. Research Bull.* **198**, Part 1.

Arnon, D. I. 1938. *Am. J. Botany* **25**, 322–325.

Arnon, D. I. 1940. *Chronica Botan.* **6**, 56–57.

Arnon, D. I. 1958. This volume. Chapter I.

Arnon, D. I., and Stout, P. R. 1939. *Plant Physiol.* **14**, 599–602.

Arnon, D. I., and Wessel, G. 1953. *Nature* **172**, 1039–40.

Arnon, D. I., Ichioka, P. S., Wessel, G., Fujiwara, A., and Woolley, J. T. 1955. *Physiol. Plantarum* **8**, 538–551.

Baltscheffsky, H., and Baltscheffsky, M. 1953. *Pubbl. staz. zool. Napoli* **24**, 447-451.

Bass, A. D., Tepperman, J., Richert, D. A., and Westerfeld, W. W. 1950. *Proc. Soc. Exptl. Biol. Med.* **73**, 687–689.

Bechi, E. 1879. *Atti Acad. nazl. Lincei, Mem., classe sci. fis., mat. e nat.* **3**, 186.

Bernheim, F., and Bernheim, M. L. C. 1939a. *J. Biol. Chem.* **127**, 353–360.

Bernheim, F., and Bernheim, M. L. C. 1939b. *J. Biol. Chem.* **128**, 79–82.

Bertrand, D. 1940. *Compt. rend.* **211**, 512–514.

Bertrand, D. 1941. *Bull. soc. chim. biol.* **23**, 467–71.

Bertrand, D. 1942a. *Bull. soc. chim. Paris* **9**, 128–133.

Bertrand, D. 1942b. *Ann. Inst. Pasteur* **68**, 58–68.

Bertrand, D. 1943 *Bull. soc. chim. biol.* **25**, 36–39.

Bertrand, D. 1950. *Bull. Am. Museum Nat. Hist.* **94**, 403–456.

Bielig, H. J., Bayer, E., Califano, L., and Wirth, L. 1954. *Pubbl. staz. zool. Napoli* **25**, 26–66.

Birch-Hirschfeld, L. 1932. *Arch. Mikrobiol.* **3**, 341–361.

Blumberg, H., and Rask, O. S. 1933. *J. Nutrition* **6**, 285–288.

Bobko, E. V., and Savvina, A. G. 1940. *Compt. rend. acad. sci. U.R.S.S.* **29**, 507–509.

Borei, E., and Ehrenberg, A. 1954. *Arch. Biochem. Biophys.* **50**, 404–416.

Bortels, H. 1930. *Arch. Mikrobiol.* **1**, 333–342.

Bortels, H. 1933. *Zentr. Bakteriol., Parasitenk. Abt. II*, **87**, 476.

Bortels, H. 1936. *Zentr. Bakteriol., Parasitenk. Abt. II*, **95**, 193–218.

Bortels, H. 1937. *Arch. Mikrobiol.* **8**, 13–26.

Bortels, H. 1940. *Arch. Mikrobiol.* **11**, 155–186.

Bowen, W., Jr. 1940. *Biol. Bull.* **79**, 114–130.

Boyd, T. C., and De, N. K. 1933. *Indian J. Med. Research* **20**, 789–800.

Brenchley, W. E., and Warington, K. 1942. *Nature* **149**, 196.

Burema, S. J., and Wieringa, K. T. 1942. *Antonie van Leeuwenhoek. J. Microbiol. Serol.* **8**, 123–133.

Burk, D. 1934. *Ergeb. Enzymforsch.* **3**, 22–56.

Burk, D., and Horner, C. K. 1935. *Intern. Soc. Soil Sci., 3rd Congr. Trans.* **1**, 152–155.

Burk, D., and Horner, C. K. 1937. *Soil Sci. Am. Proc.* **1**, 213–274.

Burk, D., and Lineweaver, H. 1931. *Arch. Mikrobiol.* **2**, 155 (cited by Burk, 1934).

Burris, R. H. 1956. *Symposium on Inorg. Nitrogen Metabolism, Baltimore, 1955,* pp. 316–343.

Califano, L., and Boeri, E. 1950. *J. Exptl. Biol.* **27**, 253–256.

Califano, L., and Caselli, P. 1948 *Pubbl. staz. zool. Napoli* **21**, 261–271.

Califano, L., and Caselli, P. 1950. *Pubb. staz. zool. Napoli* **22**, 138–145.

Cantacuzène, J., and Tchakirian, A. 1932. *Compt. rend.* **195**, 846–849.

Chiu, T. F. 1953. *Agr. Research (Taiwan)* **4**, 48–59.

Ciereszko, L. S. 1954. *Yearbook Am. Phil. Soc.* p. 392.

Commissiong, K., and Nicholas, D. J. D. 1957. *Nature* **180**, 555–556.

Cuningham, H. M., Brown, J. M., and Edie, A. E. 1953. *Can. J. Agr. Sci.* **33**, 254–260.

Curran, G. L. 1954. *J. Biol. Chem.* **210**, 765–70.

Daniel, E. P., and Hewston, E. M. 1942. *Am. J. Physiol.* **136**, 772–775.

De Renzo, E. C. 1954. *Ann. New York Acad. Sci.* **57**. 905–908.

De Renzo, E. C., Kaleita, E., Heytler, P. G., Oleson, J. J., Hutchings, B. L., and Williams, J. H. 1953a. *J. Am. Chem. Soc.* **75**, 753.

De Renzo, E. C., Kaleita, E., Heytler, P. G., Oleson, J. J., Hutchings, B. L., and Williams, J. H. 1953b. *Arch. Biochem. Biophys.* **45**, 247–253.

De Renzo, E. C., Heytler, P. G., and Stolzenberg, S. 1956. *Symposium on Inorg. Nitrogen Metabolism, Baltimore, 1955,* pp. 507–512.

Dick, A. T. 1953a. *Australian Vet. J.* **29**, 18–26.

Dick, A. T. 1953b. *Australian Vet. J.* **29**, 233–239.

Dick, A. T. 1954. *Australian J. Agr. Research* **5**, 511–544.

Dick, A. T. 1956a. *Symposium on Inorg. Nitrogen Metabolism, Baltimore, 1955,* pp. 445–473.

Dick, A. T. 1956b. *Soil Sci.* **81**, 229–236.

Dick, A. T., and Bull, L. B. 1945. *Australian Vet. J.* **21**, 70–72.

Dimitriev, K. A. 1939. *Pedology (U.S.S.R.)* No. **4**, 114–133.

Drea, W. F. 1934. *J. Nutrition* **8**, 229–234.

Drea, W. F. 1935. *J. Nutrition* **10**, 350–355.

Endean, R. 1953. *Nature* **172**, 123.

Endean, R. 1954. *Australian J. Marine and Freshwater Research* **6**, 35–59.

Evans, H. J. 1956. *Soil Sci.* **81**, 199–208.

Evans, H. J., and Hall, N. S. 1955. *Science* **22**, 922–923.

Evans, H. J., and Nason, A. 1953. *Plant Physiol.* **28**, 233–254.

Evans, H. J., Purvis, E. R., and Bear, F. E. 1950. *Plant Physiol.* **25**, 555–556.

Ferguson, W. S., Lewis, A. H., and Watson, S. J. 1938. *Nature* **141**, 553.

Fogg, G. E. 1949. *Ann. Botany (London)* **13**, 241–259.

Gericke, S. 1940. *Umschau Forschr. Wiss. u. Tech.* **44**, 597–598 (*Chem. Abstr.* **36**, 5498, 1942).

Gericke, S. 1941. *Bodenk. u. Pfanzenernähr.* **23**, 342–350.

Gericke, S., and Von Rennenkampff, E. 1939–1940. *Prakt. Bl. Pflanzenbau u. Pflanzenschutz* **17**, 17–22.

Gericke, S., and Von Rennenkampff, E. 1940. *Bodenk. u. Pfanzenernähr.* **18**, 305–315.

Gest, H., Judis, J., and Peck, H. D., Jr. 1956. *Symposium on Inorg. Nitrogen Metabolism, Baltimore, 1955*, pp. 298–315.

Geyer, C. F. 1953. *J. Dental Research* **32**, 590–595.

Glenn, J. L., and Crane, F. L. 1956. *Biochim. et Biophys. Acta* **22**, 111–115.

Goldberg, E. D., McBlair, W., and Taylor, K. M. 1951. *Biol. Bull.* **101**, 84–94.

Gray, L. F., and Daniel, L. J. 1954. *J. Nutrition* **53**, 43–51.

Green, D. E., and Beinert, H. 1953. *Biochim. et Biophys. Acta* **11**, 599–600.

Hecht, S. 1918. *Am. J. Physiol.* **45**, 157–187.

Henze, M. 1911. *Z. physiol. Chem.* **72**, 494–501.

Henze, M. 1912. *Z. physiol., Chem.* **79**, 215–228.

Henze, M. 1913. *Z. physiol. Chem.* **83**, 340–344.

Henze, M., Stohr, R., and Muller, R. 1932. *Z. physiol. Chem.* **213**, 125–135.

Hewitt, E. J. 1951. *Ann. Rev. Plant. Physiol.* **2**, 25–52.

Hewitt, E. J., and Agarwala, S. C. 1954. *Nature* **169**, 545–546.

Hewitt. E. J., Jones, E. W., and Williams, A. H. 1947. *J. Pomol. Hort. Sci.* **23**, 254.

Higgins, E. S., Richert, D. A., and Westerfeld, W. W. 1956. *J. Nutrition* **59**, 539–560.

Hoagland, D. R. 1945. *Soil Sci.* **60**, 119–123.

Hoch, G. E., Little, H. N., and Burris, R. H. 1957. *Nature* **179**, 430–431.

Horner, C. K., Burk, D., Allison, F. E., and Sherman, M. S. 1942. *J. Agr. Research* **65**, 173–193.

Ichioka, P. S., and Arnon, D. I. 1955. *Physiol. Plantarum* **8**, 552–560.

Ishibashi, M. 1951. *Bull. Inst. Chem. Research, Kyoto Univ.* **24**, 68.

Jacobs, E. 1956. *Biochim. et Biophys. Acta* **22**, 583–585.

Jensen, H. L. 1945. *Proc. Linnean Soc. N. S. Wales* **70**, 203–210.

Jensen, H. L. 1947. *Proc. Linnean Soc. N. S. Wales* **72**, 73–86.

Jensen, H. L. 1948. *Proc. Linnean Soc. N. S. Wales* **72**, 265–293.

Keeler, R. F., and Varner, J. E. 1957. *Arch. Biochem. Biophys.* **70**, 585–590.

Keeler, R. F., Bulen, W. A., and Varner, J. E. 1956. *J. Bacteriol.* **72**, 394–396.

Kluyver, A. J., and Van Reenen, W. J. 1933. *Arch. Mikrobiol.* **4**, 280–300.

Kobayashi, S. 1935. *Science Repts. Tôhoku Univ.* **28**, 185.

Kobayashi, S. 1949. *Science Repts. Tôhoku Univ.* **18**, 185–193.

Konishi, K., and Tsuge, T. 1933a. *J. Agr. Chem. Soc. Japan* **9**, 129–144. (From *Chem. Abstr.* **27**, 2621, 1933.)

Konishi, K. and Tsuge, T. 1933b. *J. Agr. Chem. Soc. Japan* **9**, 510–520. (From *Chem. Abstr.* **27**, 4333, 1933.)

Kurnick, A. A., Reid, B. L., Burroughs, R. N., Stelzner, A. D., and Couch, J. R. 1957. *Proc. Soc. Exptl. Biol. Med.* **95**, 353–356.

Lee, S. B., and Wilson, P. W. 1943. *J. Biol. Chem.* **151**, 377.

Leeper, G. W. 1941. *J. Australian Inst. Agr. Sci.* **7**, 161.

Lowater, F., and Murray, M. M. 1937. *Biochem. J.* **31**, 837–841.

Luzzato, R. 1902. *Sperimentale* **56**, 137.

Lyonnet, 1899. *Presse méd.* **59**, 33.

Mackler, B., Mahler, H. R., and Green, D. E. 1954. *J. Biol. Chem.* **210**, 149–164.

Magee, W. E., and Burris, R. H. 1956. *J. Bacteriol.* **71**, 635–643.

Mahler, H. R., Mackler, B., Green, D. E., and Bock, R. M. 1954. *J. Biol. Chem.* **210**, 465–480.

Mazé, P., and Mazé, P. J. 1939. *Compt. rend. soc. biol.* **132**, 375–377.

Miller, R. F., Price, N. O., and Engel, R. W. 1956. *J. Nutrition* **60**, 539–547.

Mountain, J. T., Stockwell, F. R., Jr., and Stokinger, H. E. 1956. *Proc. Soc. Exptl. Biol. Med.* **92**, 582–587.

Mulder, E. G. 1948. *Plant and Soil* **1**, 94–119.

Nason, A., and Evans, H. K. 1953. *J. Biol. Chem.* **202**, 655–673.

Neuberg, C., and Kobel, M. 1926. *Biochem. Z.* **174**, 680.

Newell, J. M., and McCollum, E. V. 1931. *U.S. Dept. Com., Bur. Fisheries Invest. Repts.* **5**, 1–9.

Nicholas, D. J. D., and Nason, A. 1954a *J. Biol. Chem.* **207**, 353–360.

Nicholas, D. J. D., and Nason, A. 1954b. *J. Biol. Chem.* **211**, 183–197.

Nicholas, D. J. D., and Nason, A. 1955a. *Plant Physiol.* **30**, 135–138.

Nicholas, D. J. D., and Nason, A. 1955b. *J. Bacteriol.* **69**, 580–583.

Nicholas, D. J. D., Nason, A., and McElroy, W. D. 1954. *J. Biol. Chem.* **207**, 341–351.

Nicholas, D. J. D., and Stevens, H. M. 1955. *Nature* **176**, 1066–1067.

Noddack, I., and Noddack, W., 1940. *Arkiv. Zool.* **32** (4), 35 pp.

Phillips, A. H. 1918. *Am. J. Sci.* **46**, 473–475.

Pied, H., and Azéma, M. 1930. *Compt. rend.* **190**, 220–222.

Piper, C. S. 1940. *J. Australian Inst. Agr. Sci.* **6**, 162–164.

Portes and Benoit. 1923. Cited by Bertrand (1950).

Possingham, J. V. 1954. *Australian J. Biol. Sci.* **7**, 221–224.

Reid, B. L., Kurnick, A. A., Burroughs, R. N., Svacha, R. L., and Couch, J. R. 1957. *Proc. Soc. Exptl. Biol. Med.* **94**, 737.

Reiman, C. K., and Minot, A. S. 1920. *J. Biol. Chem.* **42**, 329–345.

Remy, C. N., Richert, D. A., Doisy, R. J., Wells, I. C., and Westerfeld, W. W. 1955. *J. Biol. Chem.* **217**, 293–305.

Richert, D. A., and Westerfeld, W. W. 1953. *J. Biol. Chem.* **203**, 915–923.

Richert, D. A., and Westerfeld, W. W. 1954. *J. Biol. Chem.* **209**, 179–189.

Rosenblum, E. D., and Wilson, P. W. 1950. *J. Bacteriol.* **59**, 83–91.

Rygh, O. 1949a. *Bull. soc. chim. biol.* **31**, 1052, 1403, 1408.

Rygh, O. 1949b. *Research (London)* **2**, 340–341.

Rygh, O. 1953. *Bull. soc. chim. biol.* **33**, 133.

Schroder, M. 1931–1932. *Zentr. Bakteriol. Parasitenk. Abt. II* **85**, 177–212.

Shibuya, K., and Saeki, H. 1934. *J. Soc. Trop. Agr., Japan* **6**, 721.

Shug, A. L., Wilson, P. W., Green, D. E., and Mahler, H. R. 1954. *J. Am. Chem. Soc.* **76**, 3355–3356.

Shug, A. L., Hamilton, P. B., and Wilson, P. W. 1956. *Symposium on Inorg. Nitrogen Metabolism, Baltimore, 1955*, pp. 344–360.

Spencer, D. 1954. *Australian J. Biol. Sci.* **7**, 151–160.

Steinberg, R. A. 1936. *J. Agr. Research* **52**, 439–448.

Steinberg, R. A. 1937. *J. Agr. Research* **55**, 891–902.

Stout, P. R., and Meagher, W. R. 1948. *Science* **108**, 471.

Takahashi, H., and Nason, A. 1957. *Biochim. et Biophys. Acta* **23**, 433–435.

Taniguchi, S., Sato, R., and Egami, F. 1956. *Symposium on Inorg. Nitrogen Metabolism, Baltimore, 1955*, pp. 87–108.

Totter, J. R., Burnett, W. T., Jr., Monroe, R. A., Whitney, I. B., and Comar, C. L. 1953. *Science* **118**, 555.

Van Niel, C. B. 1935. *Arch. Mikrobiol.* **6**, 215–218.

Van Reen, R. 1954. *Arch. Biochem. Biophys.* **53**, 77–83.

Van Reen, R., and Williams, M. A. 1956. *Arch. Biochem. Biophys.* **63**, 1–8.

Vanslow, A. P., and Datta, N. P. 1949. *Soil Sci.* **67**, 363–375.

Vinogradov, A. P. 1934. *Compt. rend. acad. sci. U.R.S.S.* **3**, 454–459.

Warington, K. 1951. *Ann. Appl. Biol.* **38**, 624–41.

Webb, D. A. 1937. *Sci. Proc. Roy. Dublin Soc.* **21**, 505–539.

Webb, D. A. 1939. *J. Exptl. Biol.* **16**, 499–523.

Webb, D. A. 1956. *Pubbl. staz. zool. Napoli* **28**, 273–288.

Webb, D. A., and Fearon, W. R. 1937. *Sci. Proc. Roy. Dublin Soc.* **21**, 487–504.

Westerfeld, W. W., Richert, D. A., and Higgins, E. S. 1956. *Symposium on Inorg. Nitrogen Metabolism, Baltimore, 1955,* pp. 492–506.

Westerfeld, W. W., Richert, D. A., and Higgins, E. S. 1957. *J. Biol. Chem.* **227**, 379–391.

Wilson, R. D., and Waring, E. J. 1948. *J. Australian Inst. Agr. Sci.* **141**, 41.

Winfield, M. E. 1955. *Revs. Pure and Appl. Chem. (Australia)* **5**, 217–246.

Witz, G., and Osmond, F. 1886. *Bull. soc. Chim. Paris* **45**, 309–314.

Wolfe, M. 1954. *Ann. Botany (London)* **18**, 299–309, 309–325.

Wright, N. C., and Papish, J. 1929. *Science* **69**, 78.

Wynne, K. N., and McClymont, G. L. 1955. *Nature* **175**, 471–472.

Zbinden, C. 1931. *Lait* **11**, 114–123.

Chapter 20

The Metabolism of Molybdate and Tungstate in *Azotobacter**

Richard F. Keeler and J. E. Varner

Department of Agricultural Biochemistry
Ohio State University, Columbus, Ohio

		Page
I.	Introduction	297
II.	Materials and Methods	298
III.	Results	299
IV.	Discussion	307
V.	Summary	307
	References	308

I. Introduction

There is an absolute molybdenum requirement for *Azotobacter* and other organisms growing on either N_2 or NO_3^- as nitrogen sources (Bortels, 1930; Burk and Horner, 1939; Mulder, 1948; Jensen, 1948; Keeler, 1955). The exact reasons for this requirement have not been elucidated. Nason and Evans (1953) and Nicholas and Nason (1954) have isolated from *Neurospora crassa* a molybdenum-requiring nitrate reductase. It is likely that the nitrate reductase system of *Azotobacter* is also a molybdoenzyme, and presumably the nitrogenase system involves molybdenum. There are other instances of a molybdenum requirement in enzyme systems, i.e., xanthine oxidase (Richert and Westerfeld, 1953; Totter *et al.*, 1953), aldehyde oxidase (Mahler *et al.*, 1954), and perhaps hydrogenase (Shug *et al.*, 1954). *Azotobacter* may also utilize molybdenum in these three systems. Keeler (1955) has shown that *Azotobacter vinelandii* strain O will incorporate more than 100 times as much molybdenum as is required for optimum growth rate, and that this molybdenum is firmly bound to a nondialyzable fraction. Because the quantity of molybdate incorporated into the cells is a direct function of the oxygen tension, and an inverse function of the iron level (Keeler, 1957), mo-

* This work was supported in part by a grant from the Research Corporation.

lybdenum may be involved in an alternate terminal electron transport system similar to that suggested for *Pseudomonas* (Lenhoff *et al.*, 1956). Thus there exists a number of possible sites of molybdenum utilization as a cofactor in molybdoprotein enzyme systems in *Azotobacter*.

A competitive inhibition of molybdenum by tungsten in the growth of *Azotobacter* has been reported by Keeler and Varner (1957), and Takahashi and Nason (1957). This antagonism introduces the possibility that tungsten may be incorporated into intracellular sites in place of molybdenum.

This paper compares the uptake of tungsten-185 and molybdenum-99 into *Azotobacter*. It is shown that a large proportion of the molybdenum and tungsten taken up is incorporated into molybdo- and tungstoproteins. In both cases ammonium sulfate fractionation and paper electrophoresis showed only one labeled fraction regardless of the nitrogen source on which the cells were grown. In a comparison of the molybdenum metabolism of *Azotobacter vinelandii* strain O and *Azotobacter chroococcum* C44, it is demonstrated that the latter does not have the ability of the former to incorporate excessive molybdenum into protein. In contrast with *A. vinelandii* which shows no variation in the incorporation of Mo^{99} with various nitrogen sources (Keeler, 1957), *A. chroococcum* incorporates only one-fifth to one-tenth as much molybdenum on NH_4^+ as on N_2 or NO_3^-. Further comparisons of the metabolism of molybdenum and the incorporation into protein in both organisms are discussed.

II. MATERIALS AND METHODS

Azotobacter vinelandii strain O and *Azotobacter chroococcum* C44 (supplied by R. H. Burris and P. W. Wilson, respectively) were cultured on a sterilized, modified Burk's medium (Burk and Lineweaver, 1930) containing 4 times the suggested level of phosphate to further buffer the medium against pH changes. The medium contained 3 per cent sucrose as an energy source plus added molybdenum, tungsten, Mo^{99}, or W^{185} at 1 p.p.m. or at the levels specified in each experiment. When combined nitrogen was used, it was added at a level of 0.7 mg. per ml. of medium as KNO_3 or $(NH_4)_2SO_4$. All routine components of the medium including sucrose were reagent grade.

In experiments where large volumes of cells were required, such as the centrifugal distribution, ammonium sulfate fractionation, and paper electrophoresis experiments, the cells were grown in 3 to 8-liter volumes under forced aeration. When it was desirable to change the oxygen tension in these cultures, the level of air supplied was altered by changing the pressure of the air supplied to the cultures. Cells for other experiments were grown as shake cultures of 25 ml. in 125 ml. Erlenmeyer flasks. Cells were grown at 34°C. in all cases.

The Mo^{99} and W^{185} were supplied as $Na_2Mo^{99}O_4$, and $K_2W^{185}O_4$. All radioactive assays were performed with a Geiger-Müller end window tube and standard scaling circuits. The radioactivity levels reported were corrected for background. Cell growth was determined turbidimetrically during the log phase by optical density readings at 660 mμ. Log phase optical density readings were considered proportional to growth rate since the length of the log phase was not altered by the treatments.

The cells were harvested by centrifugation, washed twice, and re-suspended in 0.25 M sucrose containing 0.1 M phosphate (pH 7.2). The cells were disrupted by sonic oscillation in a 10 KC Raytheon. The various centrifugal fractions were obtained as described previously (Keeler et al., 1956). Uptake of the labeled anions was measured by centrifuging the log phase cells from the labeled medium and measuring the loss of activity from the medium. Protein was determined by the optical density values at 260 and 280 mμ according to the method of Warburg and Christian (1941).

The supernatant fraction after 90 minutes centrifugation at 25,000 × g was used as the material for further fractionation by ammonium sulfate. To 10 ml. of the extract was added 1.0 or 0.5 ml. increments of 3.9 M ammonium sulfate with removal of the precipitate after each step until all the activity had been precipitated.

The paper electrophoresis experiments were also conducted on the 25,000 × g supernatant fraction using veronal buffer at pH 9 and an ionic strength of 0.01. A current of 40 milliamperes at 400 volts was applied to Whatman No. 3 MM paper in sheets 9 by 22.5 inches. The runs were of about 10 hours duration at 4°C. Protein color was developed by Bromo-phenol Blue staining.

III. RESULTS

A comparison of the intracellular distribution in *A. vinelandii* of tungsten with that reported for molybdenum (Keeler et al., 1956) is shown in Table I. It is evident that a large proportion of both the Mo^{99} and W^{185} incorporated are found in the R-144-6 fraction. This fraction also contains the highest specific activity (counts per min. per mg. protein) of both labels. The W^{185}/Mo ratio added to the cultures was 10, and the incorporation of W^{185} was about one-third that of the in-corporation of Mo^{99} in the molybdenum experiment in terms of mg. of metal per mg. of protein.

It had been found earlier that tungsten inhibits molybdenum uptake

TABLE I

Comparison of the Intracellular Distribution and Uptake of W^{185} and Mo^{99} in
Azotobacter vinelandii

Fraction	Total activity in fraction (c./min.)	Total mg. protein	Specific activity (c./min./mg. prot.)	Total uptake (mg. of metal/mg. protein)
Mo^{99}				
R-144-1/2	3,100	105	30	0.0122
R-144-6	22,600	143	158	
S-144-6	7,900	98	81	
$W^{185\,a}$				
R-144-1/2	118	0.712	166	0.0034
R-144-6	3,650	0.300	12,100	
S-144-6	1,588	0.204	9,200	

[a] The W/Mo ratio was 10.

more than it inhibits growth (Keeler and Varner, 1957). Table II shows this to be true for a wide range of Mo/W ratios. Regardless of the ratio, the Mo^{99} uptake is affected much more than is the relative growth. However, this is not true for the uptake of the antagonist W^{185} which has been found to be constant over a large range of W/Mo ratios (10:1–500:1).

The stability of the incorporated molybdenum (Keeler, 1955; Keeler and Varner, 1957) of *A. vinelandii* against cyanide dialysis has been found to be characteristic also for the incorporated tungsten. Neither label is appreciably lost from the $25,000 \times g$ supernatant fraction of cell-free preparations by dialysis against 0.1 M phosphate or 10^{-3} M cyanide at pH 7.2. The stability of the Mo^{99} component when dialyzed, and the lack of loss by washing or exchange has been taken as evidence that the incorporation of molybdenum represented formation of molybdo-protein(s) (Keeler, 1957).

Further evidence supporting the conclusion that both molybdenum and tungsten are incorporated into protein was obtained by subjecting

TABLE II

Uptake of Mo^{99} as a Function of Tungsten Level in *Azotobacter vinelandii*

Treatment	Relative growth	Relative uptake of Mo^{99} per unit growth
1 p.p.m. Mo, 100 p.p.m. W	0.495	121
1 p.p.m. Mo, 50 p.p.m. W	0.600	200
1 p.p.m. Mo, 10 p.p.m. W	0.700	700
1 p.p.m. Mo, 0 p.p.m. W	0.680	1100

the 25,000 × g supernatant fractions of W^{185}- and Mo^{99}-grown cells to the action of proteinases, deoxyribonuclease, and ribonuclease. It is evident in Table III that treatment with papain or trypsin, both of which caused about 80 per cent degradation of trichloroacetic acid (TCA) precipitable

TABLE III

Mo^{99} Dialysis Loss from the 25,000 × g Supernatant Fraction of
Azotobacter vinelandii

Treatment	Percentage activity loss by dialysis[a]	Approximate percentage degradation[b]
RNAase and DNAase	79	20
Papain ($+10^{-3}$ M GSH)	99	80
Trypsin	96	80
Blank (34°C.)	55	0
Blank (5°C.)	35	0

[a] Incubated for 6 hours at 34°C. and subsequently dialyzed for 40 hours against 0.1 M phosphate, and then 20 hours against 10^{-3} M cyanide (pH 7.2, 5°C.).
[b] Measured by the change in TCA precipitable material.

material, resulted in the loss of nearly all the label during subsequent dialysis. Deoxyribonuclease and ribonuclease together also caused a considerable loss of activity, presumably by the liberation of some internal *Azotobacter* proteinase masked by nucleic acid since some (20 per cent) of the TCA precipitable material is lost by this treatment. Interestingly enough, the blank kept at the incubation temperature of 34°C. lost 20 per cent more label in subsequent dialysis than did the low temperature blank though no degradation of proteins was observable. This suggests that there was some hydrolysis by the endogenous proteinases at the elevated temperature.

In a similar experiment with W^{185} (Table IV), the same general pattern of results was obtained. That is, proteinases released the W^{185}, and nucleases released it to a lesser extent.

The intracellular fraction normally containing high Mo^{99} does not take up a significant amount of label by simple adsorption. In fact less than one-twentieth of the Mo^{99} normally incorporated during growth was found to be adsorbed by this fraction during incubation of the fraction along with the label. Similar experiments for W^{185} show that very little, if any, of the *in vivo* incorporation can be accounted for by simple adsorption onto proteins during preparation of the fraction. Rather, it appears that both W^{185} and Mo^{99} are incorporated into protein(s) during growth, thus representing an *in vivo* synthesis of metalloproteins. Further evidence for the protein nature of these fractions was obtained in

TABLE IV

W^{185} Dialysis Loss from the 25,000 $\times$ g Supernatant Fraction of
Azotobacter vinelandii

Treatment	Percentage activity loss by dialysis[a]
RNAase and DNAase	49
Papain ($+10^{-3}$ M GSH)	54
Trypsin	55
Blank (30°C.)	36
Blank (5°C.)	30

[a] Incubated for 5 hours at 30°C. and subsequently dialyzed for 36 hours at 5°C. against 10^{-3} M cyanide at pH 7.2.

the ammonium sulfate fractionation and paper electrophoresis experiments to be discussed next.

Magee (1955) has shown that a large proportion of the Mo^{99} taken up by *A. vinelandii* strain O can be precipitated from cell-free preparations by ammonium sulfate between 1.4 and 1.9 M. Since there is a good possibility that there is more than one molybdoprotein in *Azotobacter*, experiments were set up to examine the possibility of using the ammonium sulfate fractionation as Magee had done, but by fractionation by the addition of very small increments of ammonium sulfate in an effort to determine if one could locate more than a single molybdoprotein in cell-free preparations. Figure 1 illustrates results representative of such experi-

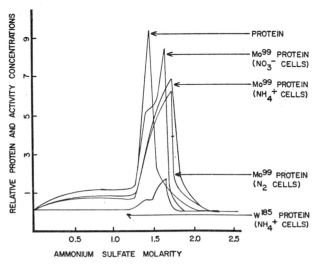

FIG. 1. Serial ammonium sulfate fractionation of the proteins of the *Azotobacter vinelandii* 25,000 $\times$ g supernatant fraction.

ments. The Mo[99] separates in one sharp peak only, at an ammonium sulfate molarity of about 1.65, regardless of the nitrogen source in the culture medium in which the cells were grown. This is somewhat surprising in view of the fact that the adaptive nitrogenase or nitrate reductase (presumably molybdoproteins) do not form except under the appropriate nitrogen source. The slight difference in the location of the peak fraction for the nitrate-grown cells is not significant. Ammonia-grown cells which incorporated W[185] show a similar fractionation pattern, that is, only one peak appears. Though not shown, for cells grown on nitrogen gas the W[185] fractionates identically. The small peak at a molarity of 1.46 may represent simple adsorption of label because a very large proportion of the total protein is recovered in that fraction. The concentrations of tungsten and molybdenum in Fig. 1 are not directly comparable as milligrams of metal per milligram of protein since specific activities of both labels were not the same. An absolute comparison of the uptake of molybdenum and tungsten was given in Table I.

The experiment in Fig. 1 was conducted on cells grown under rather high levels of aeration and only moderate iron levels which, as has been previously reported (Keeler, 1957) enhances the Mo[99] uptake. Other experiments at low oxygen tension and high levels of iron, where molybdenum uptake was reduced, failed to reveal any other peaks which might have been masked in the Fig. 1 experiment by the excessive uptake of Mo[99]. Regardless of the nitrogen source under which the cells had been grown, only one single peak was evident in all experiments. While Fig. 1 represents a plot of the total activities, a plot of the specific activities (counts per min. per mg. protein) of each fraction also fails to reveal more than one tungsto- or molybdoprotein peak.

Further experiments were conducted to compare the properties of the molybdoprotein(s) under varying culture conditions and to compare the molybdo- and tungstoproteins with one another. Partially purified preparations of sonically disrupted A. vinelandii were obtained by centrifugation of the crude homogenates for 90 minutes at 25,000 $\times$ g. The supernatant preparations were then subjected to paper electrophoresis. Autoradiographs were prepared from these paper strips. Densitometer scannings of all treatments were run on the autoradiographs and on the dye-treated electrophoretic strips, and were compared with one another. Figure 2 shows a plot of the densitometer readings on preparations from highly aerated cells grown on N_2 gas with W[185] and Mo[99] as labels. While the protein separation is not complete, it is evident that only one labeled fraction or spot is obtained on the electrophoretic strip. The mobilities of both the tungsto- and molybdoproteins are identical. Homogenates of $NH_4{}^+$- or $NO_3{}^-$-grown cells revealed the same pattern. There

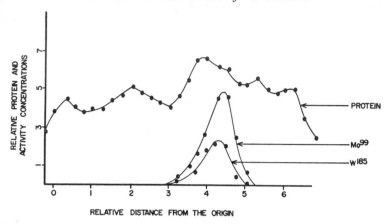

Fig. 2. Paper electrophoresis of radioactive tungsto- and molybdoproteins from partially purified homogenates of *Azotobacter vinelandii* grown on N₂.

was but one single peak in both cases and that peak had the same mobility as that of homogenates of cells grown on N₂. Electrophoretic runs on preparations of cells grown so as to limit the excessive molybdenum uptake also showed only a single peak.

The demonstration that *A. vinelandii* had the capacity of incorporating into proteins about 100 times more molybdenum than was required for optimum growth (Keeler, 1955) prompted an examination of the molybdate metabolism of another species of *Azotobacter*. It was known from the work of Horner *et al.* (1942) that for most species of *Azotobacter* one could simply leave molybdenum out of the medium and obtain a considerable decrease in growth rate, while for the *A. vinelandii* strain tested, optimum growth rate was obtained by the molybdenum present

TABLE V

Comparison of the Molybdenum Requirements of *Azotobacter vinelandii* strain O and *Azotobacter chroococcum* C44

Organism	Mo concentration added[a]	Relative growth
A. chroococcum	No Mo	0.310
	0.01 p.p.m.	0.400
	0.1 p.p.m.	0.795
	1.0 p.p.m.	0.920
A. vinelandii	No Mo	0.970
	0.01 p.p.m.	0.920
	0.1 p.p.m.	0.960
	1.0 p.p.m.	0.970

[a] Reagent grade components used—media otherwise purified in no way.

in the medium as an accidental contaminant. Keeler (1955) showed that very elaborate medium purification techniques were required to demonstrate a molybdenum deficiency with A. *vinelandii* strain O. In the light of these facts it seemed that other species of *Azotobacter* probably did not have the ability to concentrate molybdenum from a dilute medium.

A strain of A. *chroococcum* was obtained and tested to determine if it would show a molybdenum deficiency by simply leaving molybdenum out of the medium. Table V shows that while decreasing the molybdenum level in cultures of A. *vinelandii* has no significant effect, decreasing the level in A. *chroococcum* C44 cultures progressively decreased growth. Presumably if one were to repeatedly transfer molybdenum-deficient cultures on a medium purified to remove any molybdenum contamination, one could stop the growth of A. *chroococcum* completely.

The molybdenum required by this strain of A. *chroococcum* is likewise competitively inhibited by tungsten (Table VI) just as has been

TABLE VI

Competitive Inhibition of Molybdenum by Tungsten in the Growth of
Azotobacter chroococcum

W conc. (p.p.m.)	100	100	10	10	1	10	0.1	1	0.1
Mo conc. (p.p.m.)	0.001	0.01	0.001	0.01	0.001	0.1	0.001	0.1	0.01
Percentage inhibition of growth	88	88	86	64	75	52	49	32	28

shown for A. *vinelandii* (Keeler and Varner, 1957; Takahashi and Nason, 1957). The growth rate is proportional to the ratio of the metal concentrations, and not to the absolute level of tungsten.

Experiments were next designed to determine the relative uptake of Mo^{99} by A. *chroococcum* as a function of various culture conditions. The results (Table VII) show no relationship between uptake of Mo^{99} and the aeration or iron levels. This is in striking contrast to the properties of A. *vinelandii*. Further, A. *chroococcum* cells grown on NH_4^+ as a nitrogen source incorporated only one-fifth to one-tenth as much Mo^{99} as cells grown on nitrate or nitrogen gas. There is no observable difference in the incorporation of Mo^{99} in A. *vinelandii* as a function of nitrogen source (Keeler, 1957). It is also noteworthy that this uptake represents only 1 to 5 per cent of the uptake of similarly cultured A. *vinelandii*.

It thus appears that A. *chroococcum* C44, in contrast to A. *vinelandii*, cannot incorporate excessive quantities of molybdenum. The possibility immediately presented itself that these cells might prove an excellent source of cell-free preparations for ammonium sulfate fractionation and

TABLE VII

Relative Uptake of Mo[99] by *Azotobacter chroococcum* as a Function of Culture Conditions

Treatment	Mo[99] uptake per unit growth[a]
Forced aeration cultures	
NO_3^-, low aeration, 10 p.p.m. Fe, 1 p.p.m. Mo[99]	207
N_2, low aeration, 10 p.p.m. Fe, 1 p.p.m. Mo[99]	172
NH_4^+, high aeration, 0.01 p.p.m. Fe, 1 p.p.m. Mo[99]	39
N_2, high aeration, 0.1 p.p.m. Fe, 1 p.p.m. Mo[99]	132
Rapid shake cultures	
N_2	172
NH_4^+	42

[a] The absolute uptake for cells of about 0.850 optical density units was 0.02–0.05 p.p.m. in all cases for cells grown on N_2 or NO_3^-, and about one-fifth to one-tenth this amount when NH_4^+ was the nitrogen source. This is 1 to 5 per cent of what similarly cultured *Azotobacter vinelandii* will incorporate.

electrophoretic runs to demonstrate the presence of several molybdo-proteins. The possibility would be much greater here, if several molybdo-proteins exist, because the masking effect of the excess molybdenum would be absent.

Serial ammonium sulfate fractionation (Fig. 3) showed that the Mo[99] fractionated into only one peak at about 1.8 M ammonium sulfate, regardless of the nitrogen source on which the cells were grown. The low peak at 1.45 M, where most of the protein separates, is thought to

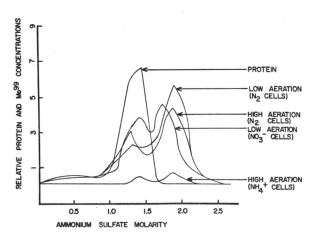

Fig. 3. Serial ammonium sulfate fractionation of the Mo[99] proteins of an *Azotobacter chroococcum* 25,000 × g supernatant fraction.

represent simple adsorption of label or coprecipitation of the molybdo-protein precipitating at 1.8 M ammonium sulfate. The incorporated Mo^{99}, regardless of nitrogen source and regardless of the level of iron or oxygen tension in the medium, fractionated identically in one peak only. The relative Mo^{99} concentrations in Fig. 3 are directly comparable in terms of absolute concentration of Mo^{99}. Furthermore, because the total protein of each fraction was approximately the same, the areas under the curves represent units of metal/unit of protein. However, the data of Fig. 1 and Fig. 3 cannot be directly compared with one another because the specific activities of the labels were not the same. An absolute comparison of the uptake of molybdenum by A. *vinelandii* with that of A. *chroococcum* is given in Table VII, footnote *a*.

IV. Discussion

According to current concepts, molybdenum can serve a number of functions in *Azotobacter*. The failure to find more than one molybdo-protein is not easily rationalized with the apparent multifunctional nature of molybdenum. It might be supposed that the results with A. *vinelandii* are due to the masking effect of the excessive Mo^{99} incorporation. How-ever, in A. *chroococcum*, where very little, if any, excessive uptake occurs, still only one molybdenum-containing fraction is found by ammonium sulfate fractionation. This suggests that either the methods are not sufficiently sensitive to show a very light labeling in other sites, or that, in fact, only one molybdoprotein exists in the cytoplasmic fraction. While the latter is not entirely unlikely, it seems a rather remote possibility. It is more probable that a demonstration of several molybdoproteins in *Azotobacter* will await the use of methods of better resolving power. A. *chroococcum* seems to be the best organism for further studies because this species does not incorporate excessive molybdenum.

V. Summary

A study of the incorporation of molybdenum and its antagonist tungsten into A. *vinelandii* strain O has revealed the following. Both the incorporated W^{185} and Mo^{99} are found largely in the same particulate fraction of cell homogenates. A large fraction of the uptake of either metal by cells represents actual formation of a molybdo- or tungsto-protein. Neither label is lost from partially purified preparations by dialysis against cyanide. However, incubation of homogenates with papain or trypsin causes release of both labels on subsequent dialysis. Both paper electrophoresis and ammonium sulfate fractionation of partially purified homogenates have revealed only a single molybdenum- or tungsten-containing fraction regardless of the nitrogen source on which the cells are grown. The fractionation characteristics of the molybdo- and tungstoproteins are identical.

In contrast with A. *vinelandii* strain O, which incorporates into proteins more than 100 times the amount of molybdenum required for optimum growth regardless of the nitrogen source, A. *chroococcum* C44 apparently incorporates only that amount actually required for growth. One-fifth to one-tenth as much molybdenum is incorporated by A. *chroococcum* on NH_4^+ as when the cells are on N_2 or NO_3^- as nitrogen sources. When molybdenum is not added to reagent grade medium in which the cells are growing, A. *chroococcum* shows a marked molybdenum deficiency not shown by A. *vinelandii*. A. *chroococcum* is competitively inhibited by tungsten just as A. *vinelandii*. Only one Mo^{99}-containing fraction has been observed when cell-free preparations of A. *chroococcum* grown on N_2, NO_3^-, or NH_4^+ are subjected to ammonium sulfate fractionation. The distribution of Mo^{99} in this fractionation procedure is identical regardless of nitrogen source.

REFERENCES

Bortels, H. 1930. *Arch. Microbiol.* 1, 333.
Burk, D., and Horner, C. K. 1939. *3rd Intern. Congr. Microbiol. Proc.* pp. 489–490.
Burk, D., and Lineweaver, H. 1930. *J. Bacteriol.* 19, 389–414.
Horner, C. K., Burk, D., Allison, F. E., and Sherman, M. S. 1942. *J. Agr. Research* 65, 173.
Jensen, H. L. 1948. *Proc. Linnean Soc. N. S. Wales* 72, 299–310.
Keeler, R. F. 1955. M.S. Thesis, Ohio State University.
Keeler, R. F. 1957. *J. Bacteriol.* 73, 582–583.
Keeler, R. F., and Varner, J. E. 1957. *Arch. Biochem. Biophys.* 70, 585–590.
Keeler, R. F., Bulen, W. A., and Varner, J. E. 1956. *J. Bacteriol.* 72, 394–396.
Lenhoff, H. M., Nicholas, D. J. D., and Kaplan, N. O. 1956. *J. Biol. Chem.* 220, 983–995.
Magee, W. E. 1955. Ph.D. Dissertation, Univ. of Wisconsin.
Mahler, H. R., Mackler, B., and Green, D. E. 1954. *J. Biol. Chem.* 210, 465–489.
Mulder, E. G. 1948. *Plant and Soil* 1, 94–119.
Nason, A., and Evans, H. J. 1953. *J. Biol. Chem.* 202, 655–673.
Nicholas, D. J. D., and Nason, A. 1954. *J. Biol. Chem.* 207, 353–360; 1954. *Arch. Biochem. Biophys.* 51, 310–312.
Richert, D. A., and Westerfeld, W. W. 1953. *J. Biol. Chem.* 203, 915–923.
Shug, A. L., Wilson, P. W., Green, D. E., and Mahler, H. R. 1954. *J. Am. Chem. Soc.* 76, 3355–3356.

Takahashi, H., and Nason, A. 1957. *Biochim. et Biophys. Acta* **23**, 433–434.

Totter, J. R., Burnett, W. T., Jr., Monroe, R. A., Whitney, I. B., and Comar, C. L. 1953. *Science* **118**, 555.

Warburg, O., and Christian, W. 1941. *Biochem. Z.* **310**, 384–421.

CHAPTER 21

The Role of Copper in Some Enzyme-Catalyzed Oxidation Reactions*

HENRY R. MAHLER

Indiana University
Bloomington, Indiana

	Page
I. Metal Enzyme-Catalyzed Oxidation Reactions	311
A. Stoichiometry	311
B. Other Characteristics	312
C. Nomenclature	313
D. Classification of Copper Enzymes	314
II. Uricase and Its Reactions	315
A. Purification of Uricase	316
B. Identification of Uricase as a Copper Protein	317
1. Preliminary Observations	317
2. Copper Analyses	319
3. Absorption Spectra	319
C. Some Properties of Purified Uricase	320
1. Kinetic and Acid Dissociation Constants	320
2. Inhibition by Purines	322
D. The Role of the Metal	323
1. Evidence for its Participation in Substrate Binding	323
2. The Nature of Some Inhibitory Complexes	323
3. The Stoichiometry of Complex Formation	324
4. The Nature of Enzyme-Bound Copper	325
5. Transformations at the Substrate Level	326
6. The Function of Copper in Electron Transfer Proper	330
References	332

I. METAL ENZYME-CATALYZED OXIDATION REACTIONS

A. *Stoichiometry*

In our discussion here we shall restrict ourselves to a consideration of some enzyme-catalyzed oxidations which use atmospheric oxygen as the

* Supported by grants-in-aid of the American Cancer Society; publication No. 820, Department of Chemistry, Indiana University.

311

eventual electron acceptor, i.e., those metal enzymes which transfer electrons by whatever mechanism from a substrate to oxygen. Closer examination demonstrates that all known reactions of this sort follow one of the stoichiometric relationships summarized in Table I. We will observe

TABLE I

Stoichiometry of Metal Enzyme-Catalyzed Oxidations

Type	Reaction	Reactants	Products
A	(1)	$SH_2 + O_2$	$= S\begin{smallmatrix}OH\\OH\end{smallmatrix}$
A	(2)	$SH_2 + O_2 + 2e^- + 2H^+$	$= S\begin{smallmatrix}H\\OH\end{smallmatrix} + H_2O$
B	(3)	$SH_2 + O_2$	$= S + H_2O_2$
B	(4)	$2SH_2 + O_2$	$= 2S + 2H_2O$

that reaction (1) is unique in that neither of the common reduction products of oxygen, i.e., water or hydrogen peroxide, appears on the right-hand side; that reaction (2) is unique in the participation besides the substrate of a second, or "external" reducing agent, which may be designated a reducing cosubstrate; while reactions (3) and (4) might be regarded as simple dehydrogenation reactions, employing oxygen as the acceptor and differing in the extent of its reduction. All the reactions have been written for neutral substrates, but it will be obvious that the reaction type would not be changed by the substitution of ionic for neutral species or even by the possible participation of moieties contributed by the aqueous solvent. Thus we might have alternative formulations, for instance:

(3a) $SH^- + O_2 = SH^+ + O_2^-$
or $SH^- + O_2 + 2H^+ = SH^+ + H_2O_2$
(3b) $SH^- + O_2 + H_2O = S\begin{smallmatrix}H\\OH\end{smallmatrix} + HO_2^-$

B. Other Characteristics

It is apparent that their stoichiometry sets apart these four possible reactions, as do some of the other properties already discussed, and summarized in the last two columns of Table II. The most fundamental difference between the reactions, however, which permits us to classify them into two quite distinct types, here called "A" and "B" respectively, has been observed by the use of oxygen labeled with the stable heavy isotope O^{18}: This is that oxygen, the electron acceptor, actually introduced into the substrate molecule in the course of the reaction, leading

TABLE II

Characteristics of Metal Enzyme-Catalyzed Oxidations

Type	Reaction	Atoms from O_2 appearing in product	"External" reducing agent required	Equivalents oxidized per molecule O_2
A	(1)	2	No	4
A	(2)	1	Yes	2
B	(3)	0	No	2
B	(4)	0	No	4

to a product containing two atoms of oxygen more, all contributed by the atmosphere, in the case of reaction (1) and one atom of oxygen in the case of reaction (2). Thus all the oxygen taken up in the case of reaction (1) finds its way into the product, while in the case of reaction (2) exactly one-half of the oxygen uptake is so utilized, the other half being reduced to water by the cosubstrate. On the other hand, the reactions of type B lead to no incorporation of O_2^{18} into the product whatever. Thus within a single group of enzymes, and thanks only to the use of refined techniques, there has been resolved the old controversy between Warburg and Wieland, as to the nature of the "activated" species in oxidation reactions. As you know the former maintained that it was the acceptor, the oxygen which was "activated," while the latter maintained just as stoutly that it was the hydrogen in the substrate which was thus affected by the enzyme. The truth, as is the case in so many scientific controversies, is that both were right some of the time, and neither one all of the time. And we now see that besides the long-established and completely respectable dehydrogenases, which one might properly regard as substrate activating enzymes, there does exist this new class of enzymes, capable of introducing, and thus indubitably of "activating," oxygen molecules as well.

C. Nomenclature

A classification of metal enzymes capable of interacting with oxygen, somewhat similar to the above, has recently been discussed by Mason (1957), who in conjunction with his collaborators has been instrumental in collecting a number of the experimental and conceptual bits and pieces on which Sections I,A and B are based (Mason et al., 1955, 1957). It is, I believe, self-evident that in the light of these findings the designation "oxidase" should be discarded. In a completely indiscriminate manner it has heretofore been applied to all the enzymes so far discussed, as well as to a large variety of others, all of which have only one thing in common, viz., the ability to utilize oxygen sometimes as the only, sometimes as one of many different, electron acceptors. Not only is this designation nondescriptive and meaningless because overly general, but it is even, at least in certain cases, misleading. Mason has suggested a system of nomenclature which is outlined in the last column of Table III. I prefer the designations of the next-to-the-last column as being more

TABLE III

Suggested Nomenclatures for Metal Enzyme-Catalyzed Oxidations

Type	Reaction	This paper	Mason's nomenclature
A	(1)	Oxygenase	Oxygen transferase
A	(2)	Hydroxylase	Mixed-function oxidase
B	(3)	Aerobic transelectronase $(O_2 \rightarrow H_2O_2)$	Two-electron transfer oxidase
B	(4)	Aerobic transelectronase $(O_2 \rightarrow H_2O)$	Four-electron transfer oxidase

descriptive, of firmer historic foundation (Hayaishi *et al.*, 1955, 1956), and consistent with the modern system of enzyme nomenclature advanced by Hoffmann-Ostenhof (1956). But either system is self-consistent and vastly preferable to the outmoded term "oxidase."

D. Classification of Copper Enzymes

Our attention is to be focused not on metal enzymes in general, but on copper enzymes in particular. In Table IV, I have attempted to arrange

TABLE IV

Reaction Types Catalyzed by Copper Enzymes

Type	Reaction	Example	Enzymes
A	(1)		None known
A	(2)		Phenolase complex, p-hydroxyphenylpyruvate oxidase
B	(3)		Uricase
B	(4)		"Catecholase," laccase, ascorbate oxidase

the known copper enzymes within the four reaction classes. No example of reaction (1) catalyzed by a copper enzyme has come to light so far, while reactions (2) and (4) are well represented by copper enzymes of good standing. In Table IV we show some typical representatives, such as the formation of an *o*-diphenol from a monophenol, representative of reaction (2), and catalyzed by "cresolase," a part of the phenolase complex (Mason *et al.*, 1955). There is also the oxidation of a dienol or *o*-diphenol to the corresponding diketone or quinone, representative of reaction (4) and exemplified by the conversions catalyzed, for instance, by ascorbate oxidase and the "catecholase" portion of phenolase. These enzymes and the reactions catalyzed by them have been studied intensively for many years and a considerable body of information is available concerning them, and accessible to the reader in several excellent reviews (Mason, 1954; Singer and Kearney, 1954).

For this reason, and for the even more valid one that we ourselves have made no contribution whatever to this body of knowledge, we shall not concern ourselves with them here. Instead I should like to report briefly on some work on uricase, identified by us as a copper enzyme only fairly recently, an enzyme the properties of which may therefore not be quite so familiar (Mahler *et al.*, 1956). Our justification for writing the reaction catalyzed by the enzyme in the manner shown in Scheme A will, I hope, become apparent in the course of this presentation. Most of the experimental work was carried out at the Enzyme Institute of the University of Wisconsin. While there I enjoyed the collaboration of Drs. Harold Baum and George Hübscher and the stimulating counsel and discussions of Prof. David E. Green.

II. Uricase and Its Reactions

The enzyme uricase, or uricooxidase, is responsible for the oxidation of uric acid to allantoin (at least in media not containing borate). As enzymes go, it can boast of considerable antiquity, having been first described by Schittenhelm (1905) and by Wiechowski (1907) some fifty years ago. Off and on, a good deal of work has been expended on the enzyme by such authorities in the enzyme field as Keilin and Hartree (1936), Schuler (Felix *et al.*, 1929; Schuler and Reindel, 1932, 1933; Schuler, 1937), Barron (Altman *et al.*, 1949), and others (Batelli and Stern, 1909; Davidson, 1938, 1942; Holmberg, 1939; Leone, 1953; Robbins *et al.*, 1955; London and Hudson, 1956) without, however, any very decisive conclusions emerging as to the nature of the active site on the enzyme, largely because of the lack of an adequate purification procedure.

Considerable effort had also gone into an elucidation of the reaction catalyzed by the enzyme. The most notable findings were those of Bentley and Neuberger (1952), who showed that all the CO_2 liberated in the reaction had its origin in C-6 of the uric acid molecule and that the enzyme functioned as an aerobic transelectronase by the demonstration that none of the oxygen taken up during the reaction appeared in the product. A little earlier, Praetorius (1948) in Kalckar's laboratory had presented evidence that, in buffers not containing borate, at least two short-lived, but spectroscopically distinct, intermediates intervened between urate and allantoin, while a different path was followed in borate buffer. Thus the status of knowledge in 1952 may be summarized by Scheme I, which is taken in essence from the paper by Bentley and Neuberger.

SCHEME I

Reaction Catalyzed by Uricase[a]

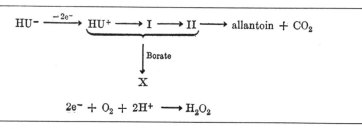

[a] Adapted from Bentley and Neuberger (1952).

A. Purification of Uricase

At about this time, we became interested in uricase and decided that the first prerequisite was the elaboration of a reproducible and convenient method for the preparation of the enzyme in good yield and high purity. In this we were successful as is indicated in the data in Table V (Mahler *et al.*, 1955). Enzyme units are defined in terms of a modification of Kalckar's spectrophotometric assay (Kalckar, 1947); we measure the disappearance of urate in a trisborate buffer at pH 8 at 293 mμ, the wavelength of maximum absorption of urate. Under our conditions one unit, i.e., a ΔA_{293} per minute equal to 1.00, corresponds to the oxidation of 0.15 micromoles of substrate per minute.

In our purification procedure we were aided greatly by the following observations: the enzyme can be extracted in excellent yield from acetone-dried pig-liver particles by means of carbonate. In our laboratory at that time, acetone-dried particles were being used as source material for a wide variety of enzymes, but all these procedures used extractions close to neutrality; thus we were able to utilize material which other people were discarding in quantity. The enzyme is remarkably stable to ex-

TABLE V

Purification of Uricase

Step	Total units	Specific activity (units $\times$ mg.$^{-1}$)	Approximate purity (%)	Recovery (%)
Pig liver homogenate	10,000	0.04	0.035	100
Alkaline carbonate extract of acetone powder of particles	5,720	0.17	0.15	57
Alkaline ammonium sulfate	5,500	0.61	0.53	55
tert-Butanol treatment	3,380	1.22	1.1	34
Precipitation at pH 4.2 extracted first with HCO$_3$$^-$ then CO$_3$$^=$	3,280	25.70	22.5	33
Precipitation by dialysis vs. HCO$_3$$^-$	2,500	37.0	32	25
Second tert-butanol treatment	2,460	66.5	58	25
Precipitation by dialysis vs. trisversenate	2,400	86.0	75	24
Ammonium sulfate fraction	1,000	100–120	85–100	10

posure to acid and has an isoelectric point close to neutrality; thus it can be precipitated in neutral or acid solution and separated from other proteins by selective precipitation and denaturation procedures. Finally, we found that the enzyme was associated with nucleic acid or nucleoprotein fragments (see also Robbins *et al.*, 1955), a fact which had been responsible for the inability of earlier investigators to proceed too far along the road to purity. We were fortunate to find that treatment with a dilute solution of *tert*-butanol in the cold was sufficient to dissociate these complexes. Table V shows that, at least to the stage of approximately 75 per cent purity by physicochemical criteria, the recoveries are quite good in spite of an overall purification of some 3000-fold.

B. Identification of Uricase as a Copper Protein

1. Preliminary Observations. Earlier investigators had identified several different metals such as iron and zinc as possible components of the active site of the enzyme (Davidson, 1938, 1942; Holmberg, 1939). None of these identifications, however, withstood the test of time and more purified enzymes (Praetorius, 1948). Nevertheless, a metal appeared strongly implicated in view of the reported extreme sensitivity of the enzyme to cyanide (Keilin and Hartree, 1936; Holmberg, 1939); this inhibition could be overcome by removal of the cyanide by means of dialysis. At first we were inclined to ascribe the cyanide inhibition to possible other reactions such as binding of a carbonyl group and, in the light of the experiences of our predecessors, were loath to look once again for a possible metal on the enzyme. The question had to be reopened, however, when we found that no other carbonyl reagent except hy-

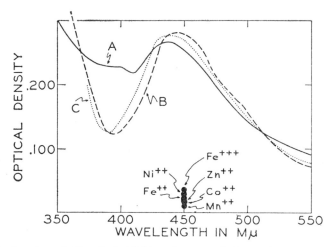

FIG. 1. Spectra of Cu diethyldithiocarbamate chelates. Curve A, uricase (Cu content, 2 μg. per ml., specific activity, 40) dialyzed for 12 hours against 0.01 M Tris Versenate, pH 8.0, followed by dialysis against the same buffer containing 0.001 M sodium diethyldithiocarbamate for 24 hours. Curve B, 2 μg. of Cu^{++} per ml. (as the sulfate) treated for 60 minutes with 0.001 M diethyldithiocarbamate in 0.01 M Tris Versenate, pH 8.0, at 38° C. Curve C, conditions as in Curve B, but 0.93 mg. per ml. of recrystallized bovine albumin or 1.0 mg. per ml. of metal-binding human globulin were added. The solid circles indicate Mn^{++}, Co^{++}, etc., obtained under conditions similar to those used for the data of Curve B, but with the appropriate ion at the same concentration substituted for Cu^{++}. (Courtesy of *J. Biol. Chem.* **216**, 625, 1955.)

droxylamine showed any ability to act as an inhibitor, while several metal complexing agents, under reducing conditions (e.g., hydroxylamine and cyanide, but not fluoride; the last, when added to hydroxylamine, however, was more effective than hydroxylamine alone) did indeed show inhibitory action. The nature of the metal became apparent in the course of experiments in which we dialyzed the enzyme against dilute solutions of metal chelating agents such as diethyldithiocarbamate for prolonged periods of time. Under these conditions we were surprised to observe colored compounds inside the dialysis bag. Figure 1 shows the spectrum of such a solution, presumably that of an enzyme-metal-diethyldithiocarbamate complex. Only copper forms a complex with an absorption spectrum and of an intensity comparable to that observed with the enzyme under similar conditions.

2. *Copper Analyses.* Thus encouraged we undertook to analyze several enzyme preparations at different stages of purification for copper by the dithizone method. The results are summarized in Table VI. We were

TABLE VI

Copper Content of Purified Uricase Preparations

Preparation	S.A.$_{Pr.}$ (units/mg. protein)	Cu (μg./mg.)	S.A.$_{Cu}$ (units/mg. Cu)
B	125	0.67[a]	180
E	40	0.18	220
D	15	0.071	211
E'$_{CN}$[b]	40	0.17	240

[a] Minimum molecular weight on a metal basis—125,000.
[b] E dialyzed vs. CN⁻.

gratified to observe a very close parallelism between copper content and specific activity of the enzyme. While copper was present in these purified preparations, spectrographic analysis disclosed the absence of all other metals (especially iron and zinc) with the exception of small and variable amounts of magnesium. Incidentally, it could also be demonstrated that prolonged dialysis against cyanide did not remove the copper from the enzyme. It thus must be bound quite tightly even, as we know, at quite acid pH. Thus cyanide inhibition must be caused by binding of the complexing agent onto enzyme-bound metal in a manner quite similar to that described previously for diethyldithiocarbamate.

3. *Absorption Spectra.* One of the reasons why we found it difficult to believe that uricase might be a metalloprotein was the fact that its absorption spectrum, both in the visible and in the ultraviolet region, did not appear to deviate significantly from the spectra of most pure metal-free proteins. (Fig. 2.) Once we knew that a metal was indeed present, we noticed certain quantitative differences, however, the most important being that the ratio A_{280}/A_{330} decreased with increasing purification and was significantly different from that of known, pure metal-free proteins. This effect is also very striking if we compare the spectra of some proteins capable of binding copper, such as crystalline bovine serum albumin or siderophyllin, the metal-binding β_2-pseudoglobulin of human plasma, in

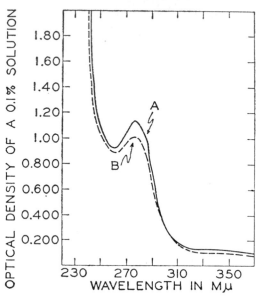

FIG. 2. Spectra of highly purified uricase. Curve A, enzyme of specific activity 120 in 1% carbonate. Curve B, enzyme of specific activity 60. (Courtesy of *J. Biol. Chem.* **216**, 625, 1955.)

the presence and in the absence of copper. We have arranged the significant ratios in tabular form in Table VII.

TABLE VII

Optical Properties of Some Copper-Containing Proteins

Protein	A_{280}/A_{330}
Uricase (S.A. = 55)	9.5
Uricase (S.A. = 120)	5.55
Bovine serum albumin	17.6
Bovine serum albumin + Cu^{++}	3.8
Metal-binding globulin	27.5
Metal-binding globulin + Cu^{++}	9.3
Metal-binding globulin + Fe^{++}	13.5

C. Some Properties of Purified Uricase[1]

1. Kinetic and Acid Dissociation Constants. We have measured the initial rate of urate oxidation by oxygen in the presence of the purified enzyme in a variety of buffers at various values of pH. We found those rates at any one pH to be identical regardless of the ionic strength and

[1] Baum *et al.,* 1956.

composition of the buffers used over a relatively wide range, and they were unaffected by either the presence or absence of borate ions. From these initial rates, the two characteristic constants of any enzymatic reaction V'_{max}, the maximal pH-independent velocity, and K_{ES}, the pH-independent Michaelis constant, can be calculated (Friden and Alberty, 1956). The enzyme inhibits the phenomenon of substrate inhibition. From plots of initial rates at high substrate concentration vs. that concentration, we can derive the value of K_{SS}, the inhibition constant for the substrate, a true dissociation constant. The activation energy for the reaction was calculated by conventional methods from the temperature-dependence of the initial rate under standard conditions. All these constants are tabulated in Table VIII.

TABLE VIII

Kinetic Constants of Highly Purified Uricase (0.01 M Tris(hydroxymethyl)amino-methane Buffer at 20°C.) and Acid Dissociation Constants of Binding Sites on Enzyme and Enzyme-Substrate Complex[a]

Kinetic constants	Value
$V'_{max} = k_3(E_t)$ (pH-independent maximal velocity)	1.7×10^{-2} μmole $\times$ min.$^{-1}$ $\times$ μg.$^{-1}$ of enzyme
k_3 (assuming a molecular weight of 100,000)	$1.7 \times 10^3 \times$ min.$^{-1}$
K_{ES} (pH-independent Michaelis constant)	1.7×10^{-5} M
K_{SS} (excess substrate inhibitor dissociation constant)	4.0×10^{-4} M
ΔE (activation energy)	1.24×10^4 cal. $\times$ mole^{-1}

Acid dissociation constants	Value
pK_{aE}	7.5
pK_{bE}	9.2
pK_{aES}	7.2
pK_{bES}	9.5

[a] From Mahler *et al.* (1955).

Recent treatments of the pH-dependence of enzymatic reactions by Dixon (1953), by Laidler (1955), by Alberty (1956), and others (Waley, 1953) have provided the worker in the field with a powerful new tool for the study of some aspects of enzyme-catalyzed reactions. Thus it is, for instance, possible on the basis of some simple assumptions to calculate the acid dissociation constants of the enzyme and the enzyme-substrate (Michaelis-Menten) complex, responsible for the typical pH-activity curves observed in so many enzyme-catalyzed reactions, including the present one. These values also are given in Table VIII. It can be seen that two acid groups on the enzyme with pK values of 7.5 and 9.2 have been identified. From a knowledge of the acid dissociation constants of the component amino acids (Klotz, 1954; Schubert, 1954), the two groups responsible may be tentatively identified as an α-amino, and an ϵ-amino (or phenolic hydroxyl) group respectively.

    2. Inhibition by Purines. It has long been known that uricase can be inhibited by xanthine and other substituted purines. We have studied the inhibition of the enzyme by a wide variety of trisubstituted purines made available to us through the kind offices of Dr. George B. Brown of the Sloan-Kettering Institute. We found the inhibition in all cases where it occurred at all to be of the competitive type, i.e., to be overcome by sufficiently high concentrations of the substrate. Inhibitions of this sort have usually been interpreted as signifying binding of the inhibitor by the very same sites on an enzyme which are responsible for substrate binding, and thus a study of inhibition patterns enables one to draw conclusions regarding the mechanism of binding of the substrate by the enzyme. A quantitative study of the phenomenon, furthermore, enables one to calculate the enzyme-inhibitor dissociation constants, the K_I's of Table IX. A consideration of the structure of the compounds responsible

TABLE IX

Enzyme-Inhibitor Dissociation Constants for Uricase-2,6,8-Trisubstituted
Purine Complexes (All in 0.01 M trisborate at pH 8.5)

Substituent in position			
2	6	8	$K_I(M)$
$-Cl$	$-Cl$	$-Cl$	8.0×10^{-7}
$-Cl$	$-Cl$	$-OH$	1.3×10^{-6}
$-OH$	$-NH_2$	$-NH_2$	1.8×10^{-6}
$-OH$	$-OH$	$-H$	1.2×10^{-5}
$-OH$	$-OH$	$-NH_2$	2.3×10^{-5}
$-OH$	$-OH$	$-OH$ (urate)	2.5×10^{-5} (K_S at pH 8.5)
$-Cl$	$-NH_2$	$-OH$	4.0×10^{-5}
$-OH$	$-NH_2$	$-OH$	1.5×10^{-4}
$-NH_2$	$-NH_2$	$-OH$	5.0×10^{-4}
$-NH_2$	$-OH$	$-NH_2$	0
$-NH_2$	$-NH_2$	$-NH_2$	0

for these inhibitions led us to the belief that effective inhibitors (and therefore probably the substrate as well) are linked to the protein at two binding sites: One cationic, providing a bond between the substituent at C-2 and the protein, and one neutral, providing the link between enzyme and the substituent at C-8 and also, to a certain extent, with N-9. The link probably occurs by means of hydrogen bonds. It is tempting to equate these two binding sites with the ϵ-amino (or phenolic hydroxyl), and α-amino groups previously referred to. Thus we have identified two groups of the active site. The third, and key one, is we believe provided by the copper.

D. The Role of the Metal

1. Evidence for its Participation in Substrate Binding. As already mentioned, the copper of uricase, corresponding to 1 gram atom of the metal per mole of enzyme (approximately 120,000 g.), is held very tenaciously by the protein and cannot be dissociated even in 5 per cent trichloroacetic acid or by prolonged dialysis against strong copper chelating agents. Thus the really decisive experiments, viz., the dissociation of the holoenzyme into apo- and coenzyme portions, followed by reconstitution by the addition of copper (Kubowitz, 1937, 1938) have not met with success so far. Nevertheless, we believe to be on firm ground in assigning an important role to the metal in the course of the enzymatic catalysis, and during its first stage, the binding of substrate to the enzyme, because of the following considerations: (*a*) There is a corresponding increase in copper content and enzymatic activity during the course of enzyme purification; (*b*) urate, like other purines is capable of chelating with metals (Albert, 1953); among these chelates those of copper are among the most tightly bound (Martell and Calvin, 1952; Williams, 1954) —chelation is believed to occur between N-7 and the oxygen at C-6 (Albert, 1953); (*c*) urate is oxidized by inorganic copper complexes, and especially by cupric cyanide, in a reaction which has several properties in common with the enzyme-catalyzed one (Griffiths, 1952; Baum, *et al.*, 1956); (*d*) the enzyme is inhibited by cyanide and by other metal complexing agents; this inhibition occurs only if the complexing agent can, like cyanide, also act as a reducing agent, or else requires the simultaneous presence of a reducing agent; (*e*) these inhibitions are either completely or partially overcome by the presence of the substrate at a low concentration; (*f*) the spectroscopically distinct complex of diethyldithiocarbamate and of enzyme-bound copper, formed on dialysis of the enzyme against the chelating agent, is dissociated on the addition of urate.

2. The Nature of Some Inhibitory Complexes. One of the puzzling features of the identification of copper as a part of the active enzymatic site has been the apparent discrepancy of this finding when contrasted with the known fact that certain heavy metal ions, most notably copper itself, are known inhibitors of the enzyme (Holmberg, 1939). Some elucidation of this problem was provided by the observations that this inhibition required the presence of certain polyvalent oxyanions and that less or no inhibition occurred if monovalent ions were substituted for them. Furthermore, the same effect could be observed in the case of the copper complex-catalyzed nonenzymatic model reactions already referred to. Here, as well, no effect was observed in the absence of the polyvalent oxyanions. Of course, while in the former case we were dealing with enhancement of inhibition, in the latter what is observed is an increase in oxidative efficiency. But in either case, the effect involved requires these ions, and it may well be that the same fundamental phenomenon is involved, especially in light of the fact that the order of effectiveness for both reactions is the same, as indicated in Scheme II. Both kinetic ob-

SCHEME II

Suggested Structures of Some Metabolically Active Copper-Oxyanion Complexes[a]

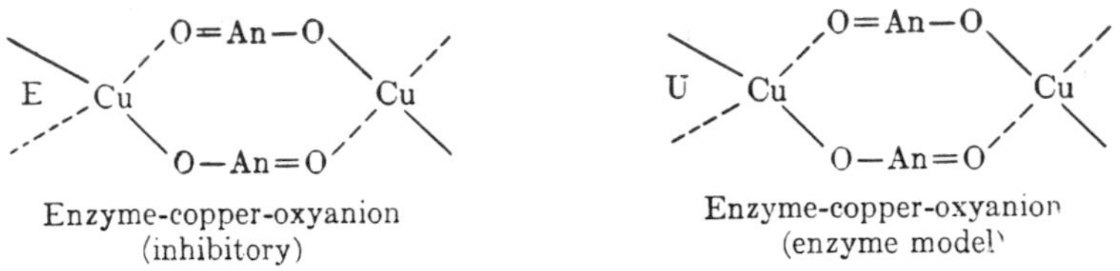

Enzyme-copper-oxyanion   Enzyme-copper-oxyanion
(inhibitory)   (enzyme model)

[a] An = borate $\simeq$ carbonate > phosphate > pyrophosphate. (Order of activity.)

servations and actual analysis of the complexes implicated in the non-enzymatic case suggest a urate:copper:anion ratio of $1:2:2$, and thus the structure shown on the scheme might not be too far-fetched. By analogy then, the inhibitory copper complex would be formulated as shown, and the essential similarity of the two effects becomes immediately apparent.

3. *The Stoichiometry of Complex Formation.* Some remarks appear germane at this point concerning the nature of the chemical reactions involved in binding various molecular species such as substrate, inhibitors, etc., onto the enzyme surface by means of the copper site. We know from observations concerning the kinetics of the reaction that the enzymatically active complex is probably one in which one substrate molecule is bound per enzyme molecule. There is some indirect evidence from the pH-dependence of the kinetic constants that this process of binding does not lead to the liberation of either a proton or a hydroxyl ion. On the other hand, the inhibitory complex formed in the presence of excess substrate is quite likely one in which two molecules of urate are bound at the same catalytically active site. The pH-dependence of this

process suggests that it almost certainly does not lead to the liberation of either ionic species (H^+ or OH^-). The binding of cyanide ion to yield the catalytically inactive cyanide complex which also seems to be a 1 : 1 complex does lead to the liberation of hydroxyl ions; the extent of binding appears to be inversely proportional to the concentration of this species. These various observations are most easily reconciled if we formulate the chemical reactions involved in the various binding processes in the manner tabulated in Scheme III.

SCHEME III

Stoichiometry of Complex Formation

---

(4) $E:Cu\overset{\cdot OH}{\cdot OH_2} + HU^- = E:Cu:U + 2H_2O$

(5a) $E:Cu\overset{\cdot OH}{\cdot OH_2} + 2HU^- = E:Cu\overset{\cdot U}{\cdot UH} + 2H_2O$

or

(5b) $E:Cu\overset{\cdot OH}{\cdot OH_2} + HU^- + H_2U = E:Cu\overset{\cdot U}{\cdot UH_2} + 2H_2O$

(6) $E:Cu\overset{\cdot OH}{\cdot OH_2} + CN^- = E:Cu\overset{\cdot CN}{\cdot OH_2} + OH^-$

---

4. The Nature of Enzyme-Bound Copper. We have just shown that the most consistent formulation for a variety of the reactions effected by the enzyme postulates the following structure for the enzyme-bound copper ion: a coordination number of 4 (perhaps arranged as a tetra-coordinated square complex); two of the valences are linked firmly to protein, and two are free to interact with ligands in the medium; in the absence of other possible complexing agents, the enzyme-bound copper exists as the aquo-hydroxo complex, a structure consistent with the observations described and with that of known copper complexes over this pH range (Bjerrum, 1941). This is shown in Scheme IV. The formation of the various other complexes we have been considering then takes place by the substitution of one or two of the "external" ligands. In the case of the catalytically active enzyme-substrate complex (see Bergmann and Dikstein, 1955, for the structure of urate monoanion), we postulate the formation of a chelate, with the oxygen at ring position-6 substituting for the uncharged donor :OH_2, and the nitrogen at position-7 (with concomitant loss of a proton) substituting for the charged donor :OH^-.

An entirely analogous situation obtains in the case of the various enzyme-purine complexes; the inhibitory enzyme-2-substrate complex is formulated as involving the same ligands as in the chelated structure, but with the ligands being provided by two different urate molecules rather

SCHEME IV

The Copper Site on the Enzyme (E)

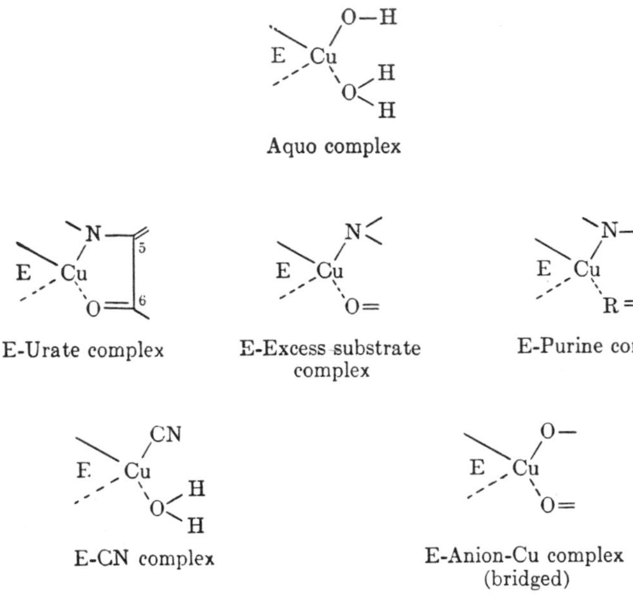

Aquo complex

E-Urate complex

E-Excess substrate complex

E-Purine complex

E-CN complex

E-Anion-Cu complex (bridged)

than by the same urate molecule. Thus low concentrations would favor the inherently more stable monourate chelate structure, while higher concentrations will lead to the formation of the diurate complex. The cyanide complex is pictured as substituting :CN⁻ for :OH⁻, while oxyanions are postulated as substituting for both moieties in an appropriate manner in the inhibitory bridged-copper complexes. The rather striking similarity of all the structures of interest in this context, makes the transformations described at least appear likely and internally consistent, even though perhaps not entirely correct.

5. *Transformations at the Substrate Level.* We have been able to show that the oxidation of urate monoanion, in the presence of the highly purified enzyme, does indeed lead to allantoin as practically the sole stable product in all buffers not containing borate (Hubscher *et al.,* 1957). Under all these conditions, the intermediates called "I" and "II" by Praetorius appear to be implicated. We were also able to demonstrate that even in borate buffers intermediate I is indeed formed, and at the same rate as when borate is excluded, but that formation of "II" is greatly decreased. Thus the two paths must diverge subsequent, and not prior, to the formation of "I," and the enzyme-catalyzed reaction proper is concerned only with the oxidation of urate to I (Scheme V).

SCHEME V

Overall Conversions in Urate Oxidation

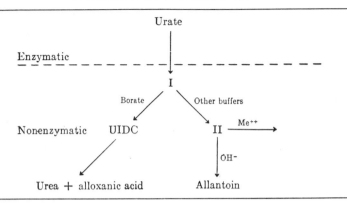

What then is the structure of this true enzymatic oxidation product? It is known that the ordinary path from urate to allantoin leads to a complete elimination of C-6 from the uric acid molecule (Bentley and Neuberger, 1952; Dalgliesh and Neuberger, 1954). Carbon atom-2, on the other hand, is retained in the product molecule (Hubscher et al., 1957), but the specific activity in the imidazolone portion corresponding to C-2 in uric acid is reduced to one-half, the other half appearing in the ureido portion (Cannelakis and Cohen, 1955). Analogous considerations also hold with respect to C-8 and with respect to the imidazolone and ureido nitrogen atoms (N-1,-3 and N-7,9 of the parent uric acid (Brown et al., 1947; Cavalieri and Brown, 1948). On the other hand, Cannelakis and Cohen also made the very important discovery that in borate buffers the end products of oxidation were alloxanate and urea, the structures of which are shown in Scheme VI. All the activity from C-2 of urate is retained in the alloxanate molecule while that from C-8 is accounted for by the urea. They also demonstrated that the immediate precursor of both the alloxanate and the urea was a compound tentatively identified as 5-ureido-4,5-diol-4-carboxylic acid or UIDC. The relationship of this compound to uric acid is immediately apparent.

Thus any postulated structure for the immediate enzymatic oxidation product (I) must fulfill the following requirements: it must still contain all the carbon atoms of urate, and it must be easily transformed into UIDC on the one hand, and by means of another intermediate (II) into carbon dioxide and allantoin. Decarboxylation may either precede or be subsequent to the formation of this intermediate II. The immediate oxidation product cannot be hydroxyacetylenediureinecarboxylate (HDC), a compound implicated in the literature in this role ever since the work

SCHEME VI

Structures of End Products of Enzymatic Oxidation of Urate

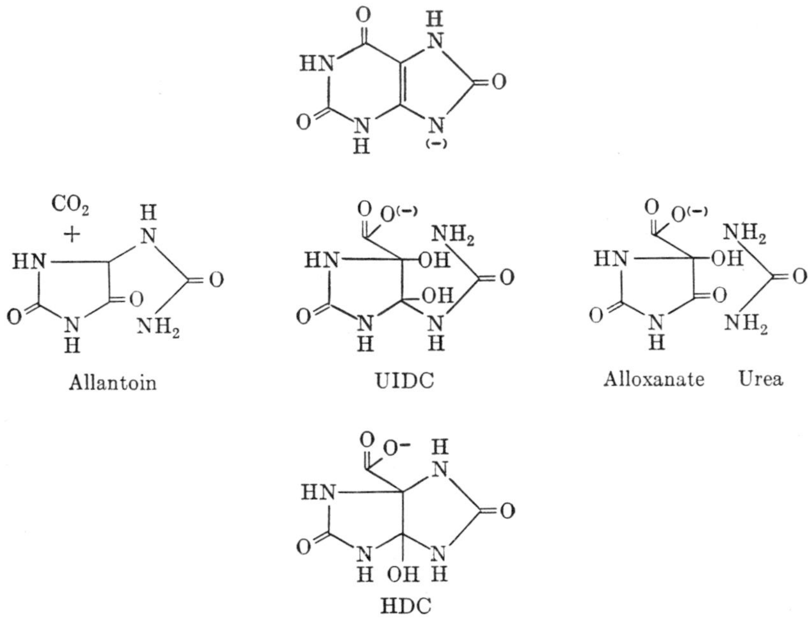

Allantoin UIDC Alloxanate Urea

HDC

of Behrend (1904) and Schuler and Reindel (1932, 1933), for this compound is relatively stable under conditions where the oxidation product is almost instantly decomposed (Hubscher *et al.*, 1957). In addition, the absorption spectrum observed by us (Mahler *et al.*, 1956; Mahler, in preparation) is completely inconsistent with the structure of HDC. This and some of the other properties of intermediate I are summarized and compared with the corresponding ones for uric acid and for intermediate II, in Table X. The value for the pK_1, derived by spectrophotometric

TABLE X

Properties of Urate and Oxidation Products

Compound	λ_{max}	pK_1	pK_2	Metal complexes	
				Metal	Evidence
Urate	293	5.4	10.2	Cu^{++}	Kinetic
"I"	305	4.5	11.5	Cu^{++}, Co^{++}	Kinetic
"II"	260	5.5	≥ 12	Cu^{++}, Co^{++}, Ni^{++}	Kinetic, spectrophotometric[a]

[a] Probably accompanied by change in structure.

means, makes it quite likely that we are indeed dealing here with a carboxylic acid rather than an imino N ionization.

We have formulated the initial, enzymatic stages during urate oxidation as shown in Scheme VII. The substrate is bound to the enzyme

SCHEME VII

The Initial Stages of the Uricase-Catalyzed Oxidation of Urate[a]

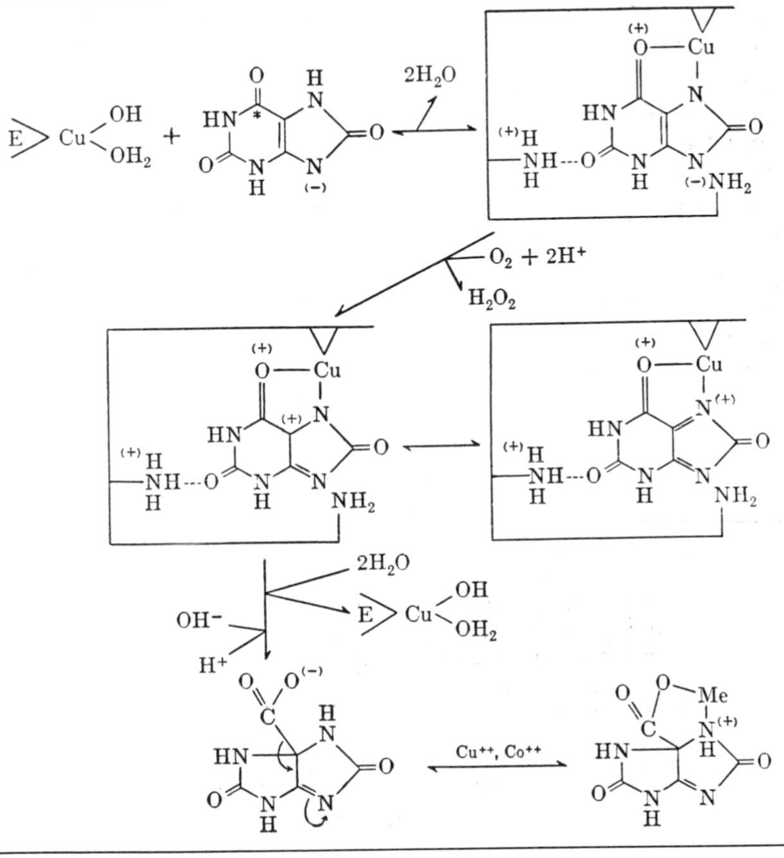

[a] Stoichiometry: $C_5N_4O_3H_3^- + O_2 + H_2O = C_5N_4O_4H_3^- + H_2O_2$

surface in the manner already described. This is then followed by the oxidation proper, i.e., the removal of two electrons from the enzyme-bound urate anion to yield a somewhat resonance-stabilized carbonium ion, in accordance with Bentley and Neuberger's (1952) earlier suggestion. Electrostatic repulsion of this positively charged moiety from the cationic copper site will facilitate its removal from the enzyme surface and free the enzyme for attack by another substrate molecule. Simultaneously with, or just subsequent to, this removal we also have a concerted attack by OH$^-$ on C-6 and by the unshared pair of electrons of N-1 on the positively charged carbon at C-5, thus leading to the formation of the carboxyl group and to ring contraction, a plausible reaction in light of precedents with similar systems (Leonard and Wildman, 1949; Leonard and Ruyle, 1949). As pointed out by Dalgliesh and Neuberger (1954), this structure, containing a double bond at a bridge-head, would be highly strained, and thus an unlikely one for the relatively stable bicyclic acid of Schuler and Reindel. But by the same token, this strained configuration and the resulting instability is completely consistent with all the observed properties of intermediate I, including its spectrum.

6. The Function of Copper in Electron Transfer Proper. In the preceding section we have discussed the possible role of the metal ion and of the other binding sites on the enzyme in the binding of the substrate prior to the enzyme-catalyzed transformations proper, and the nature of these transformations on the substrate level. We know that during this reaction two electrons have to be removed from the substrate and eventually transferred to the acceptor, oxygen. Does the metal play a vital role in this process also? Before turning to this question, let us consider very

SCHEME VIII

Some Alternative Electron Transfer Mechanisms

A. Compulsory Alternate One-Electron Steps

$(7a)$ $HU^- + Cu^{++}E \rightleftharpoons HU^-Cu^{++}E \rightarrow HU \cdot Cu^+E$

$(7b)$ $HU \cdot Cu^+E + O_2 \rightarrow HU \cdot Cu^{++}E + O_2^-$

$(7c)$ $HU \cdot Cu^{++}E \rightarrow HU^+Cu^+E \rightarrow U^+ + Cu^+E$

$(7d)$ $Cu^+E + O_2^- \rightarrow Cu^{++}E + O_2^-$

B. Formation of Binary Complex

(1)

$(8a)$ $HU^- + Cu^{++}E \rightleftharpoons Hu^-Cu^{++}E$

$(8b)$ $HU^-Cu^{++}E + O_2 \rightarrow HU^+Cu^{++}E + O_2^-$

$(8c)$ $HU^+Cu^{++}E \rightarrow HU^+ + Cu^{++}E$

(2)

$(8a)$ $HU^- + Cu^{++}E \rightleftharpoons HU^-Cu^{++}E$

$(8d)$ $HU^-Cu^{++}E \rightarrow HU \ Cu^+E$

$(8e)$ $HU \cdot Cu^+E + O_2 \rightarrow HU^+Cu^{++}E + O_2^-$

$(8f)$ $HU^+Cu^{++}E \rightarrow HU^+ + Cu^{++}E$

C. Formation of Ternary Complex

$(9a)$ $HU^- + Cu^{++}E \rightleftharpoons HU^-Cu^{++}E$

$(9b)$ $HU^-Cu^{++}E + O_2 \rightarrow HU^-Cu^{++}EO_2 \rightarrow HU^+CU^{++}EO_2^-$

$(9c)$ $HU^+Cu^{++}EO_2^- \rightarrow HU^+ + Cu^{++}E + O_2^-$

briefly the various alternatives that have been proposed for enzyme-catalyzed oxidation reactions and apply them to our particular case.

Among the suggested mechanisms, three in particular stand out (Scheme VIII): the first would postulate alternate one-electron transfers from the substrate to the metal ion, and in turn thence to the acceptor, in conformity with Michaelis' theory of alternate, compulsory univalent oxidations (1952). It will be noted that an obligatory intermediate in the reaction sequence is the semiquinoid free radical HU, at least in an enzyme-bound form. This is certainly a possible mechanism, especially in light of some recent findings by Commoner and his co-workers (1957) using microwave spectroscopy, which would seem to implicate free radicals of this sort in a wide variety of enzyme-catalyzed oxidation reactions. In the present case, however, unless the affinity of this radical for the enzyme be unusually high, one would expect its formation to be accompanied by rearrangement and dimerization reactions. No evidence for any processes of this sort has been obtained in the reaction under discussion. This line of evidence, admittedly negative, would appear to make it profitable to look for possible alternative mechanisms.

Another likely path is that found by Chance (1953) to be operative for the hydroperoxidases and suggested by him as possibly applicable to a variety of dehydrogenase reactions as well (Chance and Pappenheimer, 1954; Theorell and Chance, 1951). Two alternative formulations are described in Scheme VIII. They are similar in postulating a direct oxidation of binary enzyme-substrate complexes by O_2, but differ in that B(1) assumes the oxidation to take place without being preceded by an intramolecular dismutation on the enzyme surface, while the alternative mechanism B(2) postulates just such a dismutation. In other words, the species oxidized in B(1) is a substrate-cupric enzyme complex, while that in the B(2) is a semiquinone-cuprous enzyme complex. In B(1), the rate-limiting step would presumably be the oxidative reaction ($8b$). If this is so, K_{ES}, the Michaelis constant for the substrate would consequently be directly proportional to oxygen tension (Chance, 1953). We have measured this constant in air and in pure oxygen. Far from being higher in the latter case, it is actually slightly lower than that derived under standard conditions. This we believe is sufficient evidence for rejecting this mechanism.

In the second case, B(2), if we assume again that reaction ($8a$) cannot be rate-limiting (a sound assumption probably in view of the ready and reversible binding by the enzyme of a variety of purines structurally related to urate) then we would expect either reaction ($8d$) or ($8e$) to be rate-determining. Reaction ($8e$) cannot be the crucial one, for the same objections would then hold that have just been raised against mechanism

B(1). Thus we are left with reaction (8d). But we have found, as can be seen from a consideration of Table XI, that 2-dioxy-8-aminopurine (a very close structural analog of urate, which is bound by the enzyme with a constant almost identical with that of urate) is an alternative substrate

TABLE XI

Comparison of 2,6,8 Trioxypurine and 2,6-Dioxy-8-aminopurine

	2,6,8-Trioxypurine	2,6-Dioxy-8-aminopurine
Enzyme-substrate	$2.5 \times 10^{-5}\ M$	$2.3 \times 10^{-5}\ M$
Enzymatic turnover[a]	1700	2
Non-enzymatic turnover[a]	0.2	0.8

[a] Moles oxidized $\times$ min^{-1} $\times$ g. atom Cu

for uricase. Its oxidation rate however, is only about 1/1000th of that of urate itself. In the nonenzymatic model reaction, however, its rate of oxidation is actually 4 times that of urate. In the light of these findings, it would be very hard to understand why there should be this enormous difference in the rate of reaction (8d) for the two substrates, when we consider that in essence it is identical with the reaction actually observed in the nonenzymatic case, i.e., the reduction of a cupric complex by urate or the purine. Thus we feel justified in rejecting this alternative (8d) as well.

The most reasonable hypothesis remaining then would be that shown as alternative C: the formation of a ternary complex between enzyme, substrate, and oxygen, and occurrence of electron transfer in an intra-molecular manner within that complex. Scheme IX suggests a possible pathway for this movement of electrons.

The metal is probably in the oxidized form during the formation of the complex; reducing agents are necessary for effective inhibition of the enzyme. Williams (1956) has provided some theoretical justification for the great catalytic efficiency of cupric chelates. He postulates the d-orbitals of divalent metal ions as being able to form strong, continuous, overlapping molecular orbitals with the π-orbitals of certain ligands. We may extend this picture to include both π-orbitals of the substrate and p-orbitals of oxygen. Electrons, either singly or in pairs can then be transferred directly from the former to the latter. Although this picture does not call for an alternating valence change of the metal in a formal sense, the metallic ion participates in the enzymatic reaction in a very real manner and indeed makes it possible because it provides: (a) a locus for the actual attachment for both moieties of the actual complex within which the reaction takes place; (b) polarization of the electrons

SCHEME IX

Intramolecular Transfer of Electrons During Urate Oxidation

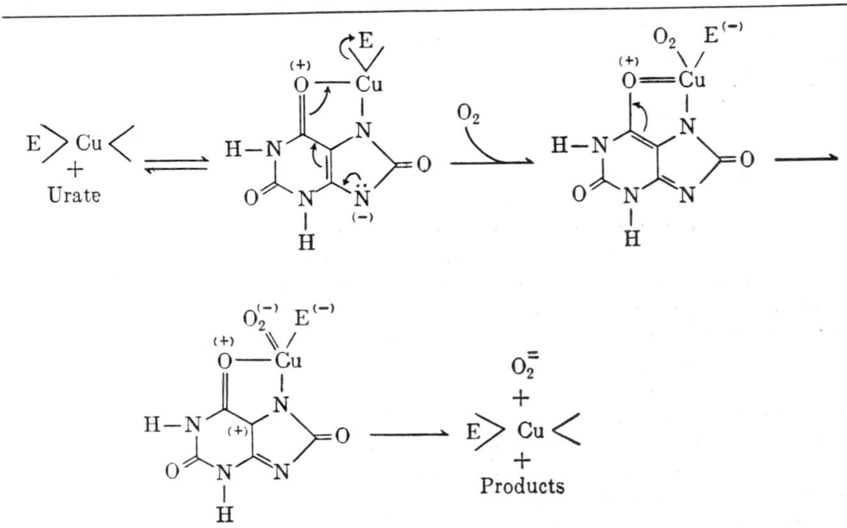

to be transferred, away from the substrate by virtue of its strong electrophilic (acceptor) character; and (*c*) permits the actual interpenetration of orbitals which makes electron transfer possible along a low-activation energy path.

It will be noted that the oxygen molecule has been pictured as actually displacing one of the protein ligands to the copper. Thus the ternary complex would be expected to be somewhat more labile and more easily dissociated with respect to its copper ion than either the free, or substrate-linked enzyme alone. This hypothesis may provide an explanation of two phenomena previously observed with other copper-containing enzymes: the exchange of labeled copper with that bound to ascorbate oxidase takes place only when enzyme, substrate, and oxygen are present simultaneously (Joselow and Dawson, 1951); a variety of copper enzymes appear to lose activity in the course of their catalytic functioning—the so-called reaction inactivation (Singer and Kearney, 1956).

REFERENCES

Albert, A. 1953. *Biochem. J.* **59**, 646–654.
Alberty, R. A. 1956. *Advances in Enzymol.* **17**, 1–64.
Altman, K. I., Smull, K., and Barron, E. S. G. 1949. *Arch. Biochem.* **21**, 158–165.
Batelli, F., and Stern, L. 1909. *Biochem. Z.* **19**, 219–253.
Baum, H., Hubscher, G., and Mahler, H. R. 1956a. *Biochim. et Biophys. Acta* **22**, 514–527.

Baum, H., Mahler, H. R., and Hubscher, G. 1956b. *Biochim. et Biophys. Acta* 22, 528–540.

Behrend, R. 1904. *Ann.* 333, 153–158.

Bentley, R., and Neuberger, A. 1952. *Biochem. J.* 56, 694–699.

Bergmann, F., and Dikstein, S. 1955. *J. Am. Chem. Soc.* 77, 691–696.

Bjerrum, J. 1941. "Metal Amine Formation in Aqueous Solution." Haase, Copenhagen, Denmark.

Brown, G. B., Roll, P. M., and Cavalieri, L. F. 1947. *J. Biol. Chem.* 171, 835–842.

Cannelakis, E. S., and Cohen, P. P. 1955. *J. Biol. Chem.* 213, 385–395.

Cavalieri, L. F., and Brown, G. B. 1948. *J. Am. Chem. Soc.* 70, 1242–1244.

Chance, B. 1953. *In* "Techniques in Organic Chemistry" (S. L. Friess and A. Weissberger, eds.), Vol. VIII. Interscience, New York.

Chance, B., and Pappenheimer, O. M., Jr. 1954. *J. Biol. Chem.* 209, 931–940.

Commoner, B., Heise, J. J., Lippincott, B. B., Norberg, R. E., Passonneau, J. V., and Townsend, J. 1957. *Science* 126, 57–63.

Dalgliesh, C. E., and Neuberger, A. 1954. *J. Chem. Soc.* pp. 3407–3414.

Davidson, J. N. 1938. *Biochem. J.* 32, 1386–1388.

Davidson, J. N. 1942. *Biochem. J.* 36, 252–258.

Dixon, M. 1953. *Biochem. J.* 55, 161–170.

Felix, F., Scheel, F., and Schuler, W. 1929. *Z. physiol. Chem.* 180, 90–98.

Frieden, C., and Alberty, R. A. 1955, *J. Biol. Chem.* 212, 859.

Griffiths, M. 1952. *J. Biol. Chem.* 197, 399–407.

Hayaishi, O., Katagiri, M., and Rothberg, S. 1955. *J. Am. Chem. Soc.* 77, 5450.

Hayaishi, O., Rothberg, S., and Mehler, A. H. 1956. *Abstr. 130th Meeting, Am. Chem. Soc.* p. 53C.

Hoffmann-Ostenhof, O. 1956. "Enzymologie." Springer, Vienna, Austria.

Holmberg, C. G. 1939. *Biochem. J.* 33, 1901–1906.

Hubscher, G., Baum, H., and Mahler, H. R. 1957. *Biochim. et Biophys. Acta* 23, 43.

Joselow, M., and Dawson, C. R. 1951. *J. Biol. Chem.* 191, 1–20.

Kalckar, H. M. 1947. *J. Biol. Chem.* 167, 429–447.

Keilin, D., and Hartree, E. F. 1936. *Proc. Roy. Soc.* B119, 141–143.

Klotz, I. M. 1954. *In* "Mechanism of Enzyme Action" (W. D. McElroy and B. Glass, eds.), Johns Hopkins Press, Baltimore, Maryland.

Kubowitz, F. 1937. *Biochem. Z.* 292, 221–229.

Kubowitz, F. 1938. *Biochem. Z.* 299, 32–57.

Laidler, K. J. 1955. *Trans. Faraday Soc.* 51, 528–560.

Leonard, N. J., and Ruyle, W. V. 1949. *J. Am. Chem. Soc.* 71, 3094–3098.

Leonard, N. J., and Wildman, W. C. 1949. *J. Am. Chem. Soc.* 71, 3089–3093.

Leone, E. 1953. *Biochem. J.* 54, 393–396.

London, M., and Hudson, P. B. 1956. *Biochim. et Biophys. Acta* 21, 291–298.

Mahler, H. R., Hubscher, G., and Baum, H. 1955. *J. Biol. Chem.* 216, 625–641.

Mahler, H. R., Baum, H., and Hubscher, G. 1956. *Science* 124, 705–708.

Martell, A. E., and Calvin, M. 1952. "Chemistry of the Metal Chelate Compounds." Prentice Hall, New York.

Mason, H. S. 1954. *Advances in Enzymol.* 15, 104–184.

Mason, H. S. 1957. *Science* 125, 1185–1188.

Mason, H. S., Foulks, W. L., and Peterson, E. W. 1955. *J. Am. Chem. Soc.* 79, 2914.

Mason, H. S., Onoprienko, I., and Buhler, D. 1957. *Biochim, et Biophys. Acta* 24, 225–227.

Michaelis, L. 1952. *In* "The Enzymes" (J. B. Sumner and K. Myrbäck, eds.), Vol. II, Part 1, pp. 1–46. Academic Press, New York.

Praetorius, E. 1948. *Biochim. et Biophys. Acta* **2**, 602–613.

Robbins, K. C., Barnett, E. L., and Grant, N. H. 1955. *J. Biol. Chem.* **216**, 27–35.

Schittenhelm, A. 1905. *Z. physiol. Chem.* **46**, 354–359.

Schubert, J. 1954. *In* "Chemical Specificity in Biological Interactions" (F. R. N. Gurd, ed.), pp. 114–160. Academic Press, New York.

Schuler, W. 1937. *Z. physiol. Chem.* **208**, 237–247.

Schuler, W., and Reindel, W. 1932. *Z. physiol. Chem.* **208**, 248.

Schuler, W., and Reindel, W. 1933. *Z. physiol. Chem.* **214**, 258–269.

Singer, T. P., and Kearney, E. 1954. *In* "The Proteins" (H. Neurath and K. Bailey, eds.), Vol. II, Part A, pp. 124–276. Academic Press, New York.

Theorell, H., and Chance, B. 1951. *Acta. Chem. Scand.* **5**, 1127.

Waley, S. G. 1953. *Biochim. et Biophys. Acta* **10**, 27–34.

Wiechowski, W. 1907. *Beitr. chem. physiol. Pathol.* **9**, 295–305.

Williams, R. J. P. 1954. *J. Phys. Chem.* **58**, 121–145.

Williams, R. J. P. 1956. *Nature* **177**, 304–307.

CHAPTER 22

The Metabolic Role of Zinc

FREDERIC L. HOCH AND BERT L. VALLEE

*The Biophysics Research Laboratory of
the Department of Medicine,
Harvard Medical School and
Peter Bent Brigham Hospital,
Boston, Massachusetts*

		Page
I.	Introduction	337
II.	Zinc Metalloproteins	339
	A. Carbonic Anhydrase	339
	B. Bovine Pancreas Carboxypeptidase	341
	C. Pyridine Nucleotide-Dependent Zinc Metallodehydrogenases	342
	1. Yeast Alcohol Dehydrogenase	342
	2. Equine Liver Alcohol Dehydrogenase	346
	3. Bovine Liver Glutamic Dehydrogenase	348
	4. Rabbit Skeletal Muscle Lactic Dehydrogenase	349
	5. Other Pyridine Nucleotide-Dependent Metallodehydrogenases	349
	D. Miscellaneous Enzymes	351
	1. Hexokinase	351
III.	Enzymatic Consequents of Zinc Deficiency	351
IV.	Porcine Parakeratosis	354
V.	Postalcoholic Hepatic Cirrhosis in the Human	356
	References	359

I. INTRODUCTION

Some 90 years ago, zinc was shown to be essential for the growth of *Aspergillus niger* (Raulin, 1869). It was found to be present in the tissues of plants, animals, and man soon thereafter (Lechartier and Bellamy, 1877; Raoult and Breton, 1877). Since that time, zinc has been classified as a "trace element" and, like the other members of this group, has been the subject of nutritional, physiological, toxicological, and biochemical investigations, which are reviewed elsewhere in detail (Lutz, 1926; Warburg, 1949; Foster, 1949; Vallee and Altschule, 1949; Lehninger, 1950; James, 1953; Underwood, 1956; Vallee, 1951, 1952, 1956, 1957). Early studies all indicated that zinc is a constant component of tissues in representative species of the various phyla. Only in the last 20 years have specific metabolic roles been assigned to this element, however, probably as a consequence of the parallel improvements in methodology in biochemistry and in metal analyses.

The investigation of the roles of such traces of metals in metabolism has come to follow certain principles, which have been discussed elsewhere (Vallee, 1951, 1952, 1955). The studies of the function of zinc to be discussed here have followed these precepts.

Operationally, the functional interaction of zinc—or of any metal ion—with enzymes may be defined (Vallee, 1955) as falling into one of two categories: *metal-enzyme complexes* or *metalloenzymes*. The *metal-enzyme complexes* apparently involving zinc are numerous (Lehninger, 1950; James, 1953; Williams, 1953; Malmstrom, 1956), but these relatively nonspecific, easily dissociable complexes have been studied extensively only *in vitro*, and the activating effect of a metal ion upon an enzyme *in vitro* defines neither its structural association with the enzyme nor a unique metabolic function of the metal. The activating effects of zinc ions upon enzymes are likely to be important *in vivo*, but at the present time it is very difficult to assign precise metabolic roles to zinc through studies of zinc-enzyme complexes.

The *metalloenzymes*, on the other hand, are defined to incorporate a single specific metal into the protein matrix so firmly that the two can be thought of as an "entity" in nature, and homogeneous metalloenzymes can be isolated and identified. This specificity and firmness of binding endow metalloenzymes with certain operational characteristics which are of advantage in discerning specific metabolic roles of metals found present in tissues. If both the metal and the enzyme activity are detected, it may be said with some confidence that they are associated, and, even further, that they are manifestations of the same protein molecule. A metabolic function of the metal may then be identified with the significance that the enzyme-catalyzed chemical reaction plays in the cellular economy. For these reasons, the known zinc metalloenzymes will be discussed here; their functions constitute, at present, the best intellectual link to the metabolic role of zinc.

With one exception, all of the information on zinc metalloenzymes is of very recent origin. The phenomena of some of the reported physiological effects of zinc deprivation can now be approached from a different viewpoint, and metabolic events not previously considered to involve zinc may be explored on the basis of biochemical knowledge. Certain nutritional studies of organisms which show specific enzymatic changes when deprived of zinc will be discussed, as will be porcine parakeratosis and human postalcoholic hepatic cirrhosis.

II. Zinc Metalloproteins

Using the operational definitions for a *metalloprotein* and a *metallo-enzyme* (Vallee, 1955), 7 zinc metalloproteins have been characterized thus far: the carbonic anhydrase of bovine erythrocytes (Keilin and Mann, 1940a,b); a zinc-containing protein of human leucocytes (Hoch and Vallee, 1952; Vallee *et al.*, 1954); the carboxypeptidase of bovine pancreas (Vallee and Neurath, 1954, 1955); the alcohol dehydrogenase of yeast (Vallee and Hoch, 1955a,b) and of equine liver (Theorell *et al.*, 1955; Vallee and Hoch, 1956, 1957); the glutamic dehydrogenase of bovine liver (Vallee *et al.*, 1955); and the lactic dehydrogenase of rabbit skeletal muscle (Vallee and Wacker, 1956). Recent findings are consistent with the existence of yet additional pyridine nucleotide-dependent metallodehydrogenases (Vallee *et al.*, 1956a), although their final inclusion in this group of zinc enzymes awaits their purification from extraneous proteins and metals, and their characterization in this homogeneous state. A number of other enzymes have also been thought to involve zinc in their mechanism of action. Until 5 years ago, the only conclusively proven role of zinc in metabolism was as a component of carbonic anhydrase.

A. Carbonic Anhydrase

Carbonic anhydrase was first described as a protein catalyst in 1932 (Brinkman *et al.*) and was purified from erythrocytes shortly thereafter (Meldrum and Roughton, 1932a,b, 1933). The most frequently used preparative method extracts the enzyme from bovine erythrocytes (Keilin and Mann, 1940a). Carbonic anhydrase has never been obtained in ultra-centrifugally or electrophoretically pure form; the claims of its crystallization (Scott and Fisher, 1942) have been questioned (Keilin and Mann, 1944). The molecular weight of carbonic anhydrase from bovine erythrocytes is approximately 30,000 (Eirich and Rideal, 1940; Smith, 1940; Petermann and Hakala, 1942).

The ecological distribution of carbonic anhydrase, methods for measurement of its activity, and procedures for its isolation and purification have been amply reviewed (Van Goor, 1948; Vallee and Altschule, 1949; Roughton and Clark, 1951; Weier and Stocking, 1952; Gibian, 1954).

Zinc was first identified as a constituent of bovine erythrocyte carbonic anhydrase (Keilin and Mann, 1939, 1940a), and this was quickly confirmed (Leiner and Leiner, 1940; Hove *et al.*, 1940). Plant carbonic anhydrase also contains zinc (Day and Franklin, 1946). The exact molar stoichiometry of zinc in carbonic anhydrase is not known, possibly because adequately purified samples have not been analyzed simultaneously for zinc, extraneous metals, and protein dispersity. Based on a molecular weight of 30,000, the reported zinc contents of bovine erythrocyte carbonic anhydrase vary from 0.92 and 1.04 (Scott and Mendive, 1941) to 1.52 (Keilin and Mann, 1940a) and 1.46 (Hove et al., 1940) gram atoms per mole. The zinc contents of carbonic anhydrase from the erythrocytes of the ox, sheep, and human may differ (Keilin and Mann, 1940a).

Although the chemical details of the bonding between the metal and the protein are not known, it is reported (Van Goor, 1945; Keller, 1955) that the enzyme can be split into thermolabile and thermostable fractions. The latter fraction is described (Keller, 1955) as a zinc-containing tripeptide with two glutamic acid residues and one glycine residue. This fragment does not itself exhibit carbonic anhydrase activity but increases the activity of dilute enzyme solutions. These studies are incomplete and preliminary in nature, and substantiation is necessary before this fragment can be considered a prosthetic group of carbonic anhydrase.

Although the manner of zinc-protein binding is obscure, the bond is firm, as shown by electrodialysis (Scott and Mendive, 1941) and exchange experiments with Zn^{65} (Tupper et al., 1951); Zinc-65 ions did not exchange with enzyme zinc over a period of 32 days.

The zinc content and the carbonic anhydrase activity of human erythrocytes are correlated to a high degree (Vallee et al., 1949), indicating that all, or at least the great preponderance, of the zinc in these cells is present in this enzyme; the presence of pyridine nucleotide-dependent zinc metallodehydrogenases in erythrocytes may eventually account for a small fraction of the total zinc. It is feasible, however, to estimate the carbonic anhydrase content of human erythrocytes from activity measurements (Keilin and Mann, 1940a): 100 milliliters of packed human red cells contain 0.21 gram of carbonic anhydrase (Vallee and Altschule, 1949).

This enzyme is inhibited by a number of agents known to form complexes with metal ions, and which are thus thought to inhibit by combining with zinc: cyanide, sulfide, and azide (Meldrum and Roughton, 1933), 2,3-dimercaptopropanol (Webb and Van Heyningen, 1947), and thiocyanate (Davenport, 1939). The inhibition by sulfide is disputed (Van Goor, 1948; Leiner and Leiner, 1940). Cyanide is a very potent reversible inhibitor, 85 per cent inactivation occurring at 4×10^{-6} M (Keilin and Mann, 1940a). The inactivations caused by these complexing agents indicate that zinc may be an active enzymatic site (Keilin and Mann, 1940b); no data either on the kinetics of these inhibitions or on the effects of chelating agents have been published. No information is extant to indicate that the inhibitory action of the sulfonamides (Keilin and Mann, 1940b) is exerted through the zinc atoms of the enzyme.

Carbonic anhydrase activity in plants has been reported (Neish, 1939; Day and Franklin, 1946; Bradfield, 1947; Waygood and Clendenning, 1950, 1951; Sibly and Wood, 1951). Plant carbonic anhydrase contains zinc (Day and Franklin, 1946), but the purest preparations of Sibly and Wood, as estimated polarographically, contained only 0.056 per cent, not removable by dialysis against water. Besides this low zinc content, the plant enzymes appear to be more resistant to inhibition by potassium cyanide, although azide inhibits about 75 per cent at 10^{-3} M.

In studies on oat plants at various stages of their life cycle, and on tomato plants, carbonic anhydrase was found only in nonchloroplast fractions of leaves (Wood and Sibly, 1952). Plants grown in zinc-deficient media showed correlated low zinc, carbonic anhydrase activity, and protein nitrogen levels.

Wood and Sibly (1952) interpreted their results to indicate that zinc deficiency lowers enzyme activity through its effects on protein synthesis in general. This interpretation implied that carbonic anhydrase be thought of as a metal-enzyme complex. It is equally feasible, however, and more nearly in accord with experimental data, to consider it as a metallo-enzyme, allowing the interpretation that zinc deficiency lowers activity by limiting the synthesis of the active metalloenzyme by interfering with the incorporation of zinc into the protein matrix. Similar interpretations extend to the analogous situation of zinc deficiency in *Neurospora* and the ensuing effect on alcohol dehydrogenase activity (see Section III).

B. Bovine Pancreas Carboxypeptidase

The carboxypeptidase, first crystallized in 1937 (Anson, 1937) and purified from bovine pancreatic juice (Green and Neurath, 1954), has a molecular weight of 34,300 (Putnam and Neurath, 1946). Recent quantitative spectrographic analyses and chemical measurements demonstrate that this carboxypeptidase is a zinc metalloenzyme (Vallee and Neurath, 1954, 1955; Vallee, 1955). Each enzyme molecule contains 1 atom of zinc, and all other metals detected, including magnesium, are present in stoichiometrically insignificant amounts.

The active role of zinc in the carboxypeptidase molecule is illustrated by the concomitant rise of the zinc:protein and the activity:protein ratios in the course of enzyme purifications (Vallee and Neurath, 1955). Other extraneous metals decrease in concentration as zinc and specific activity increase. With the first crystallization, the zinc content becomes 0.98 gram atoms per mole of carboxypeptidase; repeated crystallizations do not change this ratio, but there is a concomitant increase of specific activity with further removal of extraneous metals.

The zinc atom is firmly bound to the protein of carboxypeptidase, as is indeed the case with all the known zinc metalloenzymes. Prolonged dialysis against water or ammoniacal solutions does not alter the zinc content of the crystalline enzyme, but 1,10-phenanthroline removes zinc. On the other hand, some zinc not firmly associated with the enzyme is removed during the purification from pancreatic juice; this zinc may derive from contamination introduced in reagents, water, or glassware, or may represent other zinc-containing organic moieties or ionic zinc in pancreatic juice. A large fraction of administered Zn^{65} is rapidly excreted in pancreatic juice (Montgomery et al., 1943); part of this zinc is associated with carboxypeptidase.

Carboxypeptidase is inhibited by a number of agents which can form complexes with metals. The apparent inhibitions by sulfide, cyanide, citrate, oxalate, pyrophosphate, and cysteine were taken to corroborate earlier conclusions that carboxypeptidase was a metalloenzyme (Smith and Hanson, 1948, 1949). Some of these substances (pyrophosphate, oxalate, citrate) did not, however, affect initial rates of hydrolyses (Neurath and DeMaria, 1950).

On the other hand, metal chelating agents such as 1,10-phenanthroline, α-α'-dipyridyl, and others (Vallee and Neurath, 1955) which form strong complexes with zinc ions, inhibit initial rates completely. These agents do not inhibit when first exposed to equimolar amounts of zinc, cupric, or ferrous ions. Addition of zinc ions to carboxypeptidase already inhibited by 1,10-phenanthroline restores enzymatic activity, demonstrating the reversibility of this reaction. The sulfonamides, which inhibit carbonic anhydrase strongly, are without effect on carboxypeptidase.

C. Pyridine Nucleotide-Dependent Zinc Metallodehydrogenases

1. Yeast Alcohol Dehydrogenase. An alcohol dehydrogenase was crystallized from brewer's yeast in 1937 (Negelein and Wulff) and is usually now prepared from baker's yeast (Racker, 1950). The enzyme, prepared according to Racker (Hayes and Velick, 1954) has a molecular weight of 150,000 and binds 3.6 diphosphopyridine nucleotide molecules; it usually contains an inactive component comprising up to 20 per cent of the mass of the crystalline enzyme.

The crystalline yeast alcohol dehydrogenase (YADH), prepared from baker's yeast according to Racker, contains 4 atoms of zinc per molecule (Vallee and Hoch, 1955a,b) as measured by spectrographic and chemical (Vallee and Gibson, 1948; Hoch and Vallee, 1949) analyses. Recent studies, in which baker's yeast was grown in the presence of Zn^{65}, demonstrate directly the biosynthetic incorporation of zinc to form [(YADH)Zn$_4$[65]]; the zinc content of these crystals, as measured by radioactivity and chemically, is 4.0 gram atoms per mole. These zinc atoms are not miscible with zinc present from extraneous sources (Vallee *et al.*, 1958b).

Reports that a crystalline alcohol dehydrogenase preparation from brewer's yeast (Wallenfels and Sund, 1957a) contains 5 atoms of zinc (Wallenfels *et al.*, 1957), binds 5 diphosphopyridine nucleotide molecules (Wallenfels and Sund, 1957b), and can utilize added zinc ions to form up to 35 active enzymatic sites (Wallenfels *et al.*, 1957) are open to question. The protein purity of these preparations is not stated, nor is the accuracy of the method for zinc analysis, by X-ray fluorescence (Wallenfels *et al.*, 1957), validated in detail. Further, the assay used for enzyme activity incorporates semicarbazide, an inhibitor of yeast alcohol dehydrogenase (unpublished data), so that observed increases of activity by added ions, such as zinc, might be attributed to the nullification of an inhibition rather than to the accession of new enzymatic sites.

A preliminary report (Keleti, 1956) indicates that the enzyme prepared from baker's and that from brewer's yeast are not identical. Although they have certain properties in common, their isoelectric points and ultraviolet extinction coefficients differ, suggesting differences in their structure and composition. Immunological studies (Antoni and Keleti, 1957) further indicate a dissimilarity of these enzymes; both enzymes completely absorb the homologous as well as the heterologous rabbit antiserum, but the quantitative interactions are not identical. They both appear to be zinc metalloenzymes, both being inhibited by chelating agents, but their zinc contents are not reported (Keleti, 1956). This raises questions concerning the identity of the enzymes which different investigators have studied.

The metalloenzyme nature of yeast alcohol dehydrogenase is attested by the firm incorporation of zinc in the apoenzyme. The intrinsic zinc atoms are not miscible with extraneous zinc ions at neutral pH values as mentioned. Zinc in excess of 4 atoms can be removed, however, by dialysis against 0.1 M phosphate buffer at pH 6, together, presumably, with other contaminating metals; increases in enzymatic activity are effected by removal of these extraneous metals. The enzyme is known to be sensitive to traces of cupric ion (Negelein and Wulff, 1937) and to zinc. Addition of low concentrations of certain chelating agents may increase activity by similarly removing traces of inhibiting metals (Redetzki and Nowinski, 1957), although higher concentrations of chelators inhibit (see below).

Exposure of yeast alcohol dehydrogenase to pH levels below 6 results in rapid loss of activity; the loss of activity is directly proportional to the removal of intrinsic zinc from the enzyme. Thus, on dialysis, 50 per cent of the intrinsic zinc and the activity are lost at pH 5, and all zinc and activity at pH 4.5.

The crucial operational differences between metalloenzymes and metal-enzyme complexes are emphasized by the fact that efforts to restore activity to this zinc-depleted enzyme by additions of zinc ions alone, together with coenzyme, substrates, or sulfhydryl-containing compounds, or by variation of pH or anions have thus far been unsuccessful. Sulfhydryl groups are apparently not involved in the action of the enzyme zinc atoms (Hoch and Zotos, 1957).

This correlation between zinc content and enzyme activity is further borne out by the concomitant *rises* in zinc content and activity during the progressive purification of the enzyme (Vallee and Hoch, 1955b). Here, again, the extraneous metals are removed with increasing purity of the enzyme. These findings are all consistent with an active role for the zinc atoms in the mechanism of yeast alcohol dehydrogenase action.

Inhibition studies further demonstrate this role; a large number of chelating and complexing agents capable of combining with zinc inhibit the enzyme (Vallee and Hoch, 1955b; Hoch and Vallee, 1956a) under various conditions. The degree of inhibition is dependent on inhibitor concentration, on the duration of contact between enzyme and inhibitor prior to measurement of activity, and on the pH and temperature of this preincubated mixture.

The features of the inhibition by one of these chelating agents, 1,10-phenanthroline, have been studied intensively in an effort to elucidate the role of the yeast alcohol dehydrogenase zinc atoms by examining their reactivity toward this agent. Two types of interaction between enzyme zinc and 1,10-phenanthroline can be distinguished, both leading to characteristic inactivations. The first type is an instantaneous reversible combination between each zinc atom on the enzyme and one 1,10-phenanthroline (OP) molecule (Hoch *et al.*, 1958):

$$\text{YADH·Zn} + \text{OP} \overset{K_I}{\rightleftarrows} \text{YADH·Zn·OP} \qquad (1)$$

The formula YADH·Zn represents each zinc atom of $[(\text{YADH})\text{Zn}_4]$ as an independent active site. The apparent equilibrium constant of this reaction, K_I, is 1.5×10^{-3} M at pH 7.5 in 0.1 M phosphate buffer, 23°C. The existence of this reaction is substantiated by spectrophotometric studies which characterize the inactive enzyme-zinc-inhibitor complex, YADH·Zn·OP (Vallee *et al.*, 1957a, 1958a). The inhibition proceeding through this interaction is competitive between 1,10-phenanthroline and diphosphopyridine nucleotide (DPN) or reduced diphosphopyridine nucleotide (DPNH), but noncompetitive between 1,10-phenanthroline and ethanol or acetaldehyde (Hoch *et al.*, 1958). This is consistent with the following mechanism for yeast alcohol dehydrogenase action:

$$YADH \cdot Zn + DPN \rightleftharpoons YADH \cdot Zn \cdot DPN \tag{2}$$

$$YADH \cdot Zn \cdot DPN + C_2H_5OH \rightleftharpoons YADH \cdot Zn \cdot DPNH + CH_3CHO + H^+ \tag{3}$$

$$YADH \cdot Zn \cdot DPNH \rightleftharpoons YADH \cdot Zn + DPNH \tag{4}$$

Zinc is here depicted as a site for binding of DPN or DPNH to form the active enzyme-coenzyme complex. The stoichiometric correspondence between the 4 atoms of zinc and the 4 molecules of coenzyme known to be capable of binding to yeast alcohol dehydrogenase, together with the observation that DPN and DPNH are attached at the same enzymatic site (Hayes and Velick, 1954) strengthen this conclusion. Calculation of the velocity constants in Equations 2 to 4 from the inhibition data indicates that the rates of dissociation of the coenzyme from the zinc sites are the rate-limiting steps in the overall reaction.

The evidence from the OP-inhibition kinetics indicates that the substrates, ethanol and acetaldehyde, do not bind to yeast alcohol dehydrogenase at its zinc atoms to form a ternary complex, although such a complex at this site has been postulated (Wallenfels and Sund 1957b; Mahler and Douglas, 1957). The reaction mechanism shown in Equations 2 to 4 relates only to the role of zinc in alcohol dehydrogenase action; the postulated ternary complexes (Nygaard and Theorell, 1955) may exist, but apparently do not involve zinc as a center of the complex.

As mentioned above, only 1 molecule of 1,10-phenanthroline combines reversibly with each zinc atom in this instantaneous (< 5 seconds) inhibition (Hoch *et al.*, 1958). Since similar concentrations of zinc ion and 1,10-phenanthroline, under these conditions, form a preponderance of the $Zn \cdot OP_3$ complex (Kolthoff *et al.*, 1951), it is apparent that each zinc atom must be attached to the yeast alcohol dehydrogenase protein molecule through at least one pair of its coordination sites, while it binds 1,10-phenanthroline through another pair of coordination bonds. The steric influence of this persistent binding to the large protein molecule is seen in the weakening of the zinc-OP interaction: the dissociation constant for enzyme-bound zinc and 1,10-phenanthroline is about $10^{-3}\ M$, while a zinc ion binds a single 1,10-phenanthroline molecule to produce a dissociation constant between 10^{-5} and $10^{-6}\ M$ (Kolthoff *et al.*, 1951).

This instantaneous interaction, however, is not the only type of reactivity of yeast alcohol dehydrogenase zinc atoms toward 1,10-phenanthroline. If the enzyme is exposed to 1,10-phenanthroline, and samples of this mixture are assayed for activity after standing for various times, a progressive inhibition occurs in addition to the immediate one (Vallee and Hoch, 1955b; Hoch and Vallee, 1956b). The kinetics of this inhibition at pH 7.5 in 0.1 M phosphate buffer at 0.2°C. are consistent with the further binding of a second molecule of 1,10-phenanthroline to each zinc atom in the inactive complex YADH·Zn·OP (Williams *et al.*, 1958):

$$\text{YADH·Zn·OP} + \text{OP} \xrightarrow{k} \text{YADH·Zn·OP}_2 \tag{5}$$

This interaction is irreversible in an enzymatic sense and proceeds at a first-order rate dependent on the velocity constant k which is -13 log (inhibited activity minus control activity) per minute of preincubation per molar concentration of 1,10-phenanthroline under these experimental conditions. The irreversibility of Equation 5, denotes that the "undissociable" YADH·Zn·OP$_2$ complex represents a pool of irretrievably inactivated enzyme derived from the dissociable YADH·Zn·OP complex. With time, the size of this pool increases, more dissociable complex is immediately formed in accord with Equation 1, and the net result is a slow loss of free active enzyme.

Here the inhibitor must be bound to the zinc atoms through two of their coordination sites, leaving one site for the attachment of the metal to the protein. It is hypothesized that the zinc atoms become slowly available to combine with the additional 1,10-phenanthroline molecule through irreversible changes in the protein.

This slow type of inhibition is observed with many other metal-binding agents and yeast alcohol dehydrogenase and other pyridine nucleotide-dependent metallodehydrogenases (Vallee and Hoch, 1955b; Vallee *et al.*, 1956a) and may have its counterpart in the large number of enzymatic inhibitions reported to depend on preincubations. The details of the enzymatic role of zinc in yeast alcohol dehydrogenase and the structure of this enzymatic site are being pursued through such studies.

2. Equine Liver Alcohol Dehydrogenase. A DPN-dependent alcohol dehydrogenase crystallized from horse liver (Bonnichsen and Wassen, 1948; Bonnichsen, 1950; Bonnichsen and Brink, 1955) differs in many respects from the yeast enzyme, although it catalyzes the same reaction. Liver alcohol dehydrogenase (LADH) is less specific enzymatically than is yeast alcohol dehydrogenase, the former also oxidizing vitamin A alcohol (Bliss, 1949, 1951) and glycerol (Holzer and Schneider, 1955). This liver alcohol dehydrogenase has a molecular weight of 73,000 and reacts with two DPN molecules at neutral pH values (Theorell and Bonnichsen, 1951).

The early studies with yeast alcohol dehydrogenase led to the prediction that liver alcohol dehydrogenase would be found to contain 2 atoms of zinc per molecule (Vallee and Hoch, 1955a,b), which was rapidly confirmed qualitatively (Theorell *et al.*, 1955) and quantitatively (Vallee and Hoch, 1956, 1957). The firmness of the zinc binding, the concomitant rise of zinc and activity during purification, and the accompanying elimination of extraneous metals therewith all confirm that liver alcohol dehydrogenase is a zinc metalloenzyme (Vallee and Hoch, 1957). Like yeast alcohol dehydrogenase, liver alcohol dehydrogenase loses zinc and activity *pari passu* upon dialysis at pH values below 5.5.

The active role of its zinc atoms is demonstrated by the inhibiting effects of metal-binding agents (Vallee and Hoch, 1957), but a difference exists in the interaction of 1,10-phenanthroline with $[(LADH)Zn_2]$ and with $[(YADH)Zn_4]$. Yeast alcohol dehydrogenase exhibits both an immediate and a time-dependent inhibition with 1,10-phenanthroline (Hoch *et al.*, 1958; Williams *et al.*, 1958); liver alcohol dehydrogenase exhibits, under identical conditions, *only* the immediate reversible inhibition. Either dilution of the inhibited enzyme, or addition of zinc or cupric ions, can reverse this OP-inhibition of liver alcohol dehydrogenase; preincubation of liver alcohol dehydrogenase and 1,10-phenanthroline produces no time-dependent further inactivation at $23°C$. Thus the zinc atoms of $[(LADH)Zn_2]$ react differently from those of $[(YADH)Zn_4]$.

The kinetics of the immediate 1,10-phenanthroline inhibition of liver alcohol dehydrogenase are similar in some respects to those with yeast alcohol dehydrogenase. One molecule of 1,10-phenanthroline reacts with each zinc atom to produce the inactivation, and the resultant $LADH \cdot Zn \cdot OP$ complex has a characteristic absorption spectrum (Vallee *et al.*, 1957a, 1958a). The application of Job's method (1928) demonstrates the formation of a 1:1 zinc-OP complex, which proves that the zinc must be bound to the enzyme while combining with OP, forming a mixed complex. The amount of zinc bound by 1,10-phenanthroline corresponds very closely to the relative loss of activity. The dissociation constants of $LADH \cdot Zn \cdot OP$ determined spectrophotometrically and kinetically are of the order of 10^{-5} M, much lower than that with yeast alcohol dehydrogenase (see above), and approaching that observed with free zinc ions and 1,10-phenanthroline, 10^{-6} M (Kolthoff *et al.*, 1951).

Both DPN and DPNH compete with 1,10-phenanthroline (unpublished data), indicating that the coenzyme is bound at or near the zinc atoms, as in yeast alcohol dehydrogenase (Equations 2 and 4). However, ethanol and acetaldehyde both deviate from pure noncompetition with 1,10-phenanthroline, so that the reaction shown for yeast alcohol dehydrogenase in Equation 3 may not be followed by liver alcohol dehydrogenase. This difference may be related to the ability of liver alcohol dehydrogenase to reduce DPN without the addition of ethanol (Kaplan and Ciotti, 1954).

Extracts of the livers of the cow and the pig show a reduction of DPN in the presence of added ethanol, and it appears that there is a bovine liver alcohol dehydrogenase and a porcine liver alcohol dehydrogenase.

3. *Bovine Liver Glutamic Dehydrogenase.* The DPN-dependent glutamic dehydrogenase crystallized after purification from beef liver (Olson and Anfinsen, 1952) differs from the other enzymes of this group in some important aspects. The zinc metallodehydrogenases described in this section and other enzymes depending on pyridine nucleotides all act on primary or secondary alcoholic groups, while the glutamic dehydrogenase is the only known enzyme of this group which catalyzes the reversible oxidative deamination of an amino acid. Having a molecular weight of 1,000,000 (Olson and Anfinsen, 1952), this glutamic dehydrogenase is a much larger molecule than the other pyridine nucleotide-dependent dehydrogenases that have been studied.

The glutamic dehydrogenase of beef liver is a zinc metallodehydrogenase (Vallee *et al.*, 1955; Adelstein and Vallee, 1956); all crystalline preparations contain zinc in stoichiometrically significant amounts and do not consistently contain significant amounts of other metals. The average zinc content of 8 different crystalline preparations was 3.4 ± 1.0 atoms per molecule. This is a rather high coefficient of variation, 30 per cent, which derives both directly and indirectly from the large molecular weight of the protein. The mass ratio of zinc to protein is about 1:20,000, which is 1/10 of the mass ratio observed with the zinc metalloenzymes, carboxypeptidase, yeast alcohol dehydrogenase, and liver alcohol dehydrogenase. The demands on precise spectrochemical analysis are therefore much greater with glutamic dehydrogenase. Although these demands could theoretically be met by analyzing larger samples of glutamic dehydrogenase, that procedure would introduce excessive amounts of crystallizing and solvent electrolytes into the ash, which themselves interfere with the spectrochemical analysis. Until the resolution of this difficulty, the exact number of gram atoms of zinc in glutamic dehydrogenase cannot be specified better than stating that there are between 2 and 4 atoms per molecule.

Because of the low zinc:protein mass ratio of glutamic dehydrogenase, and the relatively large amounts of other zinc metalloproteins in liver, the correlation between zinc content and glutamic dehydrogenase activity is not striking until successive crystallizations are performed. At that time, the greatest elimination of other metals occurs, and a concomitant rise of zinc content and activity is observed.

The zinc metalloenzyme nature of glutamic dehydrogenase is further shown by the inhibiting effects of metal-binding agents. 1,10-phenanthroline inhibition of this enzyme, as with the yeast and liver alcohol dehydrogenases, is competitive with the coenzyme, indicating that the coenzyme is attached to glutamic dehydrogenase at or near its zinc atoms.

4. Rabbit Skeletal Muscle Lactic Dehydrogenase. The redox interconversion of lactic and pyruvic acids is catalyzed by a DPN-dependent enzyme isolated and crystallized from rabbit skeletal muscle (Beisenherz et al., 1953). This enzyme has not yet been completely characterized, and its molecular weight is not known. The crystalline enzyme is not homogeneous, showing at least three components of different mass on ultracentrifugation (unpublished data). The heterogeneity of the lactic dehydrogenases isolated from the same organ of an animal, from different organs of the same animal, and from different animals, has been demonstrated recently (Pfleiderer and Jeckel, 1957; Wieland and Pfleiderer, 1957).

There is zinc in all preparations of the crystalline rabbit muscle lactic dehydrogenase, or perhaps more properly, dehydrogenases, analyzed (Vallee and Wacker, 1956; Vallee et al., 1956a), the average being 637 micrograms of zinc per gram of protein. These preparations have all contained metals other than zinc as well, but in very variable amounts. With purification, the zinc content alone rises with increasing activity; the concentration of the other metals does not follow any consistent course. The unhomogeneity of the enzyme and the existence of many different lactic dehydrogenases in one organ (Pfleiderer and Jeckel, 1957), however, makes it difficult to interpret the variable zinc content.

Like the zinc metallodehydrogenases discussed above, this enzyme is inhibited either immediately or after preincubation with a number of metal-binding reagents; and some of these inhibitions can be prevented and reversed by an addition of Zn^{++} ions. The inhibition by 1,10-phenanthroline is competitive with DPN, indicating that this coenzyme is bound at or near a zinc atom. Apparently, zinc plays a functional role in the activity of rabbit skeletal muscle lactic dehydrogenase.

Rabbit skeletal muscle lactic dehydrogenase thus resembles yeast alcohol dehydrogenase, liver alcohol dehydrogenase, and glutamic dehydrogenase in all major respects. The final establishment of the molar stoichiometry of zinc awaits further purification of this enzyme.

5. Other Pyridine Nucleotide-Dependent Metallodehydrogenases. The hypothesis that a metal is a component of many, if not all, of the pyridine nucleotide-dependent dehydrogenases is a natural extension of the studies on yeast alcohol dehydrogenase, liver alcohol dehydrogenase, glutamic dehydrogenase, and rabbit skeletal muscle lactic dehydrogenase discussed in Section II. The remaining enzymes have not, for the most part, been obtained in completely pure form, and absolute proof of the hypothesis awaits their examination at that time. However, the hypothesis is strengthened if further consistencies are found, and can be discarded if major inconsistencies appear. The presence of metals in highly active, though not necessarily pure, enzyme preparations, together with the demonstration of inhibition by metal-binding agents, would validate this suggestion. These considerations apply equally to complete purified and to partially purified proteins, and it follows that the metalloprotein nature of the pyridine nucleotide-dependent dehydrogenases can be examined by investigation of readily available enzyme preparations.

Accordingly, a series of active but not completely purified dehydrogenases were examined. Zinc, copper, and iron were the only metals found (Vallee et al., 1956a) consistently in significant concentrations in the glyceraldehyde 3-phosphate dehydrogenase of yeast (Cori et al., 1948) and rabbit muscle (Beisenherz et al., 1953), the α-glycerophosphate dehydrogenase of rabbit muscle (Beisenherz et al., 1953), the malic dehydrogenase of pig heart (Straub, 1942), and the glucose 6-phosphate dehydrogenase of yeast, a triphosphopyridine nucleotide-dependent enzyme (Kornberg, 1950). These three elements all form strong complexes with 1,10-phenanthroline, 8-hydroxyquinoline, and sodium diethyldithiocarbamate, and these reagents all inhibit these enzymes under appropriate conditions (Vallee et al., 1956a). Magnesium, calcium, barium, and aluminum were also present in all enzyme preparations, but these form complexes only with 8-hydroxyquinoline. Thus the inhibitions observed are best explained by an interaction of the complexing agents with zinc, copper, or iron. Neither a metal-free active pyridine nucleotide-dependent dehydrogenase was found, nor a pyridine nucleotide-dependent dehydrogenase that was not inhibited under the appropriate constellation of experimental conditions.

In addition to these enzymes, it has been reported that the DPN-dependent formic dehydrogenase of peas is inhibited by azide, cyanide, and 8-hydroxyquinoline (Davidson, 1951), and the DPN-dependent isocitric dehydrogenase of yeast, by azide and cyanide (Kornberg and Pricer, 1951). The inhibitions of these and other dehydrogenases with cyanide and semicarbazide are ambiguous because of the presumed interaction of these reagents with either the pyridine nucleotide or a substrate. Interpretation of these findings must now include a possibility that these inhibitors may combine with a functional metal atom of the apoenzyme. In the absence of stated conditions of exposure of enzyme to inhibitor, reported absences of inhibitions of dehydrogenases with metal-binding agents cannot be interpreted.

D. Miscellaneous Enzymes

1. *Hexokinase*. The isolation of a "zinc-dependent" hexokinase from *Neurospora crassa* (Medina and Nicholas, 1957a,b) led to the suggestion that this is a zinc metalloenzyme. The criteria for this conclusion are not identical with those established to evaluate the zinc metalloenzymes described above. The hexokinase was not isolated in homogeneous form, and indeed showed a very significant phosphoglucose isomerase activity; no data on metal content of the preparations are given. The evidence for an enzymatic role for zinc is derived from the observed decrease of hexokinase activity in zinc-deficient mycelia, which is specifically over-come within 12 hours, but not immediately, by the addition of zinc to the culture. The hexokinase extracted and partially purified from the zinc-deficient felts is significantly activated by Zn^{++} ions, but that from control felts is not. Zn^{++} ions also protect the enzyme against a sulfhydryl reagent, p-chloromercuribenzoate. Versene inhibits enzyme activity, but high concentrations of KCN, NaN_3, α,α'-dipyridyl and 8-hydroxyquinoline do not. These observations, in the absence of further data, may indicate a metal-enzyme complex rather than a metalloenzyme.

The role of zinc in this enzyme requires further study. Apparently the hexokinase of yeast is not similar to this enzyme. Findings on zinc-deficient tomato plants (Reed, 1946), where inorganic phosphate ac-cumulated, were interpreted to suggest a possible role of this metal in the hexokinase of those tissues.

III. Enzymatic Consequents of Zinc Deficiency

The complexity of higher living forms often precludes the identifica-tion of the exact biochemical locus of action of a nutrient. Such difficulties may be somewhat simplified when the results of deficiencies are studied in lower organisms. Even further, the biochemical findings in such rela-tively uncomplicated organisms may often be extrapolated to interpret those in the more highly organized species, a principle of transphylar analogy of metabolic patterns. This has been shown to be possible to some extent in the case of *Neurospora crassa*, the common bread mold, which responds to zinc deficiency by displaying typical alterations of its enzyme patterns. Similar alterations are also produced by other cation and micronutrient deficiencies; this may reflect some of the occult interde-pendences which exist in higher forms.

A wild strain of *Neurospora*, 5297A, has been examined in detail as regards the activity of its tryptophan desmolase system (Nason, 1950). The activity is contained in cell-free extracts of mats and depends on the presence of pyridoxal phosphate (Umbreit *et al.*, 1946). Zinc-deficient mats grow at a rate 33–50 per cent that of the zinc-supplemented controls, and extracts of these mats form tryptophan from indole and serine only about 40 per cent as extensively as do the controls. Addition of $2 \times 10^{-6} M$ to $5 \times 10^{-2} M$ Zn^{++} to the extract fails to restore enzymatic tryptophan synthesis; indeed, the higher concentrations of Zn^{++} cause even further inhibition in a manner reminiscent of the effect of Zn^{++} on known zinc metalloenzymes. Addition of KCN or KCNS to the control extract inhibits tryptophan desmolase activity. Supplementation of the extracts with pyridoxal phosphate increases activity only slightly; the effect of increased pyridoxal in the growth medium was not mentioned. These effects are apparently specific for zinc deficiency; iron or manganese deficiency in the growing media, or additions of Cu^{++}, Mg^{++}, or Mn^{++}, to the extracts have no effect. It was concluded that "the enzyme" which converts indole and serine to tryptophan might contain zinc, or might itself be synthesized by a series of steps, one or more of which required zinc. Resolution of these or other possibilities might be accomplished by isolation and analysis of the enzyme or enzymes involved.

These studies were consistent with earlier findings in zinc-deficient tomato plants, where the metal was shown to be required for the synthesis of tryptophan, and indirectly, therefore, for auxin production (Skoog, 1940; Tsui, 1948).

Further studies on the enzyme patterns of the same strain of *Neurospora* (Nason *et al.*, 1951, 1953) revealed that zinc deficiency leads to alterations in the activity (either increases or decreases) of other enzymes as well, while certain enzymes are not affected at all. The decrease in tryptophan desmolase activity was confirmed, and the alcohol dehydrogenase normally present was often found to be completely absent in zinc-deficient *Neurospora*. A 10- to 20-fold increase in the activity of diphosphopyridine nucleotidase was observed, but fumarase, hexokinase (but see Section II, *D,1*), aldolase, and triose phosphate dehydrogenase activities were normal. These changes are not completely specific for zinc deficiency, however. While magnesium, manganese, or iron deficiencies do not affect the action of these enzymes, and while addition of Zn^{++} to zinc-deficient extracts has no effects on activities, deficiencies of other substances produce results similar to zinc deficiency. Calcium deficiency also decreases growth rate and alcohol dehydrogenase activity, and increases diphosphopyridine nucleotidase, and, slightly, fumarase activity; tryptophan desmolase is normal, however. Biotin deficiency produces results which are completely similar to zinc lack. A combined zinc and biotin deficit increases diphosphopyridine nucleotidase up to 100-fold over the controls. Markedly lowered alcohol dehydrogenase activity and high diphosphopyridine nucleotidase was noted in nitrogen or zinc deficiency in a variety of wild *Neurospora strains*.

Gradual increases of growth rate and the return of normal enzyme patterns denote recovery from these zinc deficiencies; this occurs when zinc and an appropriate nitrogen source is supplied. Similar responses occur after the other curtailed nutrients are added.

The absence of any effect when Zn^{++} is added to deficient mat extracts and the commutative nature of the enzyme activities in zinc-deficient and normal extracts indicate that ionic zinc is not involved here in the process of activation or inhibition of enzymes through formation of metal-enzyme complexes. The effect of zinc deficiency on alcohol dehydrogenase activity seems directly causal, in view of the findings detailed in Section II, *C,1* and 2.

These findings are consistent with the interpretation that the alcohol dehydrogenase of *Neurospora crassa*, like that of yeast and equine liver, is a zinc metalloenzyme. On the other hand, sufficient evidence is not on hand to interpret either the change in activity of other enzymes or the interdependences between zinc, calcium, biotin, and nitrogen in biochemical or structural terms.

The studies on *Neurospora crassa* (Nason *et al.*, 1951) also showed that *protein content* was markedly lowered in zinc-deficient mycelia. Neither protein concentration nor activity of alcohol dehydrogenase or tryptophan desmolase is increased when the zinc-deficient medium is supplemented with amino acids, vitamins, purines, and pyridines, although growth returns to normal levels. The failure of *Neurospora* to synthesize proteins was ascribed to the zinc deficiency, and this defect was thought to be the basis of the observed decreases in enzyme activities.

Zinc-deficient tomato plants also show decreased protein content, and contain about twice the total amount of amino acids and ten times the amide content of normal zinc-supplemented controls (Possingham, 1956). Especially marked are increases of extractable glutamine and asparagine, and the appearance of significant amounts of β-alanine, which is absent in the controls. Citrulline and ethanolamine, which are present in the controls are, however, absent in the zinc-deficient plants. Similar but less striking rises in amino acid content were observed in tomato shoots deprived of iron, copper, or manganese. These findings are of interest in connection with those of decreased protein synthesis in *Neurospora*. Similar findings, of lowered protein content, were reported in zinc-deficient oat plant leaves (Wood and Sibly, 1952). In these plants and in zinc-deficient tomatoes, carbonic anhydrase activity is also lowered, and the degree of diminution of protein, zinc, and carbonic anhydrase activity are all highly correlated.

Pyruvic carboxylase activity is absent in extracts of zinc-deficient *Rhizopus nigricans* (Foster and Denison, 1940), and it was concluded that zinc is necessary for synthesis of the enzyme protein itself, but that zinc is not a constituent of the enzyme.

The aldolase activity of higher plants is decreased in zinc deficiency, while copper deficiency does not affect this enzyme (Quinlan-Watson, 1951, 1953). This is of interest when compared with the conclusions of Rolinson (1951), based on the finding that the zinc requirements of *Aspergillus niger* vary for different carbon sources, although zinc is essential for all. The metal was thought to be involved in the metabolic events of the Embden-Meyerhof scheme "after the formation of the triose phosphates." While aldolase is responsible for the formation of these esters, a number of metallodehydrogenases would fit the requirements of Rolinson.

IV. PORCINE PARAKERATOSIS

The recent discovery that parakeratosis of swine involves a zinc deficiency is a significant step in our knowledge of the physiological function of the element in higher vertebrates. Spontaneous parakeratosis (Kernkamp and Ferrin, 1953) is widespread. The condition is characterized by dermatitis, diarrhea, vomiting, anorexia, severe weight loss, and eventually death. The increase of its incidence in recent years has been attributed to excessive calcium intake.

A nutritional disease can be induced in pigs (Tucker and Salmon, 1955; Luecke *et al.,* 1956), which resembles closely the spontaneous and endemic disease of hogs described as parakeratosis by Kernkamp and Ferrin (1953). By a process of systematic elimination, this disease has been defined as a zinc deficiency which is aggravated significantly by high calcium contents of the diet.

Experimental parakeratosis is induced with greatest facility in the presence of large amounts of calcium. At levels of about 30 to 35 p.p.m. of zinc, a normal dietary intake of calcium, 0.48–0.82 per cent, aggravates the signs of parakeratosis, inhibits weight gain, and increases the incidence of dermatitis. These symptoms become progressively more severe as the level of calcium is increased. A total of 80 to 100 p.p.m. of zinc in the food markedly reduces the signs of the deficiency and prevents the occurrence of dermatitis; these levels of zinc restore the parakeratotic pig to normal (Lewis *et al.*, 1956; Stevenson and Earle, 1956; Luecke *et al.*, 1957; Conrad and Beeson, 1957).

The addition of 1.33 per cent of monosodium phosphate has no effect on growth but significantly alleviates the severity of the dermatitis (Lewis *et al.*, 1956; Bellis and Philp, 1957), an effect unexplained thus far. Oral administration of vitamin A acetate neither ameliorates the skin condition nor does it increase the serum vitamin A concentration, which has been mentioned as being low (Stevenson and Earle, 1956).

Thus the requirement of zinc by the pig on practical rations appears to be very high compared to the 4–6 p.p.m. found to be essential for the mouse and rat on fortified diets. The zinc level used in purified rations fed to swine is usually less than 10 p.p.m. Yet these animals do not always develop parakeratosis, even though the calcium content of the diets is approximately the same as that of practical rations. There may be yet other unidentified factors in practical hog feeds in addition to calcium which are responsible for the apparent high zinc requirements. The absorption of zinc from the gastrointestinal tract in experimental parakeratosis is apparently normal, as studied with the isotope Zn^{65}, and parakeratosis has been induced by zinc deficiency with diets containing normal levels of calcium (Plumlee, personal communication, 1957).

Analytical information on alterations in metal distribution and on biochemical changes in this condition is limited thus far, making any localization of specific metabolic defects difficult.

Both calcium and magnesium are reported present in normal concentrations in the sera of parakeratotic animals. There are small and variable changes in serum phosphorus and in blood glucose and hemoglobin levels, and the serum albumin:globulin ratio is inverted and decreased (Stevenson and Earle, 1956). When the amount of calcium in the rations is decreased from 1.2 to 0.8 to 0.5 per cent (Lewis *et al.*, 1957), the zinc concentrations in liver, kidney, hair, and bone rise significantly, but the zinc of plasma, pancreas, skin, and intestine do not show a similar change. Increasing the zinc content of the rations to 128 or 1,028 p.p.m. produces no increase of zinc in the skin, but there are rises in zinc in the other organs (Hoekstra *et al.*, 1956; Lewis *et al.*, 1957).

Serum alkaline phosphatase activity has been assayed in these animals and is said to be extremely variable in animals receiving rations containing 32 to 44 p.p.m. of zinc (Stevenson and Earle, 1956). On the other hand, Luecke *et al.* (1957) find distinctly low serum alkaline phosphatase activities in parakeratotic animals, and they find increasing activities when such animals receive increased amounts of dietary zinc. Further investigation of metal levels and of zinc metalloenzyme activities certainly seems to be indicated in parakeratosis.

The failure of pigs with parakeratosis to gain weight and to grow, obvious anorexia, and the skin lesions are analogous to the effects of zinc deficiency in mice and rats. Since the esophagus shows marked keratosis also, it may be conjectured that this alteration in the histological structure of the upper gastrointestinal tract materially contributes to the inanition by interference with deglutition.

Parakeratosis as described so far has all of the characteristics of a conditioned deficiency, although the same disease probably can result from a primary zinc deficiency. The discovery of this spontaneous manifestation of zinc deficiency, however, provides students of the element's function with a new laboratory device to explore and delineate its physiological functions. This opportunity should shortly produce significant gains in understanding of the significance of this element in homeostasis.

V. Postalcoholic Hepatic Cirrhosis in the Human

Based on the identification of zinc in two mammalian liver enzymes, alcohol and glutamic dehydrogenase, deviations in zinc metabolism were sought in human liver disease. Marked abnormalities have recently been described in a widely prevalent liver disorder, postalcoholic cirrhosis (Vallee et al., 1956b, 1957b,c).

The concentration of zinc in the serum of these patients is markedly decreased, the degree of lowering bearing a significant relation to the fluctuating course of the hepatic dysfunction. In cases with "severe" cirrhosis, the serum zinc concentration is 66.6 ± 19 micrograms per 100 milliliters, as compared to the normal of 121 ± 19. The greatest depressions of serum zinc are noticed in comatose patients, and concentrations below 30 micrograms per 100 milliliters are a poor prognostic sign. The metal data correlate best with estimates of liver function as measured by bromosulfalein retention (Vallee et al., 1956b).

Such patients excrete abnormally large quantities of zinc in their urine, 1016 ± 196 micrograms per 24 hours, while noncirrhotic controls excrete 457 ± 120 micrograms. Oral zinc sulfate in physiologic quantities tends to restore normal excretory zinc patterns and liver function, as measured by bromosulfalein retention; serum zinc, however, did not change markedly.

The zinc content of livers of individuals dying with postalcoholic cirrhosis is also decreased (Lundegardh and Bergstrand, 1940; Vallee et al., 1957b). In cirrhotic patients 1 gram of wet liver tissue contains 29.0 ± 7.0 micrograms of zinc, as opposed to $74.0 + 23.0$ micrograms per gram in individuals dying from other causes. This difference is independent of the analytical base line chosen and is similar when expressed as zinc per gram of dried liver, or per gram of liver nitrogen. In the cirrhotic livers, only iron is similarly diminished, while calcium, manganese, aluminum, magnesium, and copper are present in concentrations identical with those observed in the noncirrhotic controls. This suggests that the altered concentrations of zinc and iron are not solely due to the structural alterations in liver tissue attending the scarification in postalcoholic cirrhosis.

The low zinc contents of serum and of liver would be most readily explained by a primary deficiency of zinc intake. The simultaneous existence of zincuria, however, raises the question of the existence of a *conditioned deficiency* in which a normal intake of the nutrient does not meet the needs of the organism owing to the presence of unusual secondary circumstances or factors. Porcine parakeratosis (see Section IV) may serve as an example of a zinc deficiency conditioned through a high calcium intake, at least in the experimentally induced disease. It is much more difficult to identify such conditioning factors or, indeed, signs of a primary zinc deficiency, in man, both because of his social habits and because of the obvious limitations imposed in experimentation.

The observed magnitude of the zincuria, caused by whatever metabolic abnormality, could deplete the zinc stores of the body to the point that inadequate amounts of zinc would be available for cellular functions, even if the intake were normal. The alterations in liver zinc and iron contents, two elements of crucial significance in oxidative catalysis, point to the metalloenzymes of these elements as possible loci of a resultant cellular biochemical defect. While separate study is necessary to assess the part that iron plays in this disease, the participation of zinc in the dehydrogenation of ethanol and of glutamic acid, two substrates that are clearly implicated in the general metabolic changes accompanying cirrhosis, enhances the hypothesis that abnormalities in zinc metabolism do contribute to pathologic manifestations.

It is certainly true that a zinc deficiency, primary or conditioned, does disturb the normal metabolic patterns of biological species other than man. Since lower forms are more accessible to experiment, it may be of value to draw transphylar analogies, and to examine the comparative biochemistry of zinc and ethanol metabolism in an effort to gain understanding of the human disease.

The lowest evolutionary forms adapt very well to the presence of ethanol, the overall equilibrium in yeast, for example, even favoring ethanol production. The liver of the horse, on the other hand, contains alcohol dehydrogenase as 1 per cent of its total protein content (Bonnichsen, 1950), which seems to prepare this animal for a considerably greater intake of ethanol than that which is considered conventional for the modern species. By analogy again, the liver of man, another mammal, should be similarly fortified against ethanol, although clinical observation indicates that these ramparts are often breached by persistent, heavy assault.

Horse liver alcohol dehydrogenase is the only purified mammalian ethanol oxidase so far available for study. While zinc has a role in ethanol oxidation in the horse and in a variety of organisms, the details of its function in this process, and the molecular structure of the catalyst, have apparently become modified by evolution, as implied by the teleology referred to above. The yeast enzyme, for example, oxidizes ethanol approximately 200 times faster than the mammalian enzyme (Theorell and Bonnichsen, 1951). Beyond this, the mammalian enzyme has gained the capacity to oxidize other alcohols, among which are glycerol (Holzer and Schneider, 1955) and vitamin A alcohol (Bliss, 1949, 1951). Thereby, this mammalian liver alcohol dehydrogenase affects several additional metabolic pathways, and interference with this enzyme will have more widespread effect.

The difference in the effect of ethanol on these two evolutionarily different enzymes may be of particular importance. The yeast alcohol dehydrogenase shows maximal activity in the presence of 0.33 M ethanol and shows no diminution of activity when ethanol concentration is raised 10-fold or more (Nygaard and Theorell, 1955). The horse liver enzyme, in contrast, at 23°C. exhibits maximal activity in the presence of 0.017 M ethanol—about 0.8 milligram of ethanol per milliliter—and is inhibited (Theorell and Chance, 1951; Theorell et al., 1955) approximately 50 per cent at 0.25 M ethanol, about 11 milligrams per milliliter. This is equivalent to a dosage level in serum that would be strongly intoxicating to a human. The mammalian enzyme, although still present in large quantities in liver and in the retina (Bliss, 1951), seems to have lost its capacity to metabolize in the presence of high concentrations of ethanol.

It may be hypothesized that the alcohol dehydrogenase of liver is particularly vulnerable to repeated or to continuous metabolic insults by high concentrations of ethanol. These episodes could set up a positive feedback system—the higher the dynamic tissue ethanol level, the lower the capacity to oxidize it, after a threshold value has been reached. Since liver alcohol dehydrogenase seems to bind ethanol in the mechanism of its enzyme action (Theorell et al., 1955), alterations of the protein structure of this enzyme particularly and of other enzymes and tissue proteins might be expected. A degradation of $[(LADH)Zn_2]$, liberating amino acids and zinc, and manifested by the observed amino-aciduria and zincuria, could then occur, the ultimate results being complete failure of zinc and protein metabolism.

Considerable evidence is at hand that zinc plays a role in protein metabolism in a higher animal, in plants, and in algae. As pointed out in Sections III and IV, zinc deficiency results in decreased protein synthesis and balance in the pig, in *Neurospora crassa,* and in oat and tomato plants. In the plants, it has been shown that the decreased protein levels are accompanied by high amino acid levels. While, as has been emphasized, these comparisons are knowingly drawn by analogy and should be considered as teleological, it must also be pointed out that similar analogies have been shown valid by the comparable effects of deficiencies of other metals and nutrients in lower and higher forms of life.

With these considerations in mind, it is possible, in fact, to reinterpret previous studies in man and to relate them to these analogies. Vitamin A metabolism, as manifested by abnormal dark adaptation, was found to be altered in human cirrhosis in 1939 (Patek and Haig). Vitamin A_1 alcohol dehydrogenase and liver alcohol dehydrogenase, in fact, appear to be the same enzyme (Bliss, 1951), which contains 0.18 per cent of zinc (Vallee and Hoch, 1957). Zinc has long been known to be present in the retina of many species in very high concentrations (Bowness *et al.,* 1952). A resistant deficiency of vitamin A exists in porcine parakeratosis (Stevenson and Earle, 1956). These studies of dark adaptation in human postalcoholic cirrhosis, therefore, seem to reflect the altered zinc metabolism in this disease.

Thus, the analogies of zinc and ethanol metabolism in microorganisms and mammals seem valid also in the human being. The metabolism of such an organism as *Neurospora* contributes to understanding *because,* and not in spite of, the fact that this organism does *not* show the anatomic consequence of a metabolic lesion, but the lesion itself is more discernible.

These studies focus on a specific area of metabolism and a metabolic component, zinc, through which a different approach to this prevalent human disease may be attained. The last few years have seen tremendous progress in the detection of basic mechanisms accounting for the diverse and varied manifestations of zinc homeostasis in plants, animals, and man. Clearly, zinc plays significant roles in fundamental life processes. Their elucidation should greatly assist our understanding of much taxonomic and phenomenologic information.

REFERENCES

Adelstein, S. J., and Vallee, B. L. 1956. *Federation Proc.* **15,** 505.
Anson, M. L. 1937. *J. Gen. Physiol.* **20,** 663.
Antoni, F., and Keleti, J. 1957. *Nature* **179,** 1020.

Beisenherz, G., Boltze, H. J., Bucher, T., Czok, R., Garbade, K. H., Meyer-Arendt, E., and Pfleiderer, G. 1953. *Z. Naturforsch.* **8b**, 555.

Bellis, D. B., and Philp, J. McL. 1957. *J. Sci. Food Agr.* **8**, Suppl., 119.

Bliss, A. F. 1949. *Biol. Bull.* **97**, 221.

Bliss, A. F. 1951. *Arch. Biochem. Biophys.* **31**, 197.

Bonnichsen, R. K. 1950. *Acta Chem. Scand.* **4**, 715.

Bonnichsen, R. K., and Brink, N. G. 1955. *In* "Biochemical Preparations" (W. W. Westerfeld, ed.), Vol. 4, p. 29. Wiley, New York.

Bonnichsen, R. K., and Wassen, A. M. 1948. *Arch. Biochem.* **18**, 361.

Bowness, J. M., Morton, R. A., Shakir, M. H., and Stubbs, A. L. 1952. *Biochem. J.* **51**, 521.

Bradfield, J. R. G. 1947. *Nature* **159**, 467.

Brinkman, R., Margaria, R., Meldrum, N. U., and Roughton, F. J. W. 1932. *J. Physiol.* (*London*) **75**, 3.

Conrad, J. H., and Beeson, W. M. 1957. *J. Animal. Sci.* **16**, 589.

Cori, G. T., Slein, N. W., and Cori, C. F. 1948. *J. Biol. Chem.* **173**, 605.

Davenport, H. W. 1939. *J. Physiol.* (*London*) **97**, 32.

Davidson, D. C. 1951. *Biochem. J.* **49**, 520.

Day, R., and Franklin, J. 1946. *Science* **104**, 363.

Eirich, F. R., and Rideal, E. K. 1940. *Nature* **146**, 541.

Foster, J. W. 1949. "Chemical Activities of Fungi," pp. 251–281. Academic Press, New York.

Foster, J. N., and Denison, F. W., Jr. 1940. *Nature* **166**, 833.

Gibian, H. 1954. *Angew. Chem.* **66**, 249.

Green, N. M., and Neurath, H. 1954. *In* "The Proteins" (H. Neurath and K. Bailey, eds.), Vol. 2, Part B, Chapter 25. Academic Press, New York.

Hayes, J. E., Jr., and Velick, S. F. 1954. *J. Biol. Chem.* **207**, 225.

Hoch, F. L., and Vallee, B. L. 1949. *J. Biol. Chem.* **181**, 295.

Hoch, F. L., and Vallee, B. L. 1952. *J. Biol. Chem.* **195**, 531.

Hoch, F. L., and Vallee, B. L. 1956a. *Federation Proc.* **15**, 93.

Hoch, F. L., and Vallee, B. L. 1956b. *J. Biol. Chem.* **221**, 491.

Hoch, F. L., and Zotos, B. 1957. *Federation Proc.* **16**, 359.

Hoch, F. L., Williams, R. J. P., and Vallee, B. L. 1958. *J. Biol. Chem.* **232**, 453.

Hoekstra, W. G., Lewis, P. K., Phillips, P. H., and Grummer, R. H. 1956, *J. Animal Sci.* **15**, 752.

Holzer, H., and Schneider, S. 1955. *Angew. Chem.* **67**, 276.

Hove, E., Elvehjem, C. A., and Hart, E. B. 1940. *J. Biol. Chem.* **136**, 425.

James, W. O. 1953. *Am. Rev. Plant Physiol.* **4**, 59.

Job, P. 1928. *Ann. chim.* (*Paris*) [10] **9**, 113.

Kaplan, N. O., and Ciotti, M. M. 1954. *J. Biol. Chem.* **221**, 431.

Keilin, D., and Mann, T. 1939. *Nature* **144**, 442.

Keilin, D., and Mann, T. 1940a. *Biochem. J.* **34**, 1163.

Keilin, D., and Mann, T. 1940b. *Nature* **153**, 107.

Keilin, D., and Mann, T. 1944. *Nature* **153**, 107.

Keleti, T. 1956. *Acta Physiol. Acad. Sci. Hung.* **9**, 415.

Keller, H. 1955. *Biochem. Z.* **229**, 104.

Kernkamp, H. C. H., and Ferrin, E. F. 1953. *J. Am. Vet. Med. Assoc.* **123**, 217.

Kolthoff, I. M., Leussing, D. L., and Lee, T. S. 1951. *J. Am. Chem. Soc.* **73**, 390.

Kornberg, A. 1950. *J. Biol. Chem.* **182**, 805.

Kornberg, A., and Pricer, W. E., Jr. 1951. *J. Biol. Chem.* **189**, 123.

Lechartier, G., and Bellamy, F. 1877. *Compt. rend.* **84**, 687.

Lehninger, A. L. 1950. *Physiol. Revs.* **30**, 393.

Leiner, M., and Leiner G. 1940. *Biol. Zentr.* **60**, 449.

Lewis, P. K., Jr., Hoekstra, W. G., and Grummer, R. H., and Phillips, P. H. 1956. *J. Animal Sci.* **15**, 741.

Lewis, P. K., Jr., Hoekstra, W. G., and Grummer, R. H. 1957. *J. Animal Sci.* **16**, 578.

Luecke, R. W., Hoefer, J. A., Brammell, W. S., and Thorp, F., Jr. 1956. *J. Animal Sci.* **15**, 347.

Luecke, R. W., Hoefer, J. A., Brammell, W. S., Schmidt, D. A. 1957. *J. Animal Sci.* **16**, 3.

Lundegardh, H. G., and Bergstrand, H. 1940. *Nova Acta Regiae Soc. Sci. Upsaliensis* [4] **12** (3).

Lutz, R. E. 1926. *J. Ind. Hyg.* **8**, 177.

Mahler, H. R., and Douglas, J. 1957. *J. Am. Chem. Soc.* **79**, 1159.

Malmstrom, B. G. 1956. "The Mechanism of Metal-Ion Activation of Enzymes. Studies on Enolase." Almqvist and Wiksells Boktryckeri AB, Uppsala, Sweden.

Medina, A., and Nicholas, D. J. D. 1957a. *Nature* **179**, 87.

Medina, A., and Nicholas, D. J. D. 1957b. *Biochem. J.* **66**, 573.

Meldrum, N. U., and Roughton, F. J. W. 1932a. *J. Physiol. (London)* **75**, 3 pp.

Meldrum, N. U., and Roughton, F. J. W. 1932b. *J. Physiol. (London)* **75**, 15 pp.

Meldrum, N. U., and Roughton, F. J. W. 1933. *J. Physiol. (London)* **80**, 113.

Montgomery, M. L., Sheline, G. F., and Chaikoff, I. L. 1943. *J. Exptl. Med.* **78**, 51.

Nason, A. 1950. *Science* **112**, 111.

Nason, A., Kaplan, N. O., and Colowick, S. P. 1951. *J. Biol. Chem.* **188**, 397.

Nason, A., Kaplan, N. O., and Oldewurtel, H. A. 1953. *J. Biol. Chem.* **201**, 435.

Negelein, E., and Wulff, H. J. 1937. *Biochem. Z.* **293**. 351.

Neish, A. C. 1939. *Biochem. J.* **33**, 300.

Neurath, H., and DeMaria G. 1950. *J. Biol. Chem.* **186**, 653.

Nygaard, A. P., and Theorell, H. 1955. *Acta Chem. Scand.* **9**, 1300.

Olson, J. A., and Anfinsen, C. B. 1952. *J. Biol. Chem.* **197**, 67.

Patek, A. J., Jr., and Haig, C. 1939. *J. Clin. Invest.* **18**, 609.

Petermann, M. N., and Hakala, N. V. 1942. *J. Biol. Chem.* **145**, 701.

Pfleiderer, G., and Jeckel, D. 1957. *Biochem. Z.* **329**, 370.

Possingham, T. V. 1956. *Australian J. Biol. Sci.* **9**, 539.

Putnam, F. W., and Neurath, H. 1946. *J. Biol. Chem.* **166**, 603.

Quinlan-Watson, T. A. F. 1951. *Nature* **167**, 1033.

Quinlan-Watson, T. A. F. 1953. *Biochem. J.* **53**, 457.

Racker, E. 1950. *J. Biol. Chem.* **184**, 313.

Raoult, F., and Breton, H. 1877. *Compt. rend.* **85**, 40.

Raulin, J. 1869. *Ann. sci. nat. Botan et biol. végétale* [5] **11**, 93.

Redetzki, H. E., and Nowinski, W. W. 1957. *Nature* **179**, 1018.

Reed, H. S. 1946. *Am. J. Botany* **33**, 778.

Rolinson, G. N. 1951. *Nature* **168**, 210.

Roughton, F. J. W., and Clark, A. M. 1951. *In* "The Enzymes" (J. B. Sumner and K. Myrbäck, eds.), Vol. I. Part 2, p. 1250. Academic Press, New York.

Scott, D. A., and Fisher, A. M. 1942. *J. Biol. Chem.* **144**, 371.

Scott, D. A. and Mendive, J. R. 1941. *J. Biol. Chem.* **140**, 445.

Sibly, P. M., and Wood, J. G. 1951. *Australian J. Sci. Research* **B4**, 500.

Skoog, F. 1940. *Am. J. Botany* **27**, 939.
Smith, E. C. B. 1940. *Biochem. J.* **34**, 1176.
Smith, E. L., and Hanson, H. T. 1948. *J. Biol. Chem.* **176**, 997.
Smith, E. L., and Hanson, H. T. 1949. *J. Biol. Chem.* **179**, 803.
Stevenson, J. W., and Earle, I. P. 1956. *J. Animal Sci.* **15**, 1036.
Straub, F. B. 1942. *Z. physiol. Chem.* **275**, 63.
Theorell, H., and Bonnichsen, R. 1951. *Acta Chem. Scand.* **5**, 1105.
Theorell, H., and Chance B. 1951. *Acta Chem. Scand.* **5**, 1127.
Theorell, H., Nygaard, A. P., and Bonnichsen, R. 1955. *Acta Chem. Scand.* **9**, 1148.
Tsui, C. 1948. *Am. J. Botany* **35**, 172.
Tucker, H. F., and Salmon, W. D. 1955. *Proc. Soc. Exptl. Biol. Med.* **88**, 613.
Tupper, R., Watts, A., and Wormall, R. W. E. 1951. *Biochem. J.* **50**, 429.
Umbreit, W. W., Wood, W. A., and Gunsalus, I. C. 1946. *J. Biol. Chem.* **165**, 731.
Underwood, E. J. 1956. "Trace Elements in Human and Animal Nutrition," p. 207. Academic Press, New York.
Vallee, B. L. 1951. *Sci. Monthly,* **62**, 368.
Vallee, B. L. 1952. *Nutrition Revs.* **10**, 65.
Vallee, B. L. 1955. *Advances in Protein Chem.* **10**, 317.
Vallee, B. L. 1956. *J. Am. Med. Assoc.* **162**, 1053.
Vallee, B. L. 1957. *A. M. A. Arch. Ind. Health* **16**, 147.
Vallee, B. L. and Altschule, M. D. 1949. *Physiol. Revs.* **29**, 370.
Vallee, B. L., and Gibson, J. G., II. 1948. *J. Biol. Chem.* **176**, 435.
Vallee, B. L., and Hoch, F. L. 1955a. *J. Am. Chem. Soc.* **77**, 821.
Vallee, B. L., and Hoch, F. L. 1955b. *Proc. Natl. Acad. Sci. U.S.* **41**, 327.
Vallee, B. L., and Hoch, F. L. 1956. *Federation Proc.* **15**, 619.
Vallee, B. L., and Hoch, F. L. 1957. *J. Biol. Chem.* **225**, 185.
Vallee, B. L., and Neurath, H. 1954. *J. Am. Chem. Soc.* **76**, 5006.
Vallee, B. L., and Neurath, H. 1955. *J. Biol. Chem.* **217**, 253.
Vallee, B. L., and Wacker, W. E. C. 1956. *J. Am. Chem. Soc.* **78**, 1771.
Vallee, B. L., Lewis, H. D., Altschule, M. D., and Gibson, J. G., II. 1949. *Blood* **4**, 467.
Vallee, B. L., Hoch, F. L., and Hughes, W. L., Jr. 1954. *Arch. Biochem. Biophys.* **48**, 347.
Vallee, B. L., Adelstein, S. J., and Olson, J. A. 1955. *J. Am. Chem. Soc.* **77**, 5196.
Vallee, B. L., Hoch, F. L., Adelstein, S. J., and Wacker, W. E. C. 1956a. *J. Am. Chem. Soc.* **78**, 5879.
Vallee, B. L., Wacker, W. E. C., Bartholomay, A. F., and Robin, E. D. 1956b. *New Engl. J. Med.* **255**, 403.
Vallee, B. L., Coombs, T. L., and Williams, R. J. P. 1957a. *Federation Proc.* **16**, 264.
Vallee, B. L., Wacker, W. E. C., Bartholomay, A. F., and Hoch, F. L. 1957b. *New Engl. J. Med.* **257**, 1055.
Vallee, B. L., Wacker, W. E. C., and Kägi, J. H. R. 1957c. *J. Clin. Invest.* **36**, 933.
Vallee, B. L., Coombs, T. L., and Williams, R. J. P. 1958a. *J. Am. Chem. Soc.* **80**, 397.
Vallee, B. L., Kägi, J. H. R., and Hoch, F. L. 1958b. *Federation Proc.* **17**, 1326.
Van Goor, H. 1945. *Rec. trav. chim.* **64**, 313.
Van Goor, H. 1948. *Enzymologia* **13**, 73.
Wallenfels, K., and Sund, H. 1957a. *Biochem. Z.* **329**, 17.
Wallenfels, K., and Sund, H. 1957b. *Biochem. Z.* **329**, 59.
Wallenfels, K., Sund, H., Faessler, A., and Burchard, W. 1957. *Biochem. Z.* **329**, 31.

Warburg, O. 1949. "Heavy Metal Prosthetic Groups and Enzyme Action." Oxford Univ. Press, London and New York.

Waygood, E. R., and Clendenning, K. A. 1950. *Can. J. Research* **C28**, 673.

Waygood, E. R., and Clendenning, K. A. 1951. *Science* **113**, 177.

Webb, E. C., and Van Heyningen, R. 1947. *Biochem. J.* **41**, 74.

Weier, T. E., and Stocking, C. R. 1952. *Botan. Rev.* **18**, 14.

Wieland, T., and Pfleiderer, G. 1957. *Biochem. Z.* **329**, 112.

Williams, R. J. P. 1953. *Biol. Revs. Cambridge Phil. Soc.* **28**, 4.

Williams, R. J. P., Hoch, F. L., and Vallee, B. L. 1958. *J. Biol. Chem.* **232**, 465.

Wood, J. G., and Sibly, P. M. 1952. *Australian J. Sci. Research* **B5**, 244.

CHAPTER 23

Iron Metabolism in Animals and Plants

S. GRANICK

*Rockefeller Institute for
Medical Research,
New York, New York*

	Page
I. Introduction	365
II. Iron Metabolism in Animals	367
A. Kinds of Iron Compounds	367
B. Functions	368
C. Location	369
D. Structure of Some Iron Compounds	370
E. Functioning Together of the Iron Compounds	370
F. Mechanisms to Make Iron Available to the Cells	372
III. Iron Metabolism in Plants	374
A. Iron Compounds of Plants	374
B. Iron Availability in Land Plants	375
C. Iron Absorption and Translocation in Land Plants	377
D. Iron in Sea Plants	379
IV. Summary and Conclusion	380
Acknowledgment	381
References	381

I. INTRODUCTION

Since this symposium is held to celebrate the 75th anniversary of the founding of the Ohio Agricultural Experimental Station, it might be of interest, by way of introduction, to take a backward glance at our state of knowledge of iron metabolism 50 to 100 years ago.

About 50 years ago, in a "System of Medicine" edited by Osler and McCrae (1908), there is given a description of chlorosis, the green sickness, which may be paraphrased as follows: "Chlorosis is a disease which appears in young women between the ages of 15 and 25. The skin color is pale or greenish. There is muscular weakness and shortness of breath. The number of red cells in the circulation is not decreased, but there is a decrease in the size and pigmentation of the red cells. The disease can be cured by feeding ferrous salts and is at present one of the 5 or 6 diseases which can be cured by a specific remedy." The article goes on

ABBREVIATIONS: ATP = adenosine triphosphate; Cyt. = cytochrome; DPNH = reduced diphosphopyridine nucleotide; EDTA = ethylene-diamine-tetra-acetic acid; FAD = flavine adenine dinucleotide.

to remark that around Boston the disease was much more common before 1890, the majority of cases having been seen in girls employed in domestic service. By the turn of the century the disease had become rare. The reason for the disappearance of the disease was not understood.

Today, from this brief summary, one might readily infer that chlorosis is an iron deficiency disease resulting in a decrease in the hemoglobin which would explain the shortness of breath and muscular weakness. However none of these correlations were made in the article. The reasons for this lack of correlation were due to the fact that 50 years ago the experiments and interpretations about iron metabolism were highly confusing (Sherman, 1907). Some investigators, considered as authorities, had made serious experimental blunders. It was considered that medicinal iron, that is, inorganic iron salts which could cure chlorosis, served merely as an irritative stimulant to the blood-forming organs (incorrect). The iron required for the body could be furnished, not by inorganic iron, but only by some complex organic compounds of the food (incorrect) including hemoglobin (correct). The idea was prevalent that iron, besides being a constituent of hemoglobin (correct), was, in addition, present in all cells in appreciable concentrations as constituents of chromatin (incorrect).

What of the status of iron metabolism in plants? Over 100 years ago it had made a good start with the outstanding paper by Eusèbe Gris. In 1844, Gris had used a nutrient solution to investigate the requirement of the elements for plant growth. He found that the lack of iron in the nutrient solution led to the formation of blanched leaves. When he painted a solution of an inorganic iron salt on the blanched leaf, it turned green in 2 or 3 days, and the green bodies in the cells could now be readily seen. The importance of iron for the greening of the plant was thus recognized early. Soon thereafter there were reports that chlorophyll contained iron, but this was disproved later by Willstatter's studies. By the end of the 19th century, systematic studies with nutrient solutions had established 10 elements as essential for plant growth.

In medical pathology, as noted above, chlorosis was used to indicate a lack of hemoglobin in man. In plant pathology, chlorosis had an independent origin and came to indicate a lack of chlorophyll.

It was during the 1920–30 period that the basic biochemical plans common to plant and animal cells were comprehended. The role of iron in the oxidative metabolism of all cells had to await the rediscovery and systematic analysis of the cytochromes by Keilin. But the whole story of the functions of iron is not yet written. The recent findings of iron flavoproteins, as well as the relatively high iron content of chloroplasts, await elucidation in terms of function. A beginning has been made in the studies of mechanisms for the absorption, transport, and storage of iron in mammals, but much remains to be learned of these mechanisms both in animals and plants.

II. Iron Metabolism in Animals

A. *Kinds of Iron Compounds*

A survey of the biological compounds containing iron in animals may be obtained by considering the iron compounds in man, where they have been most studied. In adult man, the total iron content of the body is about 4 to 5 g. (Table I). Practically all of the iron is present in some complex form bound to a number of different proteins. Only minute traces of iron are free as ferrous or ferric salts. The iron compounds may be classified into two general groups: those that contain heme or iron porphyrin and those that do not.

TABLE I

Approximate Composition of Iron-Containing Compounds in the Adult Human[a]

Compounds	Prosthetic groups per molecule	Grams	Iron in g.	Per cent of total Iron
Iron porphyrin (heme) compounds				
Blood hemoglobin	4 hemes	900	3.0	60–70
Muscle hemoglobin or Myoglobin[c]	1 heme	40	0.13	3–5
Heme enzymes				
Mitochondrial cytochromes				
c	1 heme	0.8	0.004	0.1
a_3, a, c_1, b	—	—	—	—
Microsomal cytochrome b_5 [b, d]	—	—	—	—
Catalase	—	5.0	0.004	0.1
Peroxidase	—	—	—	—
Nonheme compounds				
Flavin-Fe enzymes				
Succinic dehydrogenase[e]	1 FAD:4 Fe	—	—	—
Xanthine oxidase of liver[f]	1 FAD:4 Fe:1 Mo	—	—	—
DPNH-cytcochrome c reductase	1 FAD:4 Fe	—	—	—
Iron chelate enzyme Aconitase[g]	—	—	—	—
Transferrin	2 Fe	10.0	0.004	0.1
Ferritin	4 $(FeOOH)_n$	2–4	0.4–0.8	7–15
Total available iron stores	—	—	1.2–1.5	—
Total iron	—	—	4–5	100

[a] Modified from Granick (1954).
[b] Strittmatter and Ball (1952).
[c] Rossi-Fanelli and Antonini (1956).
[d] Strittmatter and Velick (1956).
[e] Singer *et al.* (1957).
[f] Kielley and Bradley (1955).
[g] Speyer and Diekman (1956).

The major heme protein is hemoglobin. It is also the major iron-containing protein of the body since about three-fourths of the total iron is in the form of blood and muscle hemoglobin. The other heme compounds are the cytochrome enzymes of mitochondria and microsomes and the enzymes, catalase and peroxidase. Altogether these enzymes make up only a few-thousandths of the total body iron; yet, although they are low in concentration, we shall see that all the other iron compounds of the body serve for the proper functioning of these iron-containing enzymes.

The nonheme group of iron compounds are comprised of: the iron storage protein, ferritin, which makes up some 0 to 15 per cent of the body iron; transferrin, which transports iron in the blood stream (Schade and Caroline, 1946; Laurell, 1947); the iron-flavoprotein enzymes; and enzymes like aconitase, which require iron for functioning. As may be seen from Table I, hemoglobin and ferritin are the two major iron-containing compounds of the body.

B. Functions

Another way to classify the iron compounds is according to their functions. Nine categories of functions may be considered:

(1) The heme protein that combines reversibly with O_2. (Heme + $O_2 \rightleftharpoons$ Heme·O_2). This class includes the hemoglobins of red cells, muscle hemoglobins, legume root nodule hemoglobins, etc. The kinds and distribution of the various heme proteins are summarized by Granick and Gilder (1947).

(2) The heme protein, cytochrome oxidase, that activates O_2 to accept electrons from cytochrome c. ($O_2 + 4e^- + 4H^+ \xrightarrow{\text{Cyt. oxidase}} 2H_2O$). Formally, oxidases may be considered to act to accept two or four electrons ($2AH_2 + O_2 \rightarrow 2A + 2H_2O$; $AH_2 + O_2 \rightarrow A + H_2O_2$).

(3) The heme protein, peroxidase, that activates H_2O_2 to accept two electrons from substrate A ($AH_2 + H_2O_2 \xrightarrow{\text{peroxidase}} A + 2H_2O$). Catalase in the presence of traces of H_2O_2 can act as a peroxidase.

(4) The heme protein, catalase, that dismutes H_2O_2. ($2H_2O_2 \rightarrow 2H_2O + O_2$).

(5) The oxygen transferases, iron proteins that add O_2 directly across a double bond, as shown by $O_2{}^{18}$ studies. An example is the pyrocatechol

oxidation to cis-cis muconic acid $\left(AH_2 + O_2 \rightleftharpoons A \begin{array}{c} OH \\ \diagdown \\ OH \end{array} \right)$ (Mason, 1957).

(6) The mixed function oxidases that oxidize both aromatic and aliphatic substrates with the consumption of O_2. One O atom is added to the substrate molecule as shown by $O_2{}^{18}$ tracer studies; the other is reduced by DPNH or o-diphenol to water ($AH_2 + O_2 + 2e^- + 2H^+ \rightarrow$

$$A\Big\langle \begin{array}{c} H \\ OH \end{array} + H_2O \Big).$$ This is a poorly characterized group which may include enzymes that have either Fe, Cu or Mn as prosthetic group. An example of what may be an Fe enzyme of this kind is 11-β-hydroxylase which brings about the hydroxylation of desoxy-corticosterone to form cortico-sterone (Mason, 1957).

(7) The flavoproteins which are linked to iron. Within the last few years (Mahler, 1956), a number of flavoproteins have been found, some of which are coupled with a cytochrome and some possibly through other iron chelates as electron acceptors. For example, crystalline yeast lactic dehydrogenase of molecular weight 230,000 contains 1 FMN:1 cyto-chrome b_2:8 Fe (Boeri and Tosi, 1956), and succinic dehydrogenase of molecular weight 200,000 contans 1 FAD:4 Fe (Singer $et\ al.$, 1957). These are possibly some of the enzymes which function in converting the energy of electron transfer reactions to the energy of group transfer reactions such as occurs in the formation of ATP.

(8) Those enzyme reactions where iron may act as a reaction catalyst, e.g., as a Lewis acid to attract electrons. In aconitase, the iron is essential for activity and may be an example of this kind (Speyer and Diekman, 1956).

(9) Iron compounds which serve for storage and transport; namely, ferritin and transferrin. Here one may also include some looser iron chelates such as ferric citrate or malate, etc.

C. Location

Still another way to classify the iron compounds is by their location within cells. The major part of the iron in mammals is in the red cells as hemoglobin and as ferritin in liver, spleen, and bone marrow. Many of the other iron compounds are found in cell particulates.

(1) In mitochondria are present the cytochromes of the electron transport chains including cytochrome oxidase and the coupling iron flavoproteins (Fig. 1). The membranes isolated from beef heart mito-chondria are 30 per cent lipid and contain the following approximate ratios of components (Green, 1956; Chance and Williams, 1956):

1 cyt. a_3:1cyt. a:0.3cyt. c_1:07 cyt. c:04 cyt. b:2 FAD:35 DPNH:30 Fe: 3.7 Cu*

(2) In microsomal particles of the cell, a cytochrome b_5 complex has been found which may transfer electrons from DPNH to cytochrome c (Strittmatter and Ball, 1952; Strittmatter and Velick, 1956).

(3) In phagocytic cells, lysozome bodies are found under certain conditions which may contain relatively large amounts of ferritin; per-

haps lysozomes represent digestive vacuoles which have digested hemoglobin.

(4) In chloroplasts of plant cells, no cytochrome oxidase or any other mitochondrial cytochromes have been found. Rather, there is present a cytochrome f (Hill, 1951) which may function in photosynthetic phosphorylation. Most of the iron of the leaf cell appears to be concentrated in the chloroplasts.

D. Structure of Some Iron Compounds

As illustrations of the kinds of biologically occurring iron compounds, let us briefly consider the structure of a few of them. Hemoglobin is an example of a heme protein. It has a molecular weight of 68,000 and contains 4 flat heme units that are arranged in pairs and lie roughly perpendicular to the long axis at each of the ends of an ellipsoid $55 \times 55 \times 70$ A. The iron of the heme has a coordination number of 6. In the plane of the ring, it is attached to the 4 nitrogens of the porphyrin; below the plane it is attached to an imidazole N of histidine, and above the plane it can attach to O_2 reversibly when the iron is in the ferrous state.

As an example of a nonheme protein, the structure of transferrin, the iron-transport protein of the blood, may be considered. Its molecular weight is 90,000. It is colorless when devoid of iron. It may chelate with a maximum of 2 ferric atoms to form a salmon-colored compound. Studies by Warner and Weber (1953) on a similar compound from egg white suggest that the ferric iron is coordinated with 3 phenolic groups of tyrosine, one carboxylate group, and one bicarbonate ion to form a very tight ferric chelate.

Because we shall discuss ferritin in some detail, its structure may be noted here. This iron storage protein, which is orange-brown in color (Laufberger, 1937), consists of a colorless protein, apoferritin, of molecular weight 500,000 to which may be attached several thousand iron atoms in the form of a basic hydroxide-phosphate. It is then called ferritin (Granick, 1954). The iron hydroxide is present in 4 clusters or aggregates. The iron may constitute as much as 23 per cent of the dry weight of ferritin. The highest concentration of ferritin occurs in liver, spleen, and bone marrow.

E. Functioning Together of the Iron Compounds

To summarize briefly the functioning of the various metabolically active iron compounds, let us consider the events that occur in the oxidation of succinic acid in the mitochondrion of a muscle cell and we shall see how the iron porphyrin proteins, and also nonheme iron proteins, all function together to convert electron transfer reactions into group trans-

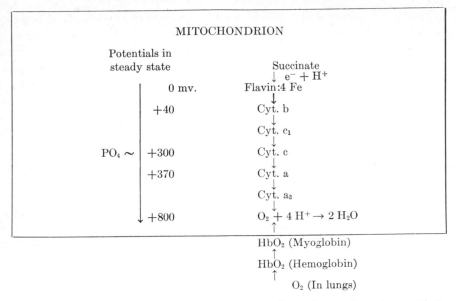

FIG. 1. Cooperation of various heme proteins in the oxidation of succinate with O_2 in a muscle mitochondrion (Green, 1956; Chance and Williams, 1956; Hartree, 1957; Wainio and Cooperstein, 1956).

fer reactions. As seen in Fig. 1, oxygen is taken into the lungs and diffuses into the blood stream where circulating erythrocytes pick up the oxygen to form oxyhemoglobin. The oxygen is transported thence to the tissues, say to the heart muscle. Here the oxygen diffuses into a muscle cell and combines temporarily with another iron porphyrin protein, muscle hemoglobin. Then the oxygen diffuses into the mitochondrion to combine with still another heme protein, cytochrome oxidase, or cytochrome a_3. Cytochrome oxidase is a catalyst which activates O_2 to take up electrons avidly.

At the same time that O_2 is moving from the lungs toward cytochrome oxidase in the mitochondria, electrons are being released from succinic acid molecules of the citric acid cycle. These electrons are activated by the enzyme succinic dehydrogenase which is an iron flavoprotein, and the electrons pass down through a series of heme proteins as cytochrome b, c_1, c, a, and finally to a_3. When the electrons combine with activated oxygen molecules, eventually to form water, perhaps H_2O_2 is produced as an intermediate, and the H_2O_2 may be acted upon by another iron porphyrin protein, peroxidase, to become a strong oxidant, or toxic accumulations of hydrogen peroxide might be destroyed by another heme protein, catalase.

The energy which is released during the transport of electrons down the potential energy hill towards oxygen is coupled in some as yet not understood fashion, possibly through heme or iron complexes, to form chemical compounds which contain bonds such as high energy phosphate bonds. Damage to the spacial configuration of the enzyme system involved does not prevent electron transfer down the potential energy hill, but damage does prevent the coupling reactions from occurring.

F. Mechanisms to Make Iron Available to the Cells

We shall review briefly the mechanisms that are required to make iron available to the mammal where the problem of iron supply becomes acute because of the high iron requirements for hemoglobin (Table I). The amount of iron is several hundred times more than is required for manufacture of the metabolically active heme enzymes. This high iron requirement and the properties of inorganic iron made it necessary to evolve mechanisms for the solubilization of iron, for its absorption and regulation, for its transport in the blood stream, and for its storage.

The available iron in food is mainly in the ferric state as ferric hydroxide and loose ferric chelates. Heme iron is less readily available (Callender et al. 1957). To be absorbed the iron must be in the ferrous form (Lintzel, 1933; Venkatachalam et al., 1956). Gastric acidity converts the iron to the free ionic state, and in the presence of SH groups and ascorbate, the ferric ions are reduced. Ferrous ions are more slowly autoxidized in acid than in neutral solution and are thus stabilized. Ferrous iron is absorbed by the mucosal cells of the duodenum and passes through the cell into the blood capillaries of the villus. Here it is picked up by a specific protein transferrin, and held as a ferric chelate; in this form it is transported to various cells of the body. The iron may go directly to the bone marrow where it may be absorbed by immature red cells. Or the iron may be stored temporarily, especially in organs like the liver, spleen, and bone marrow in the form of ferritin. The special ferric hydroxide micelles of ferritin are said to be formed on autoxidation of ferrous bicarbonate (Bayer, 1956) and attached to the apoferritin. (Since all growing cells, in addition to those forming hemoglobin, require iron for cytochromes, iron must be made available also to these other cells.) There is enough ferritin in storage so that if acute loss of blood should occur, about one-third of the total hemoglobin could be replaced without additional iron absorption. The iron of ferritin may be made soluble by reduction to the ferrous form by xanthine dehydrogenase (Green and Mazur, 1956) and possibly by flavin enzymes (Weber et al., 1956).

There is a regulatory mechanism for iron absorption which appears to reside in the mucosal cells and to be governed indirectly by the O_2 level of the blood (Granick, 1954). A decrease in O_2 tension for 2 hours results in an increased iron absorption (Smith *et al.*, 1957). Normally the mechanism permits several milligrams of iron to be absorbed per day. Iron, once it is absorbed into the body, remains there. Usually, a little more iron is absorbed than is required to replace iron lost by desquamation, etc. When red cells break down, the hemoglobin is digested within phagocytes, the porphyrin ring is oxidized to bile pigment, and iron is set free to be used over again. In cases of hemorrhage or pregnancy where demands for iron become great, iron may be absorbed at 5 to 10 times the normal rate. When a large dose of iron is fed, a "mucosal bloc" (Hahn, 1948) is established which prevents further iron absorption for several days. At the same time, the ferritin increases in the mucosal cells and especially in the fixed tissue histiocytes which are present in the lumina of the villi. Studies of these cells with the electron microscope reveal the individual ferritin molecules (S. Granick and K. Porter, unpublished). The increase and decrease in ferritin appears to parallel the formation and disappearance of the mucosal bloc. An inherited defect leading to large accumulations of iron is called hemochromatosis (Granick, 1957).

The movement and transport of specific ions across membranes by a filtration mechanism is poorly understood. Some proposed hypotheses include the following ideas: Mechanisms of respiration and synthesis set up driving forces for the accumulation of ions inside the cell, possibly by exchange of cations for H^+ and anions for HCO_3^-. Mitochondria may be involved by way of removal of anions like inorganic phosphorus to form ATP; possibly salt accumulation may also result from a spatial distribution of an electron transport chain so that one end releases H^+ and the other combines H^+ with reduction products of O_2 to form water (Fig. 1). The semipermeable membrane may contain a monolayer of protein molecules about 50 A. thick and may have properties of an exchange resin. Pores with specific permeability for certain ions may represent a space between contiguous protein molecules; the pores would be lined with certain positive and negative charges of the side chains of the protein molecules. For Fe^{++}, for example, there might be a specific pore through which it could enter, but it could enter only by displacing another Fe^{++} in the pore toward the inside of the cell. The Fe^{++} once through the pore could be removed or converted to some ferric complex. To maintain electric neutrality, H^+ could be excreted by the cell through a different pore specific for H^+ permeability or removed in some other way.

In addition to this filtration mechanism, there is evidence for mass transfer of proteins, including ferritin, between certain cells. Because ferritin molecules are large and dense enough to be visible with the electron microscope, it has been possible to show that ferritin may be transported by pinocytosis. By this means, Bessis and Breton-Gorius (1957) have shown the migration of ferritin molecules from a phagocytic cell of the bone marrow (macrophage or reticular cell) into an adjacent immature erythroblast. The active mass transfer of protein may be a far more common phenomenon than previously suspected. This development in permeability studies suggests that we should not only be guided by a concept of unity on a biochemical level but on a functional level as well. The manner in which flagellates, protozoa, etc., excrete and secrete may teach us much about problems of permeability in higher animals and plants.

Iron metabolism appears to be interrelated to some extent with copper metabolism as observed in animals and plants. In a classic study of iron and copper metabolism in yeast, Elvehjem (1931) found a marked increase in cytochrome a when the iron-containing medium was supplemented with copper. In rats, Schultze (1947) found that a lack of copper led to a decrease in cytochrome oxidase, a result which supplements the findings on yeast and suggests that copper might be a constituent of the cytochrome a–a$_3$ complex. Experiments from Wintrobe's laboratory have clearly shown that copper affects not only the absorption but the use of iron as well. Swine on a low-copper diet absorb iron only poorly from the gastrointestinal tract; the mobilization of iron from the tissues is decreased, and there is also found to be an inability to use parenterally administered iron for hemoglobin synthesis even when iron is presented to the bone marrow in normal amounts (Cartwright, 1950; Gubler et al., 1952).

III. Iron Metabolism of Plants

A. Iron Compounds in Plants

In plants, the amount of iron required to satisfy the iron protein requirements is relatively several hundred times smaller on a protoplasmic basis than for mammals. In meristematic regions where cell multiplication and enlargement are rapid, iron is required for iron enzymes of mitochondria (Hartree, 1957). In the leaves, a further and larger requirement for iron is generated by the enlarging chloroplasts at the time the leaves enlarge and turn green. In the mature leaf cell, the volume of mitochondria is tiny in comparison with the volume of the chloroplasts; the chloroplasts contain most of the iron of the leaf. In addition to an iron requirement for proplastid development, iron in the form of cytochrome f, and possibly other iron enzymes, is needed by the chloroplast for photosynthesis.

The iron in leaf blade tissue of a number of dicotyledenous plants is about 2 to 5 mg. per cent of the fresh weight or approximately 10^{-3} M with respect to iron (Hill and Lehmann, 1941). Leibich (1941) reported that 82 per cent of the iron in spinach leaves was concentrated in chloroplasts; the dried chloroplasts contained about 0.05 per cent iron, but the cell nucleus contained only traces of iron. Only 40 per cent of the chloroplast iron was dialyzable in 10^{-2} M HCl. Studies by Whatley et al. (1951) showed that in sugar beets iron and copper, but not manganese, zinc, or molybdenum, were concentrated in chloroplasts. Hill and Lehmann (1941) found that the increase in iron of the leaves preceded the increase in chlorophyll; the molar ratio of iron to chlorophyll was 1:4 to 1:10 in most plants. A number of different forms of iron were noted qualitatively. A portion of the chloroplast iron reacted with α,α'-dipyridyl on reduction; this is presumably iron in an ionic or loosely chelated form. Another portion reacted only after boiling with dilute hydrochloric acid; this may be ferric phosphate or ferric hydroxide. Still another portion reacted after ashing and was probably derived from heme.

Plant cells, in addition to the customary cytochromes of animal cells, contain a cytochrome b_3. In leaves, a cytochrome b_6 has been reported; and for the Arum spadix a cytochrome b_7 (Hartree, 1957). Chloroplasts appear to lack the electron transport system of enzymes but contain a special cytochrome f. Hill (1951) reported cytochrome f to be present in a concentration of 10^{-5} M in leaves. The molar ratio of cytochrome f to chlorophyll was 1:300. The inhibition of the Hill reaction by o-phenanthrolene is suggestive of the presence of another iron enzyme active in photosynthesis. Another indication of the high iron requirement for photosynthetic tissue is the relatively high concentration of iron (10^{-5} M) in the nutrient medium of photosynthetic bacteria required for the production of bacteriochlorophyll (Lascelles, 1956). An interesting iron compound, "ferrichrome," has been recently studied by Neilands (1957). It has been crystallized from the rust, Ustilago sphaerogena, has a molecular weight of 725, and contains one ferric atom chelated to a peptide. It may be a growth factor for Arthrobacter terregens.

B. Iron Availability in Land Plants

Since soils contain 0.5 to 5.0 per cent of iron, there is generally no deficiency of iron in the soil itself. Rather the deficiency is related to the form of iron. The form of iron best absorbed by plants appears to be ferrous (Kleman, 1937). Ferrous iron in neutral solution may exist in a concentration of 10^{-4} M, but free ferric ions in a concentration of only 10^{-17} M which is negligibly small. The availability of ferrous iron depends in general on the pH and aeration of the soil. These factors are an integrated function of the constituents of the particular soil, the bacterial, fungal, protozoan and annelid life, and the moisture and temperature. The availability of iron also depends on the particular plant. For example, iron is rendered more available if it can be reduced to the ferrous state and be kept from autoxidizing rapidly. Bacteria, acting on organic matter in the soil, will create reducing conditions; water-logging will decrease O_2 diffusion; and under acid conditions the autoxidation of ferrous ions will be slower. Also under anaerobic conditions roots excrete small quantities of organic acids as acetic, formic, oxalic which help to dissolve ferric hydroxide micelles and tend to form loose soluble ferric chelates which are more readily reduced (Stocklasa and Ernest, 1909).

Iron released from ferromagnesium minerals may be absorbed on humus and clays by ion exchange; thus monomolecularly dispersed ferric iron may be prevented from aggregating into large basic hydroxide aggregates or precipitates which would be more difficult to reduce to the ferrous state. Iron needs to be acquired throughout the life of the plant, and iron availability would depend on attaining anaerobic conditions in the soil. However, roots require O_2 for aerobic respiration and absorption. Therefore the most favorable conditions are necessarily a compromise; i.e., temporary anaerobic conditions, say after rains, and more aerobic conditions as water drains from the capillary spaces in the soil. On reclaimed muck and peat soils, where acid and anaerobic conditions have solubilized too much iron and aluminum, toxicity due to these elements may occur. On alkaline calcareous soils, a widespread deficiency called "lime induced" chlorosis is found (Brown, 1956). This condition may be related in part to the formation of insoluble basic ferric hydroxide precipitates where $HPO_4^=$ or Ca^{++} are in excess. [In mammals a diet high in phosphates also restricts iron absorption and leads to iron deficiency symptoms (Kinney et al., 1949).]

Iron availability is also a property of a particular plant (Brown, 1956). An interesting example is one studied by Holmes and Brown (1955). They found that a chlorosis-susceptible variety of soybean required a higher concentration of iron than the normal variety and that a single recessive gene was responsible.

An excess of a number of trace metals may result in iron deficiency and root damage (Brown, 1956). The deficiency may be overcome by increasing the available iron. Whether this result is due to a competition between the metal ions for entrance into the root cells, or not, is yet to be investigated. In Hawaii the high Mn^{++} content of the soil limits iron absorption. The main cause of iron deficiency in Florida orchard soils is due to excess Cu^{++}, which is said to have accumulated in the soil by application of insect sprays and fertilizers over several decades (Reuther et al. 1952).

C. Iron Absorption and Translocation in Land Plants

The germinating seed usually contains sufficient iron, stored in the cotyledons, to supply the iron requirements of the mitochondria and enlarging chloroplasts of the young plantlet. So it is evident that iron, at this stage, can be translocated from the cotyledon to the growing points of root and shoot and that sufficient iron is present for the normal development of several leaves.

After the cotyledons have fallen, the plant must depend on the soil for further inorganic elements. The mechanisms by which salts, including iron, are absorbed by the roots is poorly understood, but the problem is being actively pursued (Gauch, 1957). The region of greatest absorption of various ions is found to be several centimeters behind the root tip which is also the region of maximum water absorption (Wiebe and Kramer, 1954). Ferrous iron appears to be the form most available for absorption (Kleman, 1937); in addition absorption of ferric EDTA

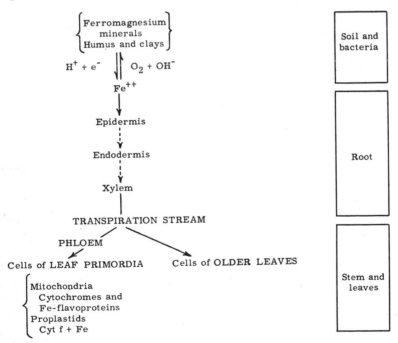

FIG. 2. Scheme for absorption and transport of iron in plants.

chelates, as such, have been reported (Brown, 1956). A scheme for iron absorption and transport is presented in Figure 2.

In general it seems clear that it is necessary for the root to metabolize oxidatively to absorb ions to any appreciable extent. Dinitrophenol not only inhibits oxidative phosphorylation but also salt accumulation. Specific pores in protoplasmic membranes, ion exchange reactions, the creation of ions by metabolism and Donnan effects may be assumed as in considerations of iron absorption in animal cells. In addition, the aqueous secretion from the endodermis into xylem must be considered; to explain this, one might postulate a process similar to the excretion performed by contractile vacuoles of flagellates where the rate of excretion may be as high as 0.5 ml. per minute per sq. cm. of surface (Kitching, 1954). Absorption of salts does not seem to be governed by the rate of water transpired; however, the water current must be considered as the primary means of conduction of salts to the older leaves. The form of iron in transport is not known. Lateral movement of K^+ has been shown to occur readily from xylem to phloem. Possibly the slowly transpiring regions of elongating shoots and young leaves may obtain iron by way of the phloem.

Translocation of iron from one portion of an older plant to another was suggested by the observation that, in the latter part of the season, the iron of green leaves is lost before chlorophyll is lost and that this iron appeared to be found in the developing seeds (Hill and Lehmann, 1941). More recent studies with tracers indicate, however, that little iron is transferred from older to younger tissues. In sunflowers, although the older leaves contained 10 times as much iron per gram dry weight as younger upper leaves, the iron did not appear to be available to the younger leaves (Glenister, 1944). Similar results were obtained with soybeans (Brown and Holmes, 1955). Nor does iron, unlike phosphorus, appear to be transferred from older leaves to meristems, since meristems are among the first tissues to suffer deficiencies when iron, calcium, or boron are involved (Biddulph, 1951).

Not only may there be a lack of availability for iron at the root surface, but a deficiency may also result from an inability to transport iron within the plant. Thus Biddulph (1951) found that bean plants grown in a nutrient solution pH 4.0, with PO_4 at 10^{-4} M were normal; at pH 7, the iron was still absorbed by the roots but precipitated out in the vein system so that the veins were green but not the blade; and at pH 7 with 10^{-3} M PO_4, the iron precipitated out on the roots and failed to enter the root resulting in a general chlorosis.

A minimal amount of iron is required for cell division in the root tip, probably mainly to satisfy mitochondrial needs. Tips of pea roots 10 mm.

in length, when grown in a tissue culture medium devoid of iron, ceased cell division although protein synthesis continued in the more mature cells adjacent to the root apex. This result is reminiscent of the finding by Lwoff (1933) that a minimum of approximately half a million heme molecules was required per cell for cell multiplication to occur.

A specific mechanism for iron absorption is suggested by the work of Jacobson and Oertli (1956). When iron feeding was interrupted for 15 to 20 days and then resumed, it was found that abnormally large amounts of iron were now absorbed from the nutrient medium. (In mammals a lack of iron also leads to an increased iron absorption.) Although chlorotic leaves took up the newly furnished iron as readily as green leaves, the chlorosis was not reversed. It would be interesting to know whether the proplastids were irreversibly damaged in the chlorotic leaf.

In some conditions, sufficient iron appears to be available for root growth but not for greening of leaves. A number of methods have been used to supply iron either to the roots or to the leaves. Ferrous sulfate has been applied under citrus trees, or injected into tree trunks, or sprayed on pineapple leaves in Hawaii. Recently iron chelating compounds have been used. These are absorbed as anions by the plants and apparently are decomposed within the plant to release the iron. High stability constants of the iron chelates are required to compete with the hydroxyl ion of alkaline soils. A cyclohexane *trans*-1,2-diaminotetraacetic acid (CDTA) and aminopolycarboxylic acid (APCA) appear to be promising compounds although their expense may limit their usefulness commercially (Holmes and Brown, 1955; Stewart and Leonard, 1954).

D. Iron in Sea Plants

The high pH of the ocean (pH 7.8), the high salt content, and the excellent aeration preclude the possibility of soluble iron. The ocean waters contain about 20 mg. iron per cubic meter, i.e., 4×10^{-10} M, which is primarily in the form of ferric hydroxide-phosphate colloidal micelles. With respect to iron alone these factors would prevent land plants from growing in ocean water. In the case of marine plant organisms, such as diatoms, studies have shown that they readily adsorb the colloidal ferric hydroxide micelles on their surface (Harvey, 1945). The scavenging of this iron is very effective. It has been estimated that all the iron in the English Channel is turned over by diatoms several times a year, i.e., the iron taken up from the ocean by the diatoms is returned after the diatoms are eaten by the zooplankton. Since it is estimated that a diatom may occlude 8×10^{-8} mg. of iron, only a small portion of this iron would suffice for the requirement of the iron enzymes in these cells.

It is not known how this iron on the surface of the diatom becomes available to the diatom. Possibly bacteria trapped in the jellylike layers make available a localized anaerobic atmosphere or the iron hydroxide micelles are phagocytized into cytoplasmic vacuoles of the diatom where acid and reducing conditions might be produced. In the open ocean where the upper waters are less dense than the water below, the upper layers may be almost free of iron especially if there is a lack of turbulence in the water. This may be one reason for the low plankton content found in the open ocean.

With an increase in human population, fresh water will soon become a limiting resource. An agriculture based on ocean water may then have to be developed. It is obvious that if the iron content of the ocean is a limiting factor it might be possible to increase the phytoplankton in limited regions of the ocean at appropriate times so that the fish-yield would be stimulated. Or it might be possible to select and test certain land plants that are suitable for human consumption to see whether they might grow in ocean or brackish waters if iron were made adequately available to them.

IV. Summary and Conclusion

Some of the known iron compounds of protoplasm have been classified according to their iron content, distribution, and functions in cells. In the mitochondria reside the ubiquitous iron compounds, the cytochromes, that serve in oxidation to release the potential energy locked in foodstuffs. Certain of these oxidative reactions are tightly coupled through other iron-containing enzymes, the iron-flavoproteins, to form "high energy phosphate bonds." In plants, in addition to the iron compounds of mito-chondria, the chloroplasts in leaf cells contain most of the iron of the cell and a special cytochrome f which is probably required for photosynthesis. Other iron compounds may serve in an auxiliary capacity. In vertebrates, hemoglobin furnishes O_2 to the mitochondria of body cells, transferrin serves to transport iron in the blood stream, and ferritin serves for storage of iron and perhaps indirectly for regulation of iron absorption.

Also discussed are mechanisms of iron absorption in animals and in land and sea plants.

As you see from the many references to recent papers, our under-standing of iron metabolism is continuing to increase at a rapid pace. However, much remains to be found and much remains to be understood of what has been found. Although the discovery of new trace elements is exciting in itself, there is much of worth still to be found in the old iron diggings.

ACKNOWLEDGMENT

I would like to acknowledge my thanks to Dr. David Mauzerall for his criticisms of this manuscript.

REFERENCES

Bayer, E. 1956. *Experientia* **12**, 365–368.
Bessis, M. E., and Breton-Gorius, J. 1957. *J. Biophys. Biochem. Cytol.* **3**, 503–504.
Biddulph, O. 1951. *In* "Mineral Nutrition in Plants" (E. Truog, ed.), pp. 261–278. Univ. Wisconsin Press, Madison, Wisconsin.
Boeri, E., and Tosi, L. 1956. *Arch. Biochem. Biophys.* **60**, 463–375.
Brown, J. C. 1956. *Ann. Rev. Plant Physiol.* **7**, 171–190.
Brown, J. C., and Holmes, R. S. 1955. *Plant Physiol.* **30**, 451–457.
Brown, R., and Possingham, J. V. 1957. *Proc. Roy. Soc.* **B147**, 145–166.
Callender, S. T., Mallett, B. J., and Smith, M. D. 1957. *Brit. J. Haematology.* **3**, 186–192.
Cartwright, G. E. 1950. *Symposium on Copper Metabolism, Baltimore* pp. 274–307.
Chance, B., and Williams, G. R. 1956. *Advances in Enzymol.* **17**, 65–134.
Elvehjem, C. A. 1931. *J. Biol. Chem.* **90**, 111–132.
Gauch, H. G. 1957. *Ann. Rev. Plant Physiol.* **8**, 31–64.
Glenister, P. R. 1944. *Botan. Gaz.* **106**, 33–40.
Granick, S. 1954. *Bull. New York Acad. Med.* **30**, 81–105.
Granick, S. 1957. *In* "Biochemical Disorders in Human Disease" (R. H. S. Thompson and E. J. King, eds.), pp. 674–684. Academic Press, New York.
Granick, S., and Gilder, H. 1947. *Advances in Enzymol.* **7**, 305–368.
Green, D. E. 1957. *Harvey Lectures.* 1956–1957, pp. 177–227. Academic Press, New York.
Green, S., and Mazur, A. 1956. *Science* **124**, 1149–1150.
Gris, E. 1844. *Compt. rend.* **19**, 1118–1119.
Gubler, C. J., Lahey, M. E., Chase, M. J., Cartwright, G. E., and Wintrobe, M. M. 1952. *Blood* **7**, 1095.
Hahn, P. F. 1948. *Federation Proc.* **7**, 493–498.
Halvorson, H. O. 1931. *Soil Sci.* **32**, 141–165.
Hartree, E. F. 1957. *Advances in Enzymol.* **18**, 1–64.
Harvey, H. W. 1945. "Recent Advances in the Chemistry and Biology of Sea Water." Cambridge Univ. Press, London and New York.
Hill, R. 1951. *Symposia Soc. Exptl. Biol.* **5**, 222–231.
Hill, R., and Lehmann, H. 1941. *Biochem. J.* **35**, 1190–1199.
Holmes, R. S., and Brown, J. C. 1955. *Soil Sci.* **80**, 167–179.
Jacobson, L., and Oertli, J. J. 1956. *Plant Physiol.* **31**, 199–204.
Kielley, W. W., and Bradley, L. B. 1955. *Federation Proc.* **14**, 235.
Kinney, T. D., Hegsted, D. M., and Finch, C. A. 1949. *J. Exptl. Med.* **90**, 137–145.
Kitching, J. A. 1954. *J. Exptl. Biol.* **31**, 76–83.
Kleman, S. 1937. *Soil Sci. Soc. Am. Proc.* **2**, 385–392.
Lascelles, J. 1956. *In* "Ciba Foundation Symposium on Porphyrin Biosynthesis and Metabolism," p. 265.
Laufberger, M. V. 1937. *Bull. soc. chim. biol.* **19**, 1575–1582.
Laurell, C. B. 1947. *Acta. Physiol. Scand.* **14**, *Suppl.* 46, 129 pp.

Leibich, H. 1941. Z. *Botan.* **37,** 129–157.

Lintzel, W. 1933. *Biochem.* Z. **263,** 173–186.

Lwoff, A. 1933. *Zentr. Bakteriol. Parasitenk. Abt. I Orig.* **130,** 498–518.

Mahler, H. R. 1956. *Advances in Enzymol.* **17,** 233–291.

Mason, H. S. 1957. *Advances in Enzymol.* **19,** 79–234.

Neilands, J. B. 1957. *Bacteriol. Rev.* **21,** 101–111.

Osler, W., and McCrae, T., eds. 1908. "System of Medicine." Oxford Univ. Press, London.

Reuther, W., Smith, P. F., and Specht, A. W. 1952. *Soil Sci.* **73,** 375–381.

Rossi-Fanelli, A., and Antonini, E. 1956. *Arch. Biochem. Biophys.* **65,** 587–590.

Schade, A. L., and Caroline, L. 1946. *Science* **104,** 340–341.

Schultze, M. O. 1947. *In* "Nutritional Anemia," pp. 99–115. Robert Gould Research Foundation, Cincinatti, Ohio.

Sherman, H. C. 1907. *U.S. Dept. Agr. Bull.* **185.**

Singer, T. P., Kearney, E. B., and Massey, V. 1957. *Advances in Enzymol.* **18,** 65–111.

Smith, O. L., Bierwagen, M. E., and Early, T. K. 1957. *Proc. Soc. Exptl. Biol. Med.* **94,** 710–711.

Speyer, J. F., and Diekman, S. R. 1956. *J. Biol. Chem.* **220,** 193–208.

Stewart, J., and Leonard, C. D. 1954. "Fruit Nutrition." Horticultural Publications, New Brunswick, New Jersey.

Stoklasa, J., and Ernest, A. 1909. *Jahrb. wiss. Bot.* **46,** 55–102.

Strittmatter, C. F., and Ball, E. G. 1952. *Proc. Natl. Acad. Sci. U.S.* **38,** 19–25.

Strittmatter, P., and Velick, S. F. 1956. *J. Biol. Chem.* **221,** 277–286.

Venkatachalam, P. S., Brading, I., George, E. P., and Walsch, R. J. 1956. *Australian J. Exptl. Biol. Med. Sci.* **34,** 389–393.

Wainio, W. W., and Cooperstein, S. J. 1956. *Advances in Enzymol.* **17,** 329–392.

Warner, R. C., and Weber, I. 1953. *J. Am. Chem. Soc.* **75,** 5094–5101.

Weber, M. M., Lenhoff, H. M., and Kaplan, N. O. 1956. *J. Biol. Chem.* **220,** 93–104.

Whatley, F. R., Ordin, L., and Arnon, D. I. 1951. *Plant Physiol.* **26,** 414–418.

Wiebe, H. H., and Kramer, P. J. 1954. *Plant Physiol.* **29,** 342–348.

CHAPTER 24

Summary of Trace Elements Symposium

C. A. ELVEHJEM

University of Wisconsin, Madison, Wisconsin

I am glad to be with you for several reasons. First, it is nice to take part in the anniversary of one of the early agricultural experiment stations in this country. About thirty years ago when I started teaching agricultural chemistry I spent a little time reviewing for the students the early development of experiment stations from Rothamsted, England, down through the various stations in this country, and the students always seemed interested in this historical approach. However, today, my colleagues seem to be so busy teaching the citric acid cycle, etc., that we don't have much time for history.

Second, I believe it is important for all of us to emphasize the contributions that agricultural experiment stations have made in this country. They have made a tremendous impact on scientific developments. The Federal government early supported research in experiment stations. Federal support is continuing, but with increasing interests in medical affairs and the cure of specific human diseases.

And third, I am of course interested to be here to listen to these papers on trace mineral elements because, after all, trace mineral elements were my first love. True, the first paper I published was on calcium, but the second paper was on iron, and for many years I worked on this as well as many other trace elements. It has been a great revelation for me to listen to these interesting papers during the past three days.

Now of course there is one reason why I am unhappy to be here and that is to attempt to give this summary. The only reason that I accepted this invitation was because my good friend Bill Krauss called me, and I couldn't say no. I am also very happy to come down here and visit my old friends and some of our old students.

Dr. Underwood made the statement to me that he understood that I was to give an intelligent summary. I want to clearly point out that the program lists my paper as a general summary. All I can do is to give my impression of and reactions to the papers given. It is certainly unnecessary to repeat in any way the presentations that have been made because as you will all agree they have been excellent, and I think if we reflect on these papers we will see that we have had excellent summaries and excellent examples of detailed studies relating to trace elements.

Almost all areas have been covered. We have dealt with the plant, the animal, microorganisms, and the soil. Work from all parts of the world has been presented by workers from several different countries. We have covered many areas of science as indicated, from physical chemistry to soil chemistry to nutrition, and so on. There have been many techniques introduced, and I think we were all fascinated by the presentation such as Dr. Mahler gave this morning on the detailed story of the isolation and characterization of a specific enzyme, how that enzyme functions, and specifically how copper enters into the picture.

In fact, we have dealt with almost every phase of life and living matter. I thought for a while that we might be neglecting the human, but we had a little better batting average today since a number of the papers this morning dealt with human subjects—Dr. Hock and Dr. Granick used the human subject in some of the work that they presented.

In making this summary, I would like first to go back to a definition of trace mineral elements or micronutrients. I do not know if a definition is too important since I think we all know what we mean when we use the term, but I was very happy that in the first papers given Monday afternoon it was clearly established what we were talking about and that we were not going to talk about the patent medicines that are on the market in certain areas of the country that contain anywhere from 20 to 30 mineral elements. Dr. Underwood clearly suggested that the trace elements included those below iron. I did not know at that time whether he was going to include iron, but Dr. Granick clearly included iron in this list, and I believe it should be since we have heard the important functions of iron in so many catalysts of the living cell.

Now I would like to emphasize, and I think it is very important, that there is nothing spectacular about trace mineral elements. Certainly they have profound effects. Fluorine when in the water we drink, but which we cannot see or taste, has a profound effect upon dental caries. The iodine in our salt, which also we cannot see or taste, makes the difference between a large incidence of goiter and no goiter. These elements do have a profound effect, but their function may be very similar to that of many nutrients. Sometimes I think there is too much hysteria about trace mineral elements, especially in human nutrition. Furthermore, after they have performed their function they can do nothing further to improve health. They saturate the enzyme systems, and they saturate the environmental fluids, but beyond that stage they may be harmful rather than beneficial.

I was interested that both Dr. Arnon and Dr. Underwood used almost the same words in describing an essential trace mineral element. Dr. Arnon said the plant cannot complete the life cycle without an essential element, the element must be specific, and it must participate in metabolism. Dr. Underwood stated there must be a growth response to the element in the animal, a specific deficiency state must develop, and this deficiency state must be correlated to some extent with changes in the blood, urine, or other tissues.

The important point in these definitions is specificity. This does not mean that one element has only one function—one element may be present in a number of enzymes and we heard this morning that zinc can be part of several enzymes. So by specificity we do not necessarily mean only one function, but that in the function this element and only this element is active. This is very important, at least for those of us who go back thirty years when we first suggested that copper was necessary for hemoglobin formation. Some of you know there was great controversy over whether copper would do it alone or whether manganese and a number of other elements would also function. Mr. Kettering indicated this point the other night, namely, that it is very difficult to accept something new, and this profound effect of a very small quantity of a trace element was difficult to accept. Thirty years ago it was difficult to recognize the possibility of contamination. Today we have a vast background of experience, and it is easier to accept additional trace mineral elements.

Next we might discuss classification. I was rather pleased that no one presented a master table classifying the elements that are necessary for each of the species of living matter. Perhaps some day we can build such a table, but I do not believe it is necessary at this stage. Many of the speakers differentiated the requirements of higher plants and lower plants, between different species of plants, between bacteria, fungi, and yeast. These variations are interesting and stimulating. Some of us are interested in the requirements of different forms of life, because we like to develop a complete picture as far as the human being is concerned. Dr. Hutner suggested that he had the organism that is ideal for this purpose, namely, *Ochromonas*. This interested me since he suggested that it might be used for measuring the antithyrotoxic substance, and I must admit that I have spent hundreds of dollars on rats for the assay of this factor. If he can do it with his organism, it would be wonderful. However, I think that no one living organism is going to tell the complete story so far as the human is concerned, and we need to accumulate facts from a number of different areas.

The next item we might mention is symptoms, description of the deficiency in various living organisms. Again there is great variation, but it is interesting that we can describe very specific symptoms in many cases, and I think Dr. Davis' paper on the description of cobalt deficiency intrigued all of us. There are many other conditions in the animal that can be clearly observed. One symptom that I heard Dr. Underwood mention this noon, namely, parakeratosis in swine, was not mentioned in the entire symposium. Here we have a very characteristic symptom.

As was mentioned by several of the speakers, standard symptoms in higher plants can be related to specific trace mineral deficiencies. In the lower forms of plant life, it is somewhat more difficult to observe gross changes, and it becomes necessary to resort to chemical or biochemical measurements. There are deficiencies in animals where the outward symptoms may not be evident. I think Dr. Bentley mentioned this yesterday in some of the vitamin B_{12}-deficiency work where there was little alteration in the growth of the animal, but he did see considerable change in the efficiency of food utilization. This is another means of determining whether all the mechanisms are proceeding in an optimum way within the organism. You may say that the symptoms themselves are not important. We are interested in the biochemical lesions, and that is certainly true. The greatest progress is going to be made when we understand all the alterations that take place within living cells whether it be plant, animal, or microorganism. Nevertheless, the external symptoms are important for several reasons. One is that if we see these symptoms we know that we have a true deficiency, and when we have a true deficiency we can proceed with our biochemical investigations with greater confidence.

Another reason was touched on by Dr. Underwood when he indicated that the work on trace mineral elements developed from two points of view—from the laboratory and from the field. Or we might say from the basic point of view and from the applied point of view. This emphasizes that there really is little distinction between applied and basic research; it does not make any difference where we start as long as we apply basic principles to the problems we want to solve. The appearance of symptoms has another important value point, and that is that when you see these symptoms you are more willing to accept the element as an essential one and you are more willing to do something about the deficiency. Dr. Davis mentioned this yesterday when he said that one of the farmers said, "I do not believe it even if I see it." Well, it helps at least to see it and very deep-seated impressions are made on investigators when they come in contact with these specific symptoms.

I know my own major professor, Professor Hart, under whom I was trained, had some very deep-seated feelings depending entirely on what he had seen in his own experience. When I took a course in agricultural chemistry under him, he emphasized that the only mineral elements we needed to worry about in animal nutrition were calcium, sodium chloride, and iodine. He paid great attention to iodine because he had seen widespread iodine deficiency both in livestock and human beings. It did not take him long, however, to add cobalt to that list after he had had personal experience with cobalt deficiency in certain areas in Wisconsin. On the other hand, he had seen extensive toxicity due to fluorine, and until his death he was not happy over the general use of fluorine in drinking water. Therefore, I think these visual deficiencies have a great effect on our thinking and on our methods of handling trace mineral problems.

The next item we might discuss is requirements. I am sure that we have a very long way to go before we can establish tables showing a specific requirement of each trace element for each species of animal, plant or microorganism. I think we are beginning to have a much more sensible attitude toward requirements; certainly we have had plenty of evidence here today that you cannot establish requirements very accurately even in the same organism, because you have such things as light, age, and many other things entering into the requirements. The fact that the plant does not contain vitamin B_{12} nor does it need vitamin B_{12}, the ruminant can make vitamin B_{12} from cobalt and nonruminants must have preformed B_{12}, are most interesting observations. The observations that certain lower forms of life need vanadium and others do not and that variation in the molybdenum requirement for different types of nitrogen metabolism are all interesting, and if we approach these requirements from that point of view, I do not think we are going to have any real blocks in our thinking—it merely means that we need to do more work.

Furthermore, I think it is important to recognize that certain statements that have been made today about requirements of certain organisms may have to be changed as the years go by. This is no criticism of the conclusions made today; it merely means that we have done the best we can with the knowledge available. I remember that when Dr. Underwood was in our laboratory we tried to see whether the rat needed cobalt or not. We found no effect whatsoever by adding cobalt. We were using milk diets supplemented with iron, copper, and manganese to produce the deficiency, and we said at that time that if a rat did need cobalt it was less than 6 μg. per day. We know today that the reason we did not get any effect with cobalt was because the milk we were using contained sufficient vitamin B_{12} to meet the demand and if that is translated into cobalt it is considerably less than 0.6 of a microgram per day. So these figures stand in light of our present knowledge, but we should be ready to change them when necessary.

It might be worthwhile to at least suggest that we do some thinking about the units used for measuring these trace mineral elements. We use parts per million and parts per billion—that may be all right in media for certain organisms—but when we come to higher animals it is a little difficult to know whether this refers to the total ration, dry weight or fresh weight, or what not. I think it might be worthwhile to think about using specific units under certain cases.

I might also mention in reference to requirements that there was little discussion during the symposium about balance experiments. Certainly for higher animals that is one of the means of determining total requirements, and in the human we will need to run balance experiments to establish final requirements for some of these trace mineral elements. It is difficult to do because of the contamination that may be encountered. The National Research Council, as many of you know, has a group both in the animal field and in the human field attempting to set requirements for humans and livestock. Little progress has been made in the case of many of the trace elements. In a few cases, very definite progress has been established. For example, the figure for the manganese requirement of the chicken is in general use because of the obvious deficiency recognized as perosis. The cobalt requirement of ruminants is also well established. So we have a long way to go, but I think progress is commensurate with the information which we have.

We should pass from requirements to sources of these elements, but I would like to interject here before we come to sources—the mechanisms. We have been most fortunate to have so many of the leaders in the field to present the mechanisms through which trace mineral elements may function.

The paper yesterday by Dr. Skok relating boron intake or boron supply to radiation injury indicates the many ramifications that work on trace mineral elements may have. The paper by Dr. Kirkwood on incorporation of iodine into thyroxine and thyroxinelike compounds, I think, was especially revealing because most of us interested in trace mineral elements, so far as nutrition is concerned, have just assumed that if you can get ample iodine into the body, the conversion of iodine into thyroxine is a very simple procedure. However, we see it is just as complex as many of the others. The papers this morning dealing with enzyme systems show the profound relationship of these trace mineral elements to basic biochemistry.

We might make one comment on the very extensive progress of our knowledge of enzymes. I liked the suggestion made by Dr. Pirson yesterday that sometimes we need to come back to the physiological effects. We need to return to the whole organism to be sure that these reactions are physiological and that they may not be artifacts, *in vitro*. Several of the speakers indicated that in some of their studies on enzyme systems these specific reactions might not occur in the intact animal or plant. Nevertheless very interesting information was gained.

We need to relate some of these enzyme systems to the specific effect. I listened very carefully during the symposium to all the extensive work on copper and copper enzymes, and the work on the iron compounds in the body. I did not hear anyone suggest specifically how copper functions in hemoglobin formation, and I would like, of course, to have that question answered for me. Another point in relation to mechanism (I think Dr. Underwood suggested this) is that even our newer techniques —use of isotopes, radioactive elements, and so on—have not necessarily eliminated the classic approach. We need to use all kinds of techniques.

I might interject a personal note here, namely, that we showed about twenty-five years ago that copper was necessary for hemoglobin formation, but it was not necessary for the absorption of iron from the tract. From the use of radioactive iron, certain workers have concluded that copper influences the absorption of iron. Well, certainly it would influence absorption indirectly because, as Dr. Granick has indicated, the body would absorb only so much iron, and when the absorbed iron cannot be converted into hemoglobin, no further iron will be absorbed. However, when copper is added, more iron is converted into hemoglobin, and the absorption will increase due to this indirect effect and not due to the fact that copper specifically affects the absorption of iron from the tract.

Finally, let us turn to a discussion of the sources of trace mineral elements. This consideration brings us back to the soil, and we had some very interesting papers on the supply of trace elements from the soil and how the supply in the soil affects our plants, our animals, and finally the human being. The paper by Beeson was a very complete survey of the relation of the soil to specific deficiences. I was especially impressed by the fact that several people talked about deficiencies in all parts of the world, which makes this a world problem as well as a local problem, as pointed out by several papers yesterday. McLean suggested that a boron deficiency may occur in soils of humid areas, and Mederski's paper described manganese deficiency in soybeans in specific areas here in the state of Ohio.

In all cases it is possible that the soil may supply a level of an element which will cause a deficiency, a level which will give an optimum supply, or one which may be toxic. The paper by Dr. Moxon on selenium gave excellent examples of these relationships: the distribution of selenium in soils may be high enough to increase the selenium content of certain plants, certain plants being more able to absorb selenium than others; and, finally, the very recent work on the possible significance of selenium as an essential element.

Fortunately, as far as the human or animal is concerned, we have the plant in between the soil and the animal, and the plant does a pretty good job in moderating the supply of the elements getting to the animal. In cases where the plant is vulnerable to these great variations, we see both deficiencies and toxicity in plants, and the method of measuring the availability of the trace mineral elements in soil becomes important. The paper yesterday by Dr. Hoff on the availability of manganese in the soil was most interesting. We must also consider the availability of mineral elements in the animal. We go back to the early work on iron where it was found that the organic forms of iron do not supply iron as readily as the simple iron salts. So we do have this interesting relationship between the soil, the plant, and the animal, and the microorganism may also play a part.

We should give a little consideration to the relationship of human health to the soil. It has not been mentioned in the symposium, although Dr. Underwood referred to it very briefly in the statement we still frequently hear "minerals taken into the system through plant foods are more available than minerals taken in separately." I know of no authentic data to substantiate this statement. Certainly plants can be excellent sources of minerals and we must rely on them, but I do not believe that the form of the trace mineral elements in plants makes them any more readily available or utilizable by the animal. In fact, in the case of iron I have already indicated that the iron in spinach is only about 20 per cent available. The only element which must be supplied in the organic form is cobalt in the form of vitamin B_{12}, and you learned that the plant does not contain vitamin B_{12} or does not need vitamin B_{12}.

It is true that in certain areas of the country the soil is sufficiently depleted in trace minerals to produce decreased production of the plants, and the plants may be low enough in certain minerals to have some effect on livestock. However, in the human this rarely takes place because of the wide sources of supply of our human food. In this connection I want to refer to a statement in Dr. Underwood's book "Trace Elements in Human and Animal Nutrition," namely, "Nutritional disabilities of man are far more likely to be associated with a poor choice of the foods consumed than with their source. Where the choice of foods is poor, so that the diet is of low nutritional value anyway, soil deficiencies are likely to accentuate the position and even to precipitate frank deficiency symptoms. But for the overwhelming bulk of mankind, a diet well-balanced and nutritionally adequate in other respects is likely on present evidence, to provide the normal individual with an abundance of all the trace elements with little chance of deleterious excess." I think that summarizes the problem of trace mineral elements in the human.

Finally, the papers in this symposium have made it obvious that we need to do a great deal more work. While we have many basic facts we need data on requirements; quantitative requirements are under different conditions. Thus we need to continue work like we have at an experiment station where we can study these problems under field conditions. We will have new conditions developing each year. We must be ready to meet these changes. We have increased greatly the rate of growth in our animals through the use of antibiotics and other growth stimulants. We have to be sure that we supply an adequate amount of trace minerals to meet this increased demand for rapid growth. If selenium and molybdenum are needed by the animal, it may be possible to demonstrate this need only if we have very rapid growth in the animal.

So it has been a happy occasion for me to listen to these papers. I am sure that each one of you could have given a different summary of the symposium, but I hope that I brought out a few points which might not have been evident to you as you listened to the papers. Thank you very much.

AUTHOR INDEX

Numbers in italics indicate the page on which the reference is listed.

A

Aaronson, S., 48, 51, 52, 59, 60, *64*
Adams, M. B., 200, *209*
Adelstein, S. J., 42, 45, *45*, 339, 346, 348, 349, 350, *359, 362*
Agarwala, S. C., 18, 29, *31*, 291, 292
Agulhon, H., 227, *242*
Ahlrogge, A. J., 110, *116*
Ahman, C. F., 194, *210*, 213, *224*
Albert, A., 323, *333*
Alberts-Dietert, F., 95, 97, 167, *173*
Alberty, R. A., 321, *333, 334*
Albiston, H. E., 36, *44*
Alexander, L. T., 128, *134*
Alexander, T. R., 230, 233, 239, *242*
Allen, M. B., 12, 21, 27, *31*, 87, 93, 97, 277, 292
Allen, P. J., 229, *242*
Allison, F. E., 277, 283, *294*, 304, *308*
Altman, K. I., 315, *333*
Altschule, M. D., 337, 339, 340, *362*
Anderson, A. J., 283, 286, *292*
Anderson, A. L., 71, *78*
Anderson, H. D., 182, 185, 186, *188, 189, 190*
Anderson, J. P., 201, 202, *209*
Andrews, E. D., 199, 201, 202, *209*
Anfinsen, C. B., 348, *361*
Anson, M. L., 341, *359*
Anthony, W. B., 208, *209*
Antoni, F., 343, *359*
Antonini, E., 367, *382*
Archibald, J. G., 208, *209*
Arnold, P. T. Dix., 196, 197, 198, 199, 200, *209*
Arnold, W., 169, *173, 174*
Arnon, D. I., 4, 5, 6, 7, 8, 10, 12, 15, 16, 20, 21, 24, 26, 27, 28, 29, 30, *31, 32*, 87, 88, 93, *97*, 160, 172, *174*, 229, *242*, 270, 278, 285, 286, *292, 294*, 375, *382*

Askew, H. O., 199, 200, *209*
Azéma, M., 271, *295*

B

Bach, M. K., 50, 52, *64*
Bailey, D. E., 176, *189*
Baker, H., 48, 51, 52, 54, 59, 60, *64, 65*
Baker, J. E., 240, *242*
Ball, E. G., 367, 369, *382*
Ballentine, R., 56, *64*
Baltscheffsky, H., 273, *292*
Baltscheffsky, M., 273, *292*
Baltzer, A. C., 196, *209*, 213, *223*
Barnes, R. H., 34, *44*, 60, *64*
Barnett, E. L., 315, 317, *335*
Barron, E. S. G., 315, *333*
Barshad, I., 76, 78, *78*
Bartholomay, A. F., 356, *362*
Bartlett, R. J., 253, *256*
Bass, A. D., 282, *292*
Bassham, J. A., 138, *154*
Batelli, F., 315, *333*
Baum, H., 315, 316, 320, 321, 323, 326, 327, 328, *333, 334*
Bayer, E., 272, *292*, 372, *381*
Beals, C. E., Jr., 69, *78*
Bear, F. E., 291, *293*
Beath, O. A., 39, *44*, 176, 177, 178, 180, 182, 183, 184, 187, *188, 190*
Bechi, E., 270, *292*
Becker, D. E., 195, 201, 207, *209, 210*, 216, *224*
Becker, R. B., 196, 197, 198, 199, 200, *209*
Beeson, K. C., 73, 74, 75, 78, 79, 195, 196, 200, 207, *209, 210*, 214, *223*
Beeson, W. M., 355, *360*
Behrend, R., 328, *334*
Beinert, H., 281, *294*
Beisenherz, G., 349, 350, *360*
Bell, J. M., 207, *210*
Bellamy, F., 337, *361*

Bellis, D. B., 355, *360*
Benoit, 271, *295*
Benoit, R. J., 58, *64*
Benson, A. A., 138, *154*
Benson, W. N., 70, *79*
Bentley, O. G., 214, 216, 217, 218, *224*
Bentley, R., 316, 327, 329, *334*
Berg, A., 126, 127, 128, 132, *134*
Berger, K. C., 229, 232, *242*, 251, 252, 253, 255, *256*
Bergmann, F., 325, *334*
Bergmann, L., 85, 86, 87, 97, 144, *154, 155,* 157, 166, 167, *174*
Bergstrand, H., 356, *361*
Berk, L., 206, *209*
Bernheim, F., 275, *292*
Bernheim, M. L. C., 275, *292*
Bersworth, F. C., 59, *64*
Bertramson, B. R., 104, *108,* 110, *116*
Bertrand, D., 11, *31,* 271, 272, 273, 274, 275, 276, 277, 278, 283, *292*
Bertrand, G., 194, *209*
Bessis, M. E., 374, *381*
Bielig, H. J., 272, *292*
Bieri, J. G., 35, *45,* 176, 184, 188, *188, 190*
Bierwagen, M. E., 373, *382*
Biddulph, O., 378, *381*
Birch-Hirschfeld, L., 283, *292*
Bird, O. D., 217, 219, *224*
Bishop, W. B. S., 167, *174*
Bjerrum, J., 325, *334*
Bliss, A. F., 346, 358, 359, *360*
Block, R. J., 139, *154*
Blumberg, H., 274, *292*
Bobko, E. V., 283, *292*
Bock, R. M., 281, *294*
Boeri, E., 272, 273, *293,* 369, *381*
Bohstedt, G., 195, 201, 203, 204, *209, 210*
Bolas, B. D., 82, *98*
Bolle-Jones, E. W., 57, *64*
Boltze, H. J., 349, 350, *360*
Bonner, J., 241, *243*
Bonnett, R., 220, *224*
Bonnichsen, R., 339, 346, 347, 357, 358, *360, 362*
Borei, E., 272, *292*
Bortels, H., 20, *31,* 271, 277, 282, 283, *292,* 297, *308*
Bossardt, D. K., 34, *44,* 60, *64*

Bowen, W., Jr., 276, *293*
Bowness, J. M., 359, *360*
Bowstead, J. E., 195, *209*
Boyce, S. G., 75, *78*
Boyd, T. C., 274, *293*
Boynton, D., 101, *107,* 229, 231, *242*
Bradfield, J. R. G., 341, *360*
Brading, I., 372, *382*
Bradley, H. C., 37, *44*
Bradley, L. B., 367, *381*
Brammell, W. S., 354, 355, *361*
Brandenburg, E., 228, *242*
Braude, R., 207, *209*
Brenchley, W. E., 228, *242,* 285, *293*
Breton, H., 337, *361*
Breton-Gorius, J., 374, *381*
Brewster, J. F., 233, *243*
Briggs, G. M., 35, *45,* 176, 188, *190*
Brink, N. G., 346, *360*
Brinkman, R., 339, *360*
Britton, J. W., 71, *78*
Brown, F. B., 220, 221, *224*
Brown, G. B., 327, *334*
Brown, J. C., 376, 378, 379, *381*
Brown, J. M., 279, *293*
Brown, T. E., 92, 94, 97, 136, 137, 139, 147, 151, *154*
Broyer, T. C., 12, *31,* 57, 60, 65, 172, *174*
Brudevold, F., 37, *44*
Buchanan, M. L., 205, *209, 210,* 222, *224*
Bucher, T., 349, 350, *360*
Buchholz, W., 10, *32*
Buhler, D., 313, *334*
Bukovac, M. J., 100, *107*
Bulen, W. A., 284, *294,* 299, *308*
Bull, L. B., 36, 40, *44,* 195, *210,* 279, *293*
Burchard, W., 343, *362*
Burchenal, J. H., 206, *209*
Burema, S. J., 283, *293*
Burghardt, H., 95, 96, *97*
Burk, D., 20, 21, 31, *31,* 158, *174,* 277, 283, *293, 294,* 297, 298, 304, *308*
Burkholder, L. M., 58, *64*
Burkholder, P. R., 58, *64*
Burns, M. J., 223, *223*
Burnett, W. T., Jr., 281, *295,* 297, *309*
Burris, R. H., 283, 284, *293, 294*
Burroughs, R. N., 282, *294, 295*

Burroughs, W., 214, *224*
Burrows, F. W., 82, 96, *98*
Burstall, F. H., 62, *65*
Burström, H., 94, 96, *97*
Burton, M. O., 54, *65*
Byers, H. G., 68, *78*, 176, 177, 178, 179, 180, *188, 189, 191*

C

Cain, J. C., 220, 221, *224*
Calfee, R. K., 99, *108*
Calhoun, B., 233, 237, *242*
Califano, L., 272, 273, *293*
Calkins, D. G., 203, *210*, 217, 219, 220, *224*
Callender, S. T., 59, *64*, 372, *381*
Calvez, J., 110, *116*
Calvin, M., 138, *154*, 323, *334*
Cameron, C. A., 180, *188*
Cannelakis, E. S., 327, *334*
Cannon, J. R., 220, *224*
Cantacuzène, J., 271, 272, *293*
Capindale, J. B., 93, *97*
Cardenas, R. R., Jr., 184, *188*
Carlton, A. B., 12, *31*, 57, *64*, 172, *174*
Carlyle, F. C., 104, *107*
Caroline, L., 368, *382*
Carpenter, L. E., 187, *188*
Carter, C. L., 70, *79*
Cartwright, G. E., 374, *381*
Cary, C. A., 221, *224*
Caselli, P., 272, *293*
Castle, W. B., 206, *209*
Catron, D. V., 204, *210*
Caughey, W. S., 49, *64*
Cavalieri, L. F., 327, *334*
Chaberek, S., Jr., 59, *64*
Chaikoff, I. L., 258, 259, 261, 262, 264, 267, 342, *361*
Chance, B., 331, *334*, 335, 358, *362*, 369, 371, *381*
Chandler, F. B., 230, *242*
Chase, M. J., 374, *381*
Chiu, T. F., 278, *293*
Chow, B. F., 221, *224*
Christian, W., 299, *309*
Church, A. W., 37, *44*
Ciereszko, L. S., 272, *293*
Ciotti, M. M., 348, *360*
Clark, A. M., 339, *361*
Clark, P. F., 53, *64*

Clendenning, K. A., 92, 97, 137, 147, *154*, 172, *174*, 341, *363*
Cline, J. H., 216, *224*
Clulo, G., 127, 128, 132, *134*
Coates, M. E., 217, *224*
Cohen, B., 266, *267*
Cohen, P. P., 327, *334*
Collett, M. E., 185, *188*
Colovos, N. F., 214, *225*
Colowick, S. P., 352, 353, *361*
Comar, C. L., 198, 201, 207, *209*, 281, 295, 297, *309*
Commissiong, K., 292, *293*
Commoner, B., 331, *334*
Connors, P., 61, *65*
Conrad, J. H., 355, *360*
Cook, J. A., 101, *107*
Cook, R. L., 104, *108*
Cooke, C. W., 73, *78*
Coolidge, A. J., 68, *78*
Coombs, T. L., 344, 347, *362*
Cooperstein, S. J., 371, *382*
Coppenet, M., 110, *116*
Cori, C. F., 350, *360*
Cori, G. T., 350, *360*
Couch, J. R., 35, *45*, 208, *209*, 282, 294, 295
Cowey, C. B., 58, *64*
Cowperthwaite, J., 53, *65*
Crane, F. L., 281, *294*
Crawford, C. L., 106, *108*
Culbertson, C. C., 204, *210*
Cuningham, H. M., 279, *293*
Cunningham, I. J., 36, 40, *44*
Curnow, D. H., 199, *210*
Curran, G. L., 275, *293*
Cuthbertson, W. F. J., 217, *224*
Czok, R., 349, 350, *360*

D

Dalgliesh, C. E., 327, 330, *334*
Daniel, E. P., 274, *293*
Daniel, L. J., 280, *294*
Datta, N. P., 291, *296*
Davenport, H. W., 340, *360*
Davidson, D. C., 350, *360*
Davidson, J. N., 315, 317, *334*
Davis, G. K., 70, 71, 77, *78*, 196, 197, 198, 199, 200, 201, 203, 204, *209*
Davis, R. L., 221, *224*
Dawson, C. R., 333, *334*

Day, H. G., 60, 65
Day, R., 339, 341, 360
De, N. K., 274, 293
Dean, L. A., 128, 134
DeMaria, G., 342, 361
Denison, F. W., Jr., 354, 360
DeRenzo, E. C., 35, 44, 281, 282, 293
de Saussure, T., 2, 31
Dick, A. T., 36, 40, 44, 76, 79, 279, 280, 293
Diekman, S. R., 367, 369, 382
Dikstein, 325, 334
Dimitriev, K. A., 278, 293
Dinusson, W. E., 205, 209, 210, 222, 224
Dion, H. G., 110, 116
Dion, H. W., 203, 210, 220, 224
Dixon, J. K., 199, 209
Dixon, M., 321, 334
Doisy, R. J., 281, 295
Dore, W. H., 240, 243
Douglas, J., 345, 361
Draize, J. H., 177, 180, 183, 187, 188
Drea, W. F., 274, 293
Droop, M. R., 58, 59, 64, 65
Dryden, L. P., 221, 224
DuBois, K. P., 186, 188
Dudley, H. C., 187, 188
Dugger, W. M., Jr., 228, 231, 232, 233, 234, 235, 236, 237, 239, 240, 242, 243
Dulaney, E. L., 56, 64
Duncan, C. W., 196, 209, 213, 223
Duncan, D. L., 70, 79
Dunn, K. M., 206, 207, 209
Durham, L. J., 93, 97
Durrum, E. L., 139, 154

E

Earle, I. P., 41, 45, 355, 359, 362
Early, T. K., 373, 382
Eaton, F. M., 229, 242
Eaton, S. V., 232, 242
Edie, A. E., 279, 293
Egami, F., 291, 295
Ehrenberg, A., 272, 292
Ehrmantraut, H. C., 92, 97, 137, 154
Eirich, F. R., 339, 360
Ellis, G. H., 196, 206, 207, 210
Eltinge, E. T., 150, 153, 155
Elvehjem, C. A., 37, 38, 44, 185, 190, 217, 224, 339, 340, 360, 374, 381

Ely, R. E., 201. 206, 207, 209
Emerson, R., 169, 174
Endean, R., 273, 293
Engel, R. W., 280, 295
Enos, H. F., Jr., 214, 225
Eppson, H. F., 39, 44, 177, 178, 180, 182, 187, 188
Ernest, A., 376, 382
Erwin, T. C., 199, 209
Evans, H. J., 283, 293, 297, 308
Evans, H. K., 286, 291, 295
Eyster, H. C. (Eyster, C.), 92, 94, 96, 97, 137, 139, 147, 151, 154, 155, 229, 242

F

Faessler, A., 343, 362
Fan, C. S., 145, 155
Fawcett, D. M., 257, 258, 259, 265, 266, 267
Fearon, W. R., 274, 296
Felix, F., 315, 334
Ferguson, W. S., 36, 39, 44, 279, 293
Ferrin, E. F., 354, 360
Filmer, J. F., 39, 45, 68, 79, 194, 195, 198, 201, 209, 211, 213, 224
Finch, C. A., 376, 381
Finck, V. A., 110, 116
Fisher, A. M., 339, 361
Fleming, G. A., 176, 191
Fogg, G. E., 21, 22, 31, 283, 293
Foltz, C. M., 35, 45, 176, 190
Ford, J. E., 51, 54, 64, 217, 218, 220, 223, 224
Foster, J. N., 354, 360
Foster, J. W., 337, 360
Foulks, W. L., 313, 315, 334
Franke, K. W., 177, 180, 182, 183, 184, 187, 188, 189, 190
Franklin, J., 339, 341, 360
Fraps, G. S., 70, 79
Fredga, A., 182, 189
Free, A. A., 207, 209
French, C. S., 145, 155
Frieden, C., 321, 334
Friederichsen, I., 83, 97
Frush, H. L., 233, 243
Fruton, J. S., 266, 267
Fudge, J. F., 70, 79
Fujiwara, A., 15, 16, 20, 31, 286, 292

G

Gaffron, H., 88, 97
Gall, L. S., 216, 224
Gallagher, C. H., 42, 44
Gant, D. E., 220, 221, 224
Garbade, K. H., 349, 350, 360
Garibaldi, J. A., 56, 64
Gauch, H. G., 228, 231, 232, 233, 234, 235, 236, 237, 239, 240, 242, 243, 377, 381
George, E. P., 372, 382
Gericke, S., 278, 293, 294
Gerloff, C. D., 12, 31
Gerretsen, F. C., 82, 92, 95, 97, 98, 99, 106, 108
Gest, H., 284, 285, 294
Geyer, C. F., 276, 295
Gibian, H., 339, 360
Gibson, J. G., II, 340, 342, 362
Gilbert, C. S., 39, 44, 177, 178, 180, 187, 188
Gilder, H., 368, 381
Glenister, P. R., 378, 381
Glenn, J. L., 281, 294
Goldberg, E. D., 272, 273, 294
Goldstein, M. N., 56, 65
Goodale, T. C., 138, 154
Gorham, P. R., 172, 174
Goss, H. J., 71, 78
Graham, J., 51, 65
Grahame, D. C., 8, 31
Grant, N. H., 315, 317, 335
Grant, W. C., 206, 209
Gray, L. F., 200, 209, 280, 294
Greathouse, L. H., 128, 134
Green, D. E., 281, 284, 294, 295, 297, 308, 369, 371, 381
Green, N. M., 341, 360
Green, S., 372, 381
Griffith, W. H., 206, 209
Griffiths, M., 323, 334
Gris, E., 366, 381
Grube, K., 87, 98
Grummer, R. H., 41, 44, 355, 360, 361
Gubler, C. J., 374, 381
Gunsalus, I. C., 352, 362

H

Haas, A. R. C., 83, 97, 99, 108
Haas, V. A., 138, 154

Hahn, P. F., 373, 381
Haig, C., 359, 361
Hakala, N. V., 339, 361
Hale, W. J., 203, 204, 209
Hall, N. S., 291, 293
Halverson, A. W., 186, 189, 190
Hambridge, G., 245, 250
Hamilton, P. B., 284, 285, 295
Hanson, H. T., 342, 362
Harington, C. R., 39, 44
Harless, E., 37, 44
Harris, R. S., 206, 210
Harrison, G. F., 217, 224
Harschfield, R. D., 186, 190
Hart, E. B., 37, 38, 44, 339, 340, 360
Hartman, A. M., 221, 224
Hartree, E. F., 315, 318, 334, 371, 374, 375, 381
Harvey, H. W., 379, 381
Harvey, R. J., 200, 211
Haselhoff, E., 228, 242
Haskins, C. P., 59, 60, 64
Hastings, A. B., 185, 190
Hayaishi, O., 314, 334
Hayes, A., 101, 108
Hayes, J. E., Jr., 342, 345, 360
Hecht, S., 271, 294
Heddleson, M. R., 253, 256
Hegsted, D. M., 61, 65, 376, 381
Heinrich, H. C., 51, 58, 64
Heintze, S. G., 110, 116
Heise, J. J., 331, 334
Hellerman, L., 49, 64
Henderson, J. A., 196, 209
Henderson, J. R., 199, 209
Hendrick, C., 187, 189
Henze, M., 37, 44, 270, 271, 272, 273, 294
Hercus, C. H., 70, 79
Hershberger, T. V., 216, 224
Heuser, G. F., 39, 45
Hewitt, E. J., 17, 18, 29, 31, 99, 108, 157, 174, 233, 242, 285, 291, 294
Hewitt, J. L., 126, 127, 134
Hewston, E. M., 274, 293
Heytler, P. G., 35, 44, 281, 293
Higgins, E. S., 35, 44, 281, 282, 294, 296
Hildebrand, E. M., 127, 134
Hill, R., 370, 375, 378, 381
Hilmoe, R. J., 181, 190

Hiltner, E., 82, 97
Hoagland, D. R., 5, 31, 234, 240, 243, 283, 285, 294
Hoch, F. L., 42, 45, 339, 342, 343, 344, 345, 346, 347, 349, 350, 356, 359, 360, 362
Hoch, G. E., 284, 294
Hodgkin, D. C., 220, 224
Hoefer, J. A., 354, 355, 361
Hoekstra, W. G., 41, 44, 202, 209, 210, 216, 224, 355, 360, 361
Hoff, D. J., 100, 103, 108, 111, 116
Hoffmann-Ostenhof, O., 314, 334
Holdsworth, E. S., 54, 64, 217, 218, 224
Holm, G. G., 205, 209
Holmberg, C. G., 315, 317, 318, 323, 334
Holmes, R. S., 376, 378, 379, 381
Holm-Hansen, O., 12, 31, 144, 151, 152, 155
Holowaychuk, N., 253, 256
Holt, A. S., 145, 155
Holt, N. B., 233, 243
Holzer, H., 346, 358, 360
Homeyer, P. G., 204, 210
Hopkins, E. F., 99, 108, 166, 174
Horner, C. K., 277, 283, 293, 294, 297, 304, 308
Hove, E., 37, 44, 339, 340, 360
Hubscher, G., 315, 316, 320, 321, 323, 326, 327, 328, 333, 334
Hudson, P. B., 315, 334
Huff, J. W., 34, 44, 60, 64
Huffman, C. F., 196, 201, 203, 206, 207, 209, 210, 213, 217, 223, 225
Hughes, W. L., Jr., 339, 362
Humphreys, J. E., 233, 237, 242
Hunt, C. H., 214, 216, 218, 224
Hunter, R. B., 202, 211
Hurd-Karrar, A. M., 180, 181, 187, 189
Hurwitz, C., 207, 210
Hutchings, B. L., 35, 44, 281, 293
Hutner, S. H., 48, 50, 51, 52, 54, 58, 59, 60, 64, 65

I

Ichioka, P. S., 16, 17, 20, 27, 31, 32, 286, 292, 294
Ijichi, W., 56, 64
Insko, W. M., 39, 44
Isbell, H. S., 233, 243

Ishibashi, M., 274, 294

J

Jack, F. H., 203, 204, 209
Jacobs, E., 281, 294
Jacobson, L., 379, 381
James, W. O., 337, 338, 360
Japha, A., 176, 189
Jeckel, D., 349, 361
Jensen, C. W., 177, 190
Jensen, H. L., 283, 294, 297, 308
Jensen, R., 72, 79
Job, P., 347, 360
Johns, A. T., 44, 44
Johnson, A. G., 177, 189
Johnson, A. W., 220, 224
Johnson, B. C., 54, 64
Johnson, C. M., 12, 31, 57, 64, 172, 174
Johnson, E. S., 240, 243
Johnson, L. R., 176, 181, 190
Johnson, R. R., 182, 189, 214, 218, 222, 224
Jones, E. W., 285, 294
Jones, L. H. P., 110, 116
Jornlin, D. F., 179, 181, 190
Joselow, M., 333, 334
Judah, J. D., 42, 44
Judis, J., 284, 285, 294

K

Kägi, J. H. R., 343, 356, 362
Kalckar, H. M., 316, 334
Kaleita, E., 281, 293
Kaluta, E., 35, 44
Kamstra, L. D., 187, 191
Kandler, O., 87, 97
Kaplan, N. O., 298, 308, 348, 352, 353, 360, 361, 372, 382
Katagiri, M., 314, 334
Kearney, E. B., 315, 333, 335, 367, 369, 382
Keast, J. C., 36, 44
Keeler, R. F., 277, 284, 294, 297, 298, 299, 300, 303, 304, 305, 308
Keener, H. A., 69, 79, 196, 206, 207, 210
Keilin, D., 315, 318, 334, 339, 340, 341, 360
Keleti, T., 343, 359, 360
Keller, H., 340, 360
Kellogg, C. E., 2, 32
Kenten, R. H., 93, 97
Kercher, C. J., 202, 210, 215, 223, 224

Kernkamp, H. C. H., 354, *360*
Kessler, E., 89, 90, 91, 95, *97, 98,* 135, 139, 144, *155*
Keston, A. S., 266, *267*
Ketchum, B. H., 15, *32*
Kidder, R. W., 196, 197, 198, 199, 200, *209*
Kielley, W. W., 367, *381*
Killham, B. J., 196, *209,* 213, *223*
King, H. H., 187, *190*
Kinney, T. D., 376, *381*
Kirk, W. G., 196, 197, 198, 199, 200, *209*
Kirkwood, S., 257, 258, 259, 265, 266, *267*
Kitching, J. A., 378, *381*
Kleman, S., 375, 377, *381*
Klosterman, E. W., 205, *209, 210,* 214, 222, *224*
Klotz, I. M., 322, *334*
Klug, H. L., 183, 185, 186, 187, *189, 190*
Kluyver, A. J., 283, *294*
Knight, S. H., 178, *189*
Kobayashi, S., 272, 273, *294*
Kobel, M., 275, *295*
Koch, B. A., 201, *210,* 216, *225*
Kohn, H. I., 169, *173*
Kolthoff, I. M., 345, 347, *360*
Kon, S. K., 54, *64,* 217, 218, *224*
Konishi, K., 277, *294*
Kornberg, A., 350, *361*
Kramer, P. J., 377, *382*
Kratz, W. A., 12, *32*
Krebs, H., 185, *189*
Krippahl, G., 10, *32*
Kubowitz, F., 323, *334*
Kuchel, R. E., 204, *210*
Kunitz, M., 261, *267*
Kunkle, L. E., 214, *224*
Kurnick, A. A., 35, *45,* 282, *294, 295*
Kylin, A., 95, *98*

L

Labes, R., 185, *189*
Lahann, H., 58, *64*
Lahey, M. E., 374, *381*
Laidler, K. J., 321, *334*
Lakin, H. W., 176, 177, 178, 179, 180, *188, 189, 191*
Lal, K. N., 168, *174*
Landolt, E., 50, *64, 65*

Langridge, J., 50, *65*
Lardy, H. A., 184, *189*
Larsen, C., 176, *189*
Larson, E. J., 41, *45*
Lascelles, J., 375, *381*
Lasley, E. L., 205, *209, 210,* 222, *224*
Latimer, L. P., 253, *256*
Laufberger, M. V., 370, *381*
Laurell, C. B., 368, *381*
Lazar, V. A., 74, 75, 78, *79*
Lechartier, G., 337, *361*
Lee, H. J., 198, 201, 202, 204, *210*
Lee, S. B., 284, *294*
Lee, T. S., 345, 347, *360*
Leeper, G. W., 110, 111, *116,* 286, *294*
Lehmann, H., 375, 378, *381*
Lehninger, A. L., 157, *174,* 337, 338, *361*
Leibich, H., 375, *382*
Leiner, G., 339, 340, *361*
Leiner, M., 339, 340, *361*
Lemley, R. E., 187, *189*
Lenhoff, H. M., 298, *308,* 372, *382*
Leonard, C. D., 379, *382*
Leonard, N. J., 330, *334*
Leone, E., 315, *334*
Leussing, D. L., 345, 347, *360*
Levey, S., 206, *210*
Levine, V. E., 187, *189*
Lewin, J. C., 61, *65*
Lewin, R. A., 58, *65*
Lewis, A. H., 36, 39, *44,* 279, *293*
Lewis, H. D., 340, *362*
Lewis, J. C., 56, *64*
Lewis, P. K., Jr., 41, *44,* 355, *360, 361*
Lewis, U. J., 217, *224*
Lindahl, I. L., 204, *210,* 215, *224*
Lines, E. W., 39, *44,* 194, 195, *210*
Lineweaver, H., 283, *293,* 298, *308*
Lintzel, W., 372, *382*
Lipman, C. B., 228, *243*
Lippincott, B. B., 331, *334*
Lissitzky, S., 262, 263, 266, *267*
Little, H. N., 284, *294*
Lochhead, A. G., 54, *65*
Lockwood, S., 48, 51, 52, 59, 60, *64*
Logothetopoulos, J. H., 266, *267*
London, M., 315, *334*
Loneragan, J. F., 15, *32*
Loosli, J. K., 195, 200, *209, 210,* 216, *224*
Lorenz, O. A., 240, *243*

Lowater, F., 274, 276, *294*
Luecke, R. W., 354, 355, *361*
Luisada-Opper, A. V., 54, *65*
Lundegårdh, H. G., 37, *44*, 94, *98*, 356, *361*
Luttgens, W., 172, *174*
Lutz, R. E., 337, *361*
Luzzato, R., 275, *294*
Lwoff, A., 379, *382*
Lyford, W. H., Jr., 69, *79*
Lyonnet, 275, *294*
Lyons, M., 39, *44*

M

McBlair, W., 272, 273, *294*
McCall, J. T., 203, 204, *209*
McClymont, G. L., 279, *296*
McCollum, E. V., 274, *295*
McCormick, T., 56, *65*
McCrae, T., 365, *382*
McCready, C. C., 17, 18, *31*
McCreary, O. C., 177, 180, 187, *188*
MacDonald, D., 62, *65*
McDonald, I. W., 195, 204, *210*
McDonald, M. R., 261, *267*
McElroy, W. D., 17, *32*, 94, *98*, 99, *108*, 233, *243*, 287, 289, 291, *295*
McGlohon, V., 217, 219, *224*
McHargue, J. S., 99, *108*
Macheboeuf, M., 194, *209*
McIlrath, W. J., 229, 231, 235, 237, 238, 239, *243*
McIntosh, R. A., 196, *210*, 213, *224*
MacKinney, G., 137, *155*, 159, 160, *174*
Mackler, B., 281, *294*, 297, *308*
McLaughlin, J. J. A., 58, 59, 60, *64*, *65*
McLean, E. O., 253, *256*
MacLeod, R. A., 60, *65*
McNaught, K. J., 195, 200, *210*
McNaught, M. L., 217, *224*
McQuillan, M. T., 266, *267*
McVickar, M. H., 251, *256*
Macy, P., 161, *174*
Madison, T. C., 176, *189*
Magee, W. E., 283, *294*, 302, *308*
Mahler, H. R., 157, *174*, 281, 284, *294*, *295*, 297, *308*, 315, 316, 320, 321, 323, 326, 327, 328, *333*, *334*, 345, *361*, *382*
Mallett, B. J., 372, *381*
Mallikarjuneswara, V. R., 57, *64*

Malmstrom, B. G., 338, *361*
Mann, P. J. G., 93, *97*, 110, *116*
Mann, T., 339, 340, 341, *360*
Mansfield, J. B., 68, *79*
Margaria, R., 339, *360*
Margolin, M., 177, *190*
Marsh, R. P., 232, *243*
Marston, H. R., 39, *44*, 68, *79*, 194, 195, 198, 201, 202, 204, *210*, 214, 216, 224
Martell, A. E., 323, *334*
Martin, A. L., 180, *189*
Martin, J. P., 83, *98*
Mason, H. S., 313, 315, *334*, 368, 369, *382*
Mason, T. G., 182, *190*
Massey, D. M., 83, *98*
Massey, V., 367, 369, *382*
Matrone, G., 73, *78*
Matsushima, K., 144, *155*
Maurer, R. L., 60, *65*
Maxwell, G. T., 197, *210*
Mazé, P., 228, *243*, 278, *295*
Mazé, P. J., 278, *295*
Mazur, A., 372, *381*
Meagher, W. R., 18, *32*, 285, *295*
Mederski, H. J., 106, *108*, 110, *116*
Medina, A., 351, *361*
Mehler, A. H., 92, *98*, 314, *334*
Meldrum, N. U., 339, *360*, *361*
Mendel, L. B., 37, *44*
Mendive, J. R., 340, *361*
Meyer-Arendt, E., 349, 350, *360*
Michaelis, L., 331, *335*
Michel, R., 262, 263, 266, *267*
Millar, C. E., 104, *108*
Miller, J. T., 177, 179, *188*
Miller, O. P., 34, *44*, 60, *64*
Miller, R. F., 280, *295*
Miller, W. T., 185, *189*
Milstrey, R., 35, *45*, 188, *190*
Minot, A. S., 275, *295*
Mitchell, R. L., 201, *210*, 217, 225
Moinuddin, M., 217, *224*
Monroe, R. A., 281, *295*, 297, *309*
Montgomery, M. L., 342, *361*
Morgan, G. T., 62, *65*
Morgan, M. F., 112, *116*
Morris, V. H., 182, *190*
Morrison, F. B., 205, *210*
Morrow, K. S., 69, *79*, 206, 207, *210*

Morton, R. A., 359, *360*
Morton, R. K., 266, *267*
Mountain, J. T., 275, *295*
Moxon, A. L., 71, *79*, 176, 177, 178, 179, 180, 181, 182, 183, 184, 185, 186, 188, *188*, *189*, *190*, 214, 216, 218, *224*
Mulder, E. G., 17, *32*, 82, *98*, 99, 106, *108*, 283, 285, 286, 291, *295*, 297, *308*
Mulford, D. J., 206, *209*
Muller, R., 273, *294*
Murnane, D., 195, *210*
Murray, M. M., 274, 276, *294*
Myant, N. B., 266, *267*
Myers, J., 12, 15, *32*, 51, *65*, 144, *155*

N

Nakamura, M., 61, *65*
Nason, A., 20, *32*, 94, 95, *98*, 99, *108*, 233, *243*, 277, 284, 286, 287, 288, 289, 290, 291, *295*, 297, 298, 305, *308*, *309*, 351, 352, 353, *361*
Nathan, H. A., 48, 51, 52, 53, 59, 60, *64*, 65
Neal, W. M., 194, *210*, 213, *224*
Negelein, E., 342, 343, *361*
Neilands, J. B., 375, *382*
Neish, A. C., 87, *98*, 341, *361*
Neiswander, C. R., 182, *190*
Neuberg, C., 275, *295*
Neuberger, A., 316, 327, 329, 330, *334*
Neurath, H., 339, 341, 342, *360*, *361*, *362*
Newell, J. M., 274, *295*
Nicholas, D. J. D., 17, 20, *32*, 95, *98*, 286, 287, 288, 289, 290, 291, 292, *295*, 297, 298, *308*, 351, *361*
Noddack, I., 272, 274, *295*
Noddack, W., 272, 274, *295*
Noland, P. R., 205, *210*
Norberg, R. E., 331, *334*
Norris, L. C., 35, 39, *44*, *45*
Nowinski, W. W., 343, *361*
Nygaard, A. P., 339, 345, 347, 358, *362*

O

O'Brien, J. R. P., 59, *64*
Ochoa, S., 93, *98*
O'Connor, R., 176, *191*

Oertli, J. J., 379, *381*
Ohlrogge, A. J., 104, *108*
Oldewurtel, H. A., 352, *361*
Oleson, J. J., 35, *44*, 281, *293*
Olson, J. A., 339, 348, *361*, *362*
Olson, O. E., 71, *79*, 177, 178, 179, 180, 181, 186, 187, *188*, *189*, *190*, *191*
Olson, R., 42, *45*
O'Moore, L. B., 176, *190*
Onofrey, E., 60, *65*
Onoprienko, I., 313, *334*
Ordin, L., 241, *243*, 375, *382*
Orten, J. M., 206, *210*
Osler, W., 365, *382*
Osmond, F., 277, *296*
Owen, E. C., 217, *224*
Owen, O., 83, *98*
Ozanne, P. G., 60, *65*, 172, *174*

P

Painter, E. P., 180, 182, *189*, *190*
Palade, G. E., 50, *65*
Palser, B. F., 235, 237, *243*
Papish, J., 274, *296*
Pappenheimer, O. M., Jr., 331, *334*
Parker, L. F. J., 220, 221, *224*
Parks, R. Q., 253, *256*
Passonneau, J. V., 331, *334*
Patek, A. J., Jr., 359, *361*
Patterson, E. L., 35, *45*, 188, *190*
Pavcek, C. L., 206, *209*
Paye, J. E., 207, *209*
Paynter, C. R., 186, *190*
Pearson, P. B., 204, *210*, 215, *224*
Pearson, R. E., 72, *79*
Peck, H. D., Jr., 284, 285, *294*
Peech, M., 128, *134*
Pegler, H. F., 217, *224*
Percival, G. P., 69, *79*, 196, 206, 207, *210*
Perkins, A. T., 187, *190*
Petermann, M. N., 339, *361*
Petersen, D. F., 183, 185, 186, *189*, *190*
Petersen, R. A., 48, 51, 52, 59, 60, *64*
Peterson, E. W., 313, 315, *334*
Peterson, R. C., 217, 219, *224*
Pfiffner, J. J., 203, *210*, 217, 219, 220, *224*
Pfleiderer, G., 349, 350, *360*, *361*, *363*
Phillips, A. H., 274, *295*

Phillips, P. H., 41, *44*, 195, 201, 202, 203, 204, *209, 210,* 216, *224,* 355, *360, 361*
Phillipson, G. T., 201, *210*
Phillis, E., 181, 182, *190*
Philp, J. McL., 355, *360*
Pickworth, J., 220, *224*
Pied, H., 271, *295*
Pinsent, J., 60, *65*
Pintner, I. J., 58, *64, 65*
Piper, C. S., 285, *295*
Pirson, A., 27, 32, 82, 83, 84, 88, 97, *98,* 139, 144, *155,* 157, 166, 167, *174*
Pitt-Rivers, R., 266, *267*
Poley, W. E., 184, 185, 188, *189, 190*
Pollard, C. J., 184, *188*
Pomerantz, E., 214, *225*
Poos, F. W., 181, *189*
Pope, A. L., 195, 201, 202, 203, 204, *209, 210,* 216, *224*
Porter, J. W. G., 54, *64,* 203, *210,* 217, 218, 220, *224*
Portes, 271, *295*
Portsmouth, G. B., 167, *174*
Possingham, J. V., 154, *155,* 291, *295,* 353, *361*
Potter, G. D., 258, 259, 261, 262, 264, 267
Potter, V. R., 183, 184, 185, 186, *189, 190*
Praetorius, E., 316, 317, *335*
Pratt, P. F., 255, *256*
Presley, H. J., 239, *243*
Price, N. O., 280, *295*
Pricer, W. E., Jr., 350, *361*
Prosen, R. J., 220, *224*
Provasoli, L., 50, 58, 59, 60, *64, 65*
Purvis, E. R., 228, 230, *243,* 291, *293*
Putnam, F. W., 341, *361*

Q

Quinlan-Watson, T. A. F., 354, *361*

R

Rabinowitch, E. I., 151, *155*
Racker, E., 342, *361*
Raleigh, G. J., 61, *65*
Ramage, H., 37, *45*
Ramig, R. E., 161, *174*
Rao, M.S.S., 168, *174*
Raoult, F., 337, *361*
Rask, O. S., 274, *292*

Raulin, J., 1, 2, *32,* 337, *361*
Ravikovitch, S., 177, *190*
Ray, S. N., 201, *210*
Redetzki, H. E., 343, *361*
Reed, H. S., 237, 239, *243,* 351, *361*
Reed, J. F., 128, *134*
Rees, K. R., 42, *44*
Reeve, E., 232, *243*
Reid, B. L., 35, *45,* 282, *294, 295*
Reiman, C. K., 275, *295*
Reindel, W., 315, 328, *335*
Reisner, G. S., 88, 94, *98,* 166, 167, *174*
Remy, C. N., 281, *295*
Reuther, W., 82, 96, *98,* 106, *108,* 377, 382
Rhian, M., 181, 184, 185, 186, *189, 190*
Rhoades, A. S., 126, *134*
Rice, T. D., 177, *189*
Richert, D. A., 35, *44, 45,* 281, 282, *292, 294, 295, 296,* 297, *308*
Rideal, E. K., 339, *360*
Robbins, K. C., 315, 317, *335*
Robertson, J. H., 220, *224*
Robin, E. D., 356, *362*
Robinson, W. O., 39, *45,* 176, 181, *190*
Robison, W. L., 222, *224*
Roche, J., 262, 263, 266, *267*
Rodriguez, E., 48, 51, 52, 59, 60, *64*
Rolinson, G. N., 354, *361*
Roll, P. M., 327, *334*
Romney, E. M., 100, *108*
Root, W. S., 206, *209*
Rose, D. H., 126, *134*
Rosenblum, E. D., 284, *295*
Rosenfeld, I., 184, *190*
Ross, G. I. M., 50, 52, *64*
Rossi-Fanelli, A., 367, *382*
Rossiter, R. C., 199, *210*
Rothberg, S., 314, *334*
Rothery, P., 207, *210*
Rothstein, A., 101, *108*
Roughton, F. J. W., 339, *360, 361*
Ruck, H. C., 82, *98*
Rupel, I. W., 208, *209*
Ruprecht, R. W., 228, 230, *243*
Russel, D. A., 251, *256*
Russell, F. C., 70, *79*
Ruyle, W. V., 330, *334*
Rygh, O., 35, *45,* 276, *295*

S

Sackville, J. P., 195, *209*
Saeki, H., 277, *295*
Sager, R., 50, *65*
Salmon, W. D., 223, *224*, 354, *362*
Salsbury, R. L., 217, *225*
Salsbury, W. H., Jr., 203, *210*
Sandals, K. M., 177, 178, *189*
Sanders, M., 48, 51, 52, 59, 60, *64*
Sato, R., 291, *295*
Savvina, A. G., 283, *292*
Sayre, J. D., 245, *250*
Schade, A. L., 368, *382*
Schatz, A., 59, 60, *64*
Scheel, F., 315, *334*
Scher, S., 60, *64*
Schittenhelm, A., 315, *335*
Schmidt, D. A., 355, *361*
Schmucker, T., 234, 239, *243*
Schneider, H. A., 186, *190*
Schneider, S., 346, 358, *360*
Schoening, H. W., 177, *189*
Schollenberger, C. J., 128, *134*
Schroder, M., 283, *295*
Schubert, J., 59, *65*, 322, *335*
Schuler, W., 315, 328, *334, 335*
Schutze, M. O., 374, *382*
Schwartz, M., 172, *174*
Schwarz, K., 35, *45*, 176, 188, *190*
Scott, D. A., 339, 340, *361*
Scott, M. L., 35, *45*, 176, 188, *190*
Seaborg, G. T., 8, *31*
Searight, W. V., 71, *79*, 177, 178, 180, *189, 190*
Sebrell, W. H., Jr., 206, *210*
Selawry, O. S., 56, *65*
Shakir, M. H., 359, *360*
Shaw, B. T., 253, *256*
Sheldon, J. H., 37, *45*
Sheline, G. F., 342, *361*
Sherman, H. C., 366, *382*
Sherman, M. S., 277, 283, *294*, 304, *308*
Shibuya, K., 277, *295*
Shive, J. W., 95, *98*, 232, 240, *243*
Shive, W., 57, *65*
Shooter, R. A., 60, *65*
Shug, A. L., 284, 285, *295*, 297, *308*
Sibly, P. M., 341, 353, *361, 363*
Siegel, S. M., 239, *243*
Simmonds, S., 266, *267*

Simon, R. H., 128, *134*
Simonis, W., 87, *98*
Sinclair, R. D., 195, *209*
Singer, T. P., 261, 267, *315*, 333, *335*, 367, 369, *382*
Sisler, E. C., 234, 236, *243*
Skok, J., 229, 230, 231, 234, 235, 236, 238, 241, *243*
Skoog, F., 12, *31*, 352, *362*
Slein, N. W., 350, *360*
Smiley, J. D., 49, *64*
Smith, A., 182, *190*
Smith, C. K., 203, *210*, 217, *225*
Smith, E. C. B., 339, *362*
Smith, E. L., 207, *209*, 220, 221, *224*, 342, *362*
Smith, J. A. B., 217, *224*
Smith, M. D., 372, *381*
Smith, M. E., 239, *243*
Smith, M. I., 182, 186, 187, *190, 191*
Smith, O. L., 373, *382*
Smith, P. F., 377, *382*
Smith, S. E., 41, *45*, 195, 200, 201, 202, 207, *209, 210*, 215, 216, 223, *224*, *225*
Smull, K., 315, *333*
Snell, N. S., 56, *64*
Snider, H. J., 110, *116*
Snyder, W. C., 5, *31*
Sobotka, H., 54, *64, 65*
Somers, G. F., 259, *267*
Somers, I. I., 95, *98*
Sommer, A. L., 228, *243*
Specht, A. W., 377, *382*
Speer, V. C., 204, *210*
Spencer, D., 18, *32*, 286, 292, *293, 295*
Speyer, J. F., 367, 369, *382*
Spinks, J. W. T., 207, *210*
Spurr, A. R., 239, *243*
Stackhouse, J. M., 255, *256*
Stanford, G. W., 187, *190*
Stanley, P. G., 266, *267*
Stark, C. N., 216, *224*
Starr, T. J., 58, *65*
Stauffer, J. F., 145, *155*
Steadman, L. T., 37, *44*
Steckel, J. E., 104, *108*, 110, *116*
Steenbock, H., 38, *44*
Stegmann, G., 12, *32*, 97, *98*
Steinberg, R. A., 17, *32*, 229, *243*, 285, *295*

Stelzner, A. D., 282, *294*
Stephens, D. G., 56, *64*
Stepka, W., 138, *154*
Stern, L., 315, *333*
Stevens, H. M., 291, *295*
Stevenson, J. W., 41, *45*, 355, 359, *362*
Stewart, J., 200, *210*, 379, *382*
Stiles, W., 232, 237, *243*
Stipek, R. W., 217, 219, *224*
Stocking, C. R., 339, *363*
Stockwell, F. R., Jr., 275, *295*
Stohr, R., 273, *294*
Stokinger, H. E., 275, *296*
Stoklasa, J., 376, *382*
Stokstad, E. L. R., 35, *45*, 176, 188, *190*
Stolzenberg, S., 281, *293*
Stotz, E., 185, *190*
Stout, P. R., 6, 7, 12, 29, *31*, *32*, 57, *64*, 172, *174*, 229, *242*, 285, *292*, *293*
Straub, F. B., 350, *362*
Strittmatter, C. F., 367, 369, *382*
Strock, L. W., 177, *190*
Struglia, L., 204, *210*, 215, *224*
Stubbs, A. L., 359, *360*
Sumner, J. B., 259, *267*
Sund, H., 343, 345, *362*
Sutherland, I., 220, *224*
Svacha, R. L., 35, *45*, 282, *295*
Svirbely, J. L., 184, *190*
Sweeney, A., 176, *191*

T

Taboury, M., 180, *190*
Takahashi, H., 277, 284, *295*, 298, 305, *309*
Taniguchi, S., 291, *295*
Tanner, H. A., 92, 94, 97, 139, 147, 151, *155*
Tappan, D. V., 217, *224*
Tarver, H., 266, *267*
Taurog, A., 258, 259, 261, 262, 264, *267*
Taylor, J. B., 185, 188, *190*
Taylor, K. M., 272, 273, *294*
Taylor, R. F., 201, *209*
Tchakirian, A., 234, *243*, 271, 272, *293*
Teeri, A. E., 214, *225*
Tepperman, J., 282, *292*
Theorell, H., 331, *335*, 339, 345, 346, 347, 358, *362*
Thomas, M. P., 283, *292*
Thomas, R. G., 195, *210*

Thompson, J. F., 88, 94, *98*, 166, 167, *174*
Thorp, F., Jr., 354, *361*
Thorvaldson, T., 176, 181, *190*
Tichy, C., 27, *32*, 82, 83, 84, 88, *98*, 139, *155*, 167, *174*
Todd, A. R., 220, *224*
Tolmach, L. J., 93, *98*
Tong, W., 259, 261, *267*
Torssell, K., 233, 239, *243*
Tosi, L., 369, *381*
Tosic, J., 217, *225*
Toth, S. J., 100, *108*
Totter, J. R., 281, *295*, 297, *309*
Townsend, J., 331, *334*
Trager, W., 53, *65*
Traux, H. E., 126, 127, *134*
Trelease, H. M., 187, *191*
Trelease, S. F., 176, 182, 184, 187, *190*, *191*
Trikojus, V. M., 266, *267*
Trotter, W. R., 266, *267*
Trueblood, K. N., 220, *224*
Tsuge, T., 277, *294*
Tsui, C., 352, *362*
Truog, E., 252, 253, 255, *256*
Tucker, H. F., 354, *362*
Tully, W. C., 184, *189*
Tupper, R., 340, *362*
Turk, K. L., 201, *210*, 216, *225*

U

Ulrich, A., 161, *174*
Umbreit, W. W., 145, *155*, 352, *362*
Underwood, E. J., 38, 39, *45*, 68, *79*, 184, *191*, 194, 199, 200, 201, 204, *210*, *211*, 213, 214, *224*, *225*, 337, *362*

V

Vallee, B. L., 42, *45*, 337, 338, 339, 340, 341, 342, 343, 344, 345, 346, 347, 348, 349, 350, 356, 359, *359*, *360*, *362*
Vandecaveye, S. C., 161, *174*
Vanecko, S., 214, 216, 218, *224*
Van Goor, H., 339, 340, *362*
Van Heyningen, 340, *363*
Van Niel, C. B., 277, *295*
Van Reen, R., 41, *45*, 280, *295*
Van Reenen, W. J., 283, *294*
Vanslow, A. P., 291, *296*

Varner, J. E., 277, 284, *294*, 298, 299, 300, 305, *308*

Velick, S. F., 342, 345, *360*, 367, 369, *382*

Venkatachalam, P. S., 372, *382*

Viets, F. G., Jr., *190*

Vinogradov, A. P., 271, 274, *296*

Vishniac, W., 93, *98*

Vitale, J. J., 61, *65*

Volk, G. W., 255, *256*

Von Rennenkampff, E., 278, *294*

W

Wacker, W. E. C., 339, 346, 349, 350, 356, *362*

Waddell, J., 38, *44*

Wahlstrom, R. C., 187, *191*

Wainio, W. W., 371, *382*

Waksman, S. A., 22, *32*

Waley, S. G., 266, 267, 321, *335*

Walker, J. B., 12, 15, 18, *32*, 97, *98*

Walker, W., 202, *211*

Walker, W. E. C., 42, *45*

Walldov, E. E., 137, *154*

Wallenfels, K., 343, 345, *362*

Walsch, R. J., 372, *382*

Walsh, T., 176, *191*

Waltner, K., 206, *211*

Warburg, O., 10, *32*, 92, *98*, 158, 172, *174*, 299, *309*, 337, *363*

Waring, E. J., 285, *296*

Waring, W. S., 159, *174*

Warington, K., 228, *243*, 278, 285, *293*, *296*

Warner, R. C., 370, *382*

Wassen, A. M., 346, *360*

Watson, J., 266, 267

Watson, S. J., 36, 39, *44*, 279, *293*

Watts, A., 340, *362*

Waygood, E. R., 341, *363*

Webb, D. A., 60, *65*, 271, 272, 273, 274, *296*

Webb, E. C., 340, *363*

Weber, I., 370, *382*

Weber, M. M., 372, *382*

Weier, T. E., 339, *363*

Weir, W. C., 201, *210*

Wells, I. C., 281, *295*

Werkman, C. H., 159, *174*

Wessel, G., 8, 15, 16, 20, 27, *31*, 270, 278, 286, *292*

Westerfeld, W. W., 35, *44*, *45*, 281, 282, 292, *294*, 295, 296, 297, *308*

Westfall, B. B., 182, 187, *190*, *191*

Whatley, F. R., 27, *31*, 87, 93, 97, 172, *174*, 375, *382*

White, E. A., 197, *211*

White, J. G., 220, *224*

White, S. N., 181, *190*

Whitehead, E. I., 179, 181, *190*

Whitney, I. B., 281, *295*, 297, *309*

Whittwer, S. H., 100, *107*

Wiebe, H. H., 377, *382*

Wiechowski, W., 315, *335*

Wieland, T., 349, *363*

Wieringa, K. T., 283, *293*

Wijmenga, H. G., 217, 220, *225*

Wildman, W. C., 330, *334*

Wilgus, H. S., 39, *45*

Wilhelmi, G., 27, *32*, 82, 83, 84, 88, *98*, 139, *155*, 167, *174*

Willard, H. H., 128, *134*

Williams, A. H., 285, *294*

Williams, G. R., 369, 371, *381*

Williams, J. H., 35, *44*, 281, *293*

Williams, K. T., 176, 177, 178, 179, 180, 185, *188*, *189*, *191*

Williams, M. A., 41, *45*, 280, *295*

Williams, R. J. P., 323, 332, *335*, 338, 344, 345, 346, 347, *360*, *363*

Williams, T. R., 51, *65*

Willis, L. G., 106, *108*

Willman, J. P., 205, *210*

Wilson, J. H., 106, *108*

Wilson, P. W., 284, 285, *294*, 295, 297, *308*

Wilson, R. D., 285, *296*

Wilson, W. O., 185, 188, *190*

Winfield, M. E., 234, 240, *243*, 285, *296*

Winter, H. F., 127, 132, *134*

Wintrobe, M. M., 374, *381*

Wirth, L., 272, *292*

Witz, G., 277, *296*

Wolfe, M., 283, *296*

Wolken, J. J., 50, *65*

Wood, J. G., 18, *32*, 341, 353, *361*, *363*

Wood, W. A., 352, *362*

Woolley, J. T., 15, 16, 20, 27, *31*, 60, *65*, 172, *174*, 286, *292*

Wormall, R. W. E., 340, *362*

Wright, C. I., 185, *191*

Wright, N. C., 274, *296*

Wulff, H. J., 342, 343, *361*
Wyatt, H. V., 60, *65*
Wynne, K. N., 279, *296*

Y

Yagi, Y., 262, 263, 266, *267*
Young, H. C., 127, 132, *134*

Z

Zahl, P. A., 58, *65*
Zbinden, C., 274, *296*
Zittle, C. A., 233, *243*
Zotos, B., 344, *360*
Zweig, G., 139, *154*

SUBJECT INDEX

A

Alfalfa
  boron requirement, 255
Ankistrodesmus
  manganese and photosynthesis, 83
Apples
  manganese toxicity, 125
Arsenic
  in red blood cells, 37
  selenium interaction, 41, 186
Anabaena
  essential elements for, 12
  molybdenum in nitrogen assimilation, 18
Aspergillus
  molybdenum in nitrate assimilation, 285
  role of zinc in, 1, 3
Azotobacter
  molybdenum in nitrogen fixation, 283
  molybdenum—tungsten uptake, 299

B

Boron
  application to soils, 256
  availability in soils, 252
  and cellular development, 237
  complexing by borate ion, 233
  deficiency symptoms in plants, 229
  distribution in the plant cell, 231
  essentiality for plants, 227, 241
  and internal bark necrosis of apple, 127, 133
  in leaf margins, 245
  in Ohio soils, 251
  requirement for alfalfa, 255
    of crops, 230, 252
  in sugar translocation, 234
  utilization by plants, 230, 252
Boron in leaves
  seasonal variation, 246
  variation in corn inbreds, 248
Brisket disease, 71

C

Calcium
  zinc interaction, 41, 355
Cattle
  cobalt deficiency, 196
Chlorella
  light and manganese requirement, 135
  manganese and CO_2 fixation, 151
  manganese deficiency, 148
    and respiration, 139
  manganese and photosynthesis, 85, 137
  mineral requirements for
    autotrophic growth, 160, 163, 173
    heterotrophic growth, 160, 163
  molybdenum in nitrogen assimilation, 18
  vanadium in, 11
Cobalt
  in animal tissues, 207
  content of forages, 73, 200, 214
  deficiency in animals, 39, 68, 72, 194
    in cattle, 196
    in sheep, 194
    in swine, 204
  in polycythemia, 206
  prevention of phalaris staggers, 204
  requirements of animals, 200, 214
  soil-plant-animal relationships, 74
  supplementation of animal rations, 198, 208
  toxicity of, 206
  in vitamin B_{12}, 43, 51, 56, 201, 205, 213, 216, 387
  in vitamin B_{12}-like substances, 219, 222
Copper
  deficiency in animals, 40, 70
  in enzymes, 42, 314, 350
  iron interactions, 374, 389
  molybdenum-inorganic sulfate interaction, 40, 279
  and molybdenum toxicity, 36, 39, 71
  oxyanion complexes, 324

407

requirement of rats, 38
  of tomato, 14
site on enzyme, 326
substrate binding, 323
toxic effect on animals, 36
in uricase, 317

E

Enzymes
  alcohol dehydrogenase, 339, 342
  aldehyde oxidase, 42, 271, 281
  ascorbic acid oxidase, 42, 314
  carbonic anhydrase, 42, 339, 341
  carboxypeptidase, 42, 339, 341
  catalase, 42, 367, 368
  cytochromes, 42, 367, 368
  glutamic dehydrogenase, 339, 348
  hexokinase, 351
  11-β-hydroxylase, 369
  laccase, 42, 314
  lactic dehydrogenase, 339, 349
  nitrate reductase, 20, 42, 286
  oxygen transferases, 314, 368
  peroxidase, 42, 367, 368
  phenolase complex, 314
  pyridine nucleotide dehydrogenases,
    42, 342, 349
  succinic dehydrogenase, 367
  uricase, 42, 314, 315
  xanthine oxidase, 35, 271, 281, 367
Essential elements, 3, 5, 6, 12
  criterion of essentiality, 6, 14, 34
Euglena
  metals as temperature factors for, 49,
    52

F

Ferritin, 367, 369, 372
Fluorine
  toxic effect in animals, 36

G

Grapes
  maganese deficiency, 117

H

Hemoglobin, 367
Hemovanadin
  occurrence in tunicates, 272

Hepatic cirrhosis
  in human, 356
Higher plants
  essential elements for, 12
Hill reaction, 92, 138, 145, 165, 375

I

Inhibition studies
  with vitamin B$_{12}$, 57
Iodine
  deficiency in animals, 39, 69, 388
  in monoiodotyrosine synthesis, 257,
    388
  in thyroxine, 42
Iron
  availability to plants, 375
  and chlorosis, 365
  copper interactions, 374, 389
  in electron transfer, 371
  in enzymes, 41, 350, 367
  ferritin, 367, 369
  in flavoproteins, 369
  functions of, 366
  for green algae, 9
  and Hill reaction, 375
  and internal bark necrosis of apple,
    127
  light interactions, 91
  in photosynthesis, 84
  requirement for *Chlorella*, 165
  in sea plants, 379
  site in enzymes, 369
  transferrin, 367, 369
Iron in animals
  biological compounds, 367
Iron in plants
  absorption and translocation, 377
  biological compounds, 374

L

Lead
  in teeth, 37

M

Magnesium
  requirement by *Chlorella*, 162
Manganese
  and CO$_2$ fixation, 151
  deficiency in animals, 39
    in *Chlorella*, 85, 135